Electromagnetic Fields and Waves

ELECTROMAGNETIC FIELDS AND WAVES

Robert V. Langmuir

PROFESSOR OF ELECTRICAL ENGINEERING
CALIFORNIA INSTITUTE OF TECHNOLOGY

McGRAW-HILL BOOK COMPANY, INC.

1961   NEW YORK   TORONTO   LONDON

ELECTROMAGNETIC FIELDS AND WAVES

II

36290

THE MAPLE PRESS COMPANY, YORK, PA.

Preface

This book is intended for relatively mature students at the senior or first-year graduate level in electrical engineering or applied physics. As is so often the case, this book arose from the lecture notes of a course in electricity and magnetism that has been given for many years. One of the objects of that course and of this book is so to familiarize the student with the meaning and content of Maxwell's equations that these equations will thereafter be the starting point for the solution of any electrical problem he may meet. Another purpose is to acquaint the student with some of the subjects of modern electrical engineering, such as waveguides, cavities, antennas, etc. This last purpose can, of course, be only partially fulfilled, for the content of any technical field changes at a very rapid rate, and any book will be out-of-date to some extent as soon as it is published. As an example, it is practically certain that the engineers of the future will need to know a great deal about plasma physics. This subject is only beginning to be understood as this book is being written and is touched upon only in the discussion of the ionosphere in the last chapter.

Just what topics should be included in a book of this type is a question that has many answers. The likes, dislikes, and prejudices of the author will of course be important in giving an answer. The choice of topics in this book is based on experience in teaching a course in which many of the materials in this text were used as "course notes." Under such circumstances topics of interest to the author will be emphasized, while subjects in which he is less interested will receive a somewhat shorter treatment. The arrangement of courses at the author's institution will also influence his choice of material. Thus this book stops short of topics that involve extensive use of particle

v

dynamics, such as klystrons and traveling wave tubes. Likewise, although the basic physics of radiation is covered extensively, the application to antennas is somewhat short. This is because both these fields are thoroughly covered in fifth-year courses at the California Institute of Technology. Another influence of modern curricula is seen in the absence of conformal transformation techniques in solving two-dimensional potential problems. This subject is usually covered in a separate course introducing the subject of "functions of a complex variable." The students who have been using this text in the form of course notes have come to it quite well prepared in vector analysis, partial differential equations, Fourier series, etc. Thus the treatment of these mathematical subjects in this book is brief but complete. The whole book, in fact, is quite brief; important points are often stated but once and not referred to again. A careful reading of the text by the student is needed to solve some of the problems. Many subjects are elaborated only in the problems at the end of each chapter rather than being treated in the text.

In such a rapidly moving field as modern electrical engineering one can scarcely do much more than train the student in the mathematical methods and basic physics of the field, using as an example the status of the field at present. It is hoped that this book will help train students in this way to meet and solve problems that are not even dreamed of now.

Robert V. Langmuir

Contents

1

Introduction to Electrostatics

Electrostatics concerns itself with the discussion of electric fields which do not change with time. Classical electricity and magnetism presume that measurements will be made on a scale considerably larger than the atomistic scale so that the graininess of matter caused by the fact that it is actually composed of atoms will not be of major interest. The various electric and magnetic quantities will be averaged over regions large compared with atomic dimensions and presumably will give answers which are valid only under such conditions.

The development of the theory of electricity and magnetism rests on certain postulates or experiments. Advanced textbooks on this subject often postulate the truth of Maxwell's equations and examine the consequences of this assumption. If the results agree with experimental evidence this is considered to be sufficient justification for the usefulness of the postulates, if not their truth.

In this book it will be more instructive to postulate the results of certain experiments that can be performed in the laboratory. Thus at the beginning of electrostatics we give the results of the physical experiments (such as Coulomb's law) and at the start of the discussion of magnetism we give the law describing the interaction of steady currents (the law of Biot and Savart). Consequences are then drawn from these basic experiments, and this makes up the body of the theory. Of course we have some freedom in the choice of which experiments we shall use for the foundations of the theory. We shall choose those experiments that best fit the development we wish to follow.

1

1.1 Coulomb's Law

Experimentally we find that charged particles are acted upon by two types of forces, electric and magnetic. An expression of this experimental law is

$$\mathbf{F} = q(\mathbf{E} + \mathbf{v} \times \mathbf{B}) \tag{1}$$

This is called the Lorentz equation. The units used here are rationalized mks units, which will be introduced gradually as needed. Here $\mathbf{F}$, the force, is measured in newtons. A mass of 1 kilogram under the influence of gravity ($g = 9.8$ m/sec/sec) represents a force of 9.8 newtons. Thus 1 newton represents the gravitational force on 0.22 pound, or about the gravitational force on a small apple. The charge q is measured in coulombs (one coulomb per second equals one ampere).

The system of units in electricity and magnetism used here (the mks-ampere system) shall not be completely defined without reference to magnetic experiments; the definition of the ampere shall be deferred to the chapter on magnetism. The magnetic force ($q\mathbf{v} \times \mathbf{B}$) shall also be discussed later in the chapter on magnetism. The units of q and $\mathbf{E}$, of course, must be so chosen that the force is measured in newtons. As we have already fixed q in terms of the ampere, $\mathbf{E}$ is determined from (1) and given the dimensions of volts per meter.

We must consider the force between two charged particles. Experimentally it is found that the force between two point charges q_1 and q_2 separated by a distance $\mathbf{r}$ is given by Coulomb's law, which is

$$\mathbf{F} = \frac{q_1 q_2 \mathbf{r}}{4\pi \epsilon_0 r^3} \tag{2}$$

The effect of q_2 on unit charge is thus given by

$$\mathbf{F} = \mathbf{E} = \frac{q_2 \mathbf{r}}{4\pi \epsilon_0 r^3} \tag{3}$$

and the force on any charge q is

$$\mathbf{F} = q\mathbf{E} \tag{4}$$

ϵ_0 is an experimental constant such that when the charge is measured in coulombs (which is defined in terms of the ampere), the force is in newtons. Its value in vacuum in the mks system of units is *measured* to be 8.85×10^{-12} farad per meter. The significance of the units "farads per meter" shall become evident when capacity is discussed. The presence of 4π in the formulas is the result of using a rationalized system of units and is merely conventional. It is conventional also to define the sign of the electric charge by calling the charge of an ordinary electron negative. When the mks system of units is extended to electricity and magnetism we must choose some arbitrary electrical unit. It would be quite simple (and it is often done) to choose q as this unit. It is more realistic, however, to use the ampere, since the experimental determination of the ampere is much more straightforward, as we shall see in Chapter 4. We shall fully discuss units in the chapter on magnetism.

1.2   Direct Vector Integration for Solving Problems

Using the above simple experimental laws together with the ordinary laws of vector algebra, we can solve a number of useful problems in electrostatics. Often the solution can be obtained more easily by using Gauss' theorem and the concept of potential, but the physical insight obtained by simple vector manipulation is often very useful. We shall now give several examples in the use of the above ideas.

Example 1. Find the electric field at a distance R from an infinitely long line charge of strength σ coulombs per meter.

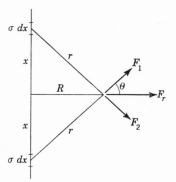

Fig. 1.2a. Field from a line charge.

Solution. The field due to an elementary charge $\sigma\,dx$ at x will be $\sigma\,dx/4\pi\epsilon_0 r^2$ in the direction of $\mathbf{F}_1$ in Figure 1.2a. There will be a corresponding elementary charge above the field point giving an equal field in the direction of $\mathbf{F}_2$. These two fields will add together to give an electric field in the radial direction $\mathbf{F}_r$. Thus the net field will be in the radial direction and the vector summation of the fields of all the elementary charges can be replaced by a scalar integration:

$$E_r = 2 \int_0^\infty \frac{\sigma\,dx\,\cos\theta}{4\pi\epsilon_0 r^2} \tag{1}$$

But $r = \sqrt{x^2 + R^2}$ and $\cos\theta = R/r$. Thus

$$E_r = \frac{\sigma R}{2\pi\epsilon_0} \int_0^\infty \frac{dx}{(x^2 + R^2)^{3/2}} = \frac{\sigma R}{2\pi\epsilon_0} \left. \frac{x}{R^2(x^2 + R^2)^{1/2}} \right|_0^\infty$$

$$= \frac{\sigma}{2\pi\epsilon_0 R} \qquad \text{volts/m} \tag{2}$$

Example 2.   Find the electric field at a distance R in front of an infinite plane having a uniform surface charge density of σ coulombs per square meter.

Solution.   By symmetry the force from an elementary ring of charge of radius x about a point opposite the field point on the charged surface will be in a direction perpendicular to the charged plane.   The net field is thus

$$
\begin{aligned}
E &= \int_0^\infty \frac{2\pi\sigma x\,dx}{4\pi\epsilon_0 r^2}\cos\theta = \frac{\sigma R}{2\epsilon_0}\int_0^\infty \frac{x\,dx}{(x^2+R^2)^{3/2}} \\
&= \frac{\sigma R}{2\epsilon_0}\frac{-1}{(x^2+R^2)^{1/2}}\bigg|_0^\infty = \frac{\sigma}{2\epsilon_0} \qquad \text{volts/m}
\end{aligned}
\tag{3}
$$

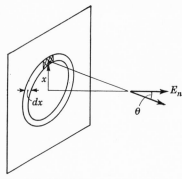

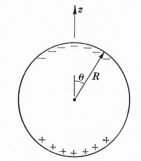

Fig. 1.2*b*. Field from a planar charge.   Fig. 1.2*c*. Field in the center of a spherical cavity in a dielectric.

Example 3.   Find the electric field at the center of a sphere of radius R that arises from a charge distribution on the surface of the sphere given by $\sigma = -P\cos\theta$, where θ is the polar angle in spherical coordinates.

Solution.   This problem seems artificial, but we shall need the solution to just this problem in Chapter 13 when we discuss dispersion in liquids and solids.   There will obviously be only an E_z, in the polar direction, and we can thus take the z component of any E we calculate.   This gives, as is clear from Figure 1.2*c*,

$$
\begin{aligned}
E_z &= \int_0^\pi \frac{P\cos\theta\cos\theta\,2\pi R\sin\theta\,R\,d\theta}{4\pi\epsilon_0 R^2} \\
&= \frac{P}{3\epsilon_0} \qquad \text{volts/m}
\end{aligned}
\tag{4}
$$

It should be noted that the above problems were solved essentially by vector integration.   In each case there was enough symmetry present so that the direction of the electric field could be found by inspection and the actual work was reduced to a scalar integration.   In more complicated problems this cannot be done, and the direct vector integration becomes difficult.   In addition, the problems above presume that the location of the charges is known at the start of the problem. This, in general, will not be the case when large conductors are present. These considerations lead to the search for a scalar, rather than a vector, method for solving electrostatic problems, and involve the use of the scalar potential.

1.3   Scalar Potentials

We show in Appendix A that a certain vector operation called "taking the gradient of a scalar function of the coordinates" will generate a vector field.   This operation, written as $\nabla\phi$, where ϕ is the scalar function, has the following properties which are proved in Appendix A:

1. If a vector $\mathbf{F}$ is the gradient of a scalar function, the line integral between two end points a and b depends *only* on the end points and not on the path.

2. If $\oint \mathbf{F} \cdot \mathbf{dr} = 0$ for every closed path in a region, there exists a ϕ such that $\mathbf{F} = \nabla\phi$.

We presume here that the reader is familiar with this operation. Appendix A should be carefully studied by those who are not completely familiar with the use of the gradient operator.   We further presume that the reader is familiar with the vector products $\mathbf{A} \cdot \mathbf{B}$ and $\mathbf{A} \times \mathbf{B}$.   This subject is adequately treated in many textbooks and will not be treated here.   The discussion of the gradient and curl in the appendix, although brief, is complete.

We now consider the work W done in moving a unit positive charge in an electric field $\mathbf{E}$.   We have

$$W = - \int_a^b \mathbf{E} \cdot \mathbf{dr} \qquad (1)$$

If the electric field is caused by a single charge q, then

$$\mathbf{E} = \frac{q}{4\pi\epsilon_0}\frac{\mathbf{r}}{r^3} = -\frac{q}{4\pi\epsilon_0}\nabla\left(\frac{1}{r}\right)$$

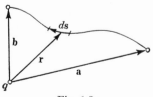

Fig. 1.3a

and we have

$$W = \frac{q}{4\pi\epsilon_0}\int_a^b \nabla\left(\frac{1}{r}\right) \cdot \mathbf{dr} = \frac{q}{4\pi\epsilon_0}\int_a^b d\left(\frac{1}{r}\right) = \frac{q}{4\pi\epsilon_0}\left(\frac{1}{b} - \frac{1}{a}\right) \qquad (2)$$

which depends only on the end points and is independent of the path of integration.

In general we will have many charges contributing to $\mathbf{E}$; the work done carrying a unit charge from a to b will still be independent of the path.   The vector $\mathbf{E}$ can be then derived from a scalar potential

$$\mathbf{E} = -\operatorname{grad} \phi \tag{3}$$

where for a single charge q one has the scalar potential

$$\phi = \frac{q}{4\pi\epsilon_0 r} \tag{4}$$

The work done in moving a unit charge from a to b is thus the difference in potentials between a and b.   Since the curl of any gradient is identically zero (see Appendix B), we also have

$$\nabla \times \mathbf{E} = 0 \tag{5}$$

Clearly only differences in potential are measurable and in any problem we can add a constant to all the potentials and the fields will be the same.

1.4   Gauss' Law

Before proceeding with the use of the concept of potential introduced above, we can profitably discuss Gauss' law.   We shall prove this law for a single charge; by superposition it will hold for a collection of an arbitrary number of point charges.   The theorem states that if a charge q is inside a volume having a surface S, then the integral over the surface S of the normal component of $\mathbf{E}$ is equal to $1/\epsilon_0$ times the charge q. Stated mathematically this is

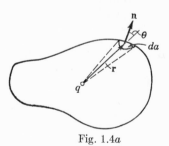

$$\int_S \mathbf{E} \cdot \mathbf{n} \, da = \frac{q}{\epsilon_0} \tag{1}$$

where $\mathbf{n}$ is a unit vector directed along the outer normal to the surface S at an elementary area da.   To prove this theorem for a single charge, consider Figure 1.4a.

Fig. 1.4a

The contribution from da to $\mathbf{E} \cdot \mathbf{n} \, da$ is $E \, da \cos \theta$.   However, $da \cos \theta$ is $r^2 \, d\Omega$, where $d\Omega$ is the solid angle subtended by da from q, and $E = q/4\pi\epsilon_0 r^2$.   Thus

$$d\Omega = \frac{da \cos \theta}{r^2}$$

$$\mathbf{E} \cdot \mathbf{n} \, da = \frac{q}{4\pi\epsilon_0 r^2} r^2 \, d\Omega = \frac{q}{4\pi\epsilon_0} \, d\Omega \tag{2}$$

Integrating over the whole surface, $\int d\Omega = 4\pi$ and Equation (2) is shown to be true for a single charge. The extension to an arbitrary number of charges is obvious:

$$\int_S \mathbf{E} \cdot \mathbf{n}\, da = \frac{\sum\limits_n q_n}{\epsilon_0} \qquad (3)$$

where $\sum\limits_n q_n$ is the sum of all the charges inside the surface S.

1.5 Use of Gauss' Law to Solve Problems

Several applications of Gauss' law can be made immediately. We shall proceed first to solve Examples 1 and 2 worked earlier in this chapter.

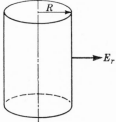

Fig. 1.5a. Field from a line charge.

Example 1a. Find the field at a distance R from an infinite line charge of strength σ coulombs per meter.

Solution. Surround the line charge by a coaxial cylindrical surface of unit length. This will be our "Gaussian surface." By symmetry, it is obvious that no flux passes through the top and bottom surfaces, and that $\mathbf{E}$ is uniform and radially directed outward on the curved surfaces. Applying Gauss' law we find that

cylinder is 1 meter high ⟶   (per meter, is implicit here)

$$\int_S \mathbf{E} \cdot \mathbf{n}\, da = 2\pi R E_r = \frac{\sigma}{\epsilon_0} \qquad (1)$$

or

$$E_r = \frac{\sigma}{2\pi\epsilon_0 R} \qquad (2)$$

The corresponding potential is

$$\phi = \frac{-\sigma}{2\pi\epsilon_0}\log r + C \qquad (3)$$

Example 2a. Find the field from a uniformly charged infinite surface having a surface charge density of σ coulombs per square meter.

Solution. Here, by symmetry, it is obvious that the field can be only perpendicular to the charged surface. We construct a "Gaussian pillbox," as in Figure 1.5b. Clearly no flux crosses

the curved surfaces, and we have

$$\int_S \mathbf{E} \cdot \mathbf{n}\, da = 2EA = \frac{\sigma A}{\epsilon_0}$$

where A is the area of the end sections. This gives

$$E = \frac{\sigma}{2\epsilon_0}$$

Fig. 1.5b. Field from a planar charge.

It is important to realize the limitations of the above method. These are hidden in the use of the words "obviously" and "by symmetry," which imply that the problem is so simple to begin with that intuitively we know quite a bit about it from inspection alone. This is a result of the simple geometry of the cases considered.

1.6 Conductors. Image Problems

Many problems in electrostatics involve the presence of charged conducting bodies. For the purposes of electrostatics a conductor will be defined as a region of space in which $\mathbf{E}$ cannot be made different from zero. This is a somewhat arbitrary definition because some sort of time scale is presumed. A charge placed on a copper conductor of laboratory size will distribute itself so as to give zero $\mathbf{E}$ inside the conductor in a time short compared with a microsecond or so. An insulator like quartz, however, will take several days to redistribute the charge so as to make $\mathbf{E}$ zero. However, most materials are clearly conductors or insulators. Discussion of insulators shall be deferred until the chapter on dielectrics.

Several immediate consequences emerge from the above definition of a conductor. The first is that a conductor is an equipotential, because if $\mathbf{E} = 0$ in a conductor, ϕ must clearly be a constant. It follows that $\mathbf{E}$ just outside the surface of a conductor must be perpendicular to it, since $\mathbf{E} = -\text{grad } \phi$, and grad ϕ is perpendicular to an equipotential surface.

Applying Figure 1.5b to a conductor, where the conductor is to the left of the plane, we have

$$\int_S \mathbf{E} \cdot \mathbf{n}\, da = EA = \frac{\sigma A}{\epsilon_0} \tag{1}$$

or $E = \sigma/\epsilon_0$ where σ is the surface charge density near the region of interest. This, of course, applies only to such a small region of the conductor that it can be considered to be planar over the region considered.   It is clear that in any problem an equipotential surface can be replaced by a conducting surface without disturbing the fields.

The fact that any equipotential surface can be replaced by a conducting surface permits us to solve a few problems by the method of images.   The method depends on the fact that if we can solve one problem, several other problems are also solved at the same time: namely, those in which the charges remain the same as in the original problem but an equipotential surface is replaced by a conducting surface.   The simplest example of this is to take as the primary problem two equal and opposite charges separated by a distance $2a$.   The solution to this problem can be immediately written as

$$\phi = \frac{q}{4\pi\epsilon_0 r_1} - \frac{q}{4\pi\epsilon_0 r_2} + C \tag{2}$$

This is not a very elegant expression, because r_1 and r_2 do not constitute a familiar coordinate system.   It is clear by symmetry that the equipotential surface midway between the two charges is an infinite

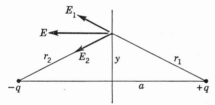

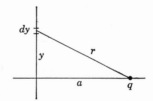

Fig. 1.6a. Point charge before a conducting plane.

Fig. 1.6b. Total charge induced on a plane by a point charge.

plane.   If we now replace this equipotential surface by a conductor, the fields to the right have not changed and we also have the solution to the problem of a point charge located a distance a from a conducting plane.   It will be convenient to take the constant C in (2) to be zero; this will place the conducting plane at zero potential, and is referred to by saying that the conducting plane is grounded.

The solution to the problem of a point charge at a distance a from a grounded conducting plane is thus given by (2) with C taken as zero. This solution holds only in the region 1, for nothing that occurs in region 2 can affect the fields in region 1.   The charge $-q$ to the left of the conducting plane is called the image charge.   We say that the problem of the point charge in front of a conducting plane can be solved in region 1 by replacing this problem with another one whose solution we know: namely, the original charge and its image, but with no conducting plane.   The charge distribution on the conducting plane can easily be found, since $\sigma = \epsilon_0 E$, and E at the conducting plane is given by

$$E_x = -\frac{2q}{4\pi\epsilon_0 r^2}\frac{a}{r} = -\frac{qa}{2\pi\epsilon_0}\frac{1}{(a^2 + y^2)^{3/2}} \tag{3}$$

and hence

$$\sigma = -\frac{qa}{2\pi}\frac{1}{(a^2 + y^2)^{3/2}} \tag{4}$$

The whole charge induced on the plate is found by integration

$$Q = -\frac{qa}{2\pi}\int_0^\infty \frac{2\pi y \, dy}{(a^2 + y^2)^{3/2}} = qa \left.\frac{1}{\sqrt{a^2 + y^2}}\right|_0^\infty = -q \tag{5}$$

An easier way to arrive at this result would be to notice that all the lines of **E** will terminate on the charged plane, and apply Gauss' law to a surface made up of the conducting plane and a hemisphere of infinite radius.

Example 4. Compute the work done in moving a charge q from infinity to a distance d in front of a conducting plane.

Solution. At any point x, E from the image is

$$E = \frac{-q}{4\pi\epsilon_0(2x)^2}$$

and the work done in moving the charge q a distance dx against this E is $dW = qE \, dx = (q^2/16\pi\epsilon_0 x^2) \, dx$. The total work done is therefore

$$W = \int_\infty^d \frac{q^2}{16\pi\epsilon_0 x^2} \, dx = \frac{-q^2}{16\pi\epsilon_0 d} \tag{6}$$

This is a negative amount of work done on the particle as the original charge is attracted to its image. Note carefully that it is not necessary to add in the work done in moving the image charge. The image charge is used only to compute E; once E is known the calculation proceeds as above. The change in E when the original charge is moved a distance dx is a second-order effect and does not appear in the calculation.

Several other types of image calculations can be made. We shall consider here one that has to do with spherical conducting surfaces. The method is based on an argument from plane geometry. Consider Figure 1.6c. The construction is such that the point P is opposite a spherical surface of radius a, P' is at a distance d from the center of this sphere along the line joining the center of the sphere, and the point P. d is chosen so that $d/a = a/x$. The triangle having the sides a, d, and r_2 is clearly similar to the triangle having sides a, r_1, and x since two of the sides are proportional and one angle is common to the two triangles.   Thus we can write

$$\frac{d}{a} = \frac{a}{x} = \frac{r_2}{r_1} \tag{7}$$

Let us now place a charge q at the point P, a charge q' at the point P', and compute the potential at a point on the spherical surface.   The potential will be

$$\phi = \frac{1}{4\pi\epsilon_0}\left(\frac{q}{r_1} + \frac{q'}{r_2}\right) + C \tag{8}$$

But $r_2 = r_1 a/x$ from (7) and hence the potential is

$$\phi = \frac{1}{4\pi\epsilon_0 r_1}\left(q + q'\frac{x}{a}\right) + C \tag{9}$$

If now we choose $q' = -(a/x)q$ we find that the potential of the spherical surface is a constant.   The image problem, i.e., a charge q at

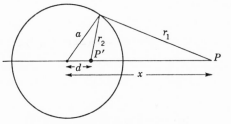

Fig. 1.6c. Spherical image system.

P and a charge $q' = -(a/x)q$ at P' leaves the spherical surface at constant potential and we can replace this equipotential by a conducting surface.   We can superimpose on this solution any other problem that will also leave the spherical surface an equipotential surface. Such another problem is clearly one that has an arbitrary charge Q at the center of the spherical surface.   Thus the problem of a point charge q at a distance x from the center of a conducting sphere of radius a can be solved in the region of interest (namely outside the sphere) by the image problem shown in Figure 1.6c, where $q' = -(a/x)q$ and $d/a = a/x$. Q is arbitrary.   The potential and electric field at any point outside the sphere can easily be written down for the image problem.   If the sphere is grounded (potential zero), we have (8) for a solution with $C = 0$ and r_1 and r_2 arbitrary.   If the sphere is given as being uncharged, the net charge inside the spherical surface must be zero.   The corresponding image problem would then have a charge $Q = -q' = +(a/x)q$ at the center of the sphere.   Several charges $q_1, q_2, \ldots$ can be placed at various points outside the sphere and suitable image charges can be arranged inside the sphere to give an easily solved image problem.

We now discuss the application of the above technique to line charges and cylindrical conducting surfaces. As before we construct $d/a = a/x$ and thus have $d/a = a/x = r_2/r_1$ on the cylinder. Consider line charges at P and P' parallel to a cylinder of radius a. The potential at any point will be

$$\phi = - \frac{\sigma}{2\pi\epsilon_0} \log r_1 - \frac{\sigma'}{2\pi\epsilon_0} \log r_2 + C \tag{10}$$

We wish the potential of the cylinder to be a constant independent of r_1 and r_2. It seems reasonable that this can be accomplished only if we can get $\phi = \phi(r_1/r_2)$. This will happen if we choose $\sigma' = -\sigma$, since then we have on the cylindrical surface

$$\phi = - \frac{\sigma}{2\pi\epsilon_0} \log \frac{r_1}{r_2} + C = - \frac{\sigma}{2\pi\epsilon_0} \log \frac{x}{a} + C$$

If we choose $\phi = 0$ on the cylinder, we have $C = \sigma/2\pi\epsilon_0 \log (x/a)$, or, at any point outside the cylinder,

$$\phi = - \frac{\sigma}{2\pi\epsilon_0} \log \left(\frac{r_1}{r_2} \frac{a}{x} \right) \tag{11}$$

As before we can superimpose the solution of an arbitrary line charge σ'' along the axis of the cylinder, as this will also keep the cylindrical surface an equipotential. If the cylinder is uncharged, we must, of course, take $\sigma'' = -\sigma' = \sigma$.

We should point out that the above spherical image problem can be inverted to obtain the potential and field of a point charge inside a conducting sphere. The image is then outside the sphere. A corresponding statement holds for a line charge inside a cylindrical conducting shell. The problem of two charged spheres can be thrown into the form of an infinite set of images of decreasing size, while the problem of two charged parallel cylinders can be solved exactly, as we shall show in the next section.

1.7 Capacity

We shall now discuss the concept of the capacity of a condenser. A condenser consists of two conductors carrying equal and opposite charge. The capacity of such a condenser is defined as the ratio of this charge to the potential difference between the two conductors. The simplest case is that of two parallel plates of area A separated by a distance d. Neglecting edge effects, the field will be normal to the plates and by Gauss' theorem we have $E = \sigma/\epsilon_0$ where σ is the charge per unit area. The potential difference between the plates is

$$\Delta V = Ed = \frac{\sigma d}{\epsilon_0}$$

and the total charge σA. The capacity is

$$C = \frac{\sigma A \epsilon_0}{\sigma d} = \frac{\epsilon_0 A}{d} \qquad \text{farads} \qquad (1)$$

where one farad is the capacity of a condenser that has a $\Delta V = $ one volt for 1 coulomb of charge on each plate. If $A = 1$ sq m and $d = 1$ m, we have $C = \epsilon_0$ so ϵ_0 is the capacity of such a condenser, and the units of ϵ_0 are clearly farads per meter.

Consider next two coaxial conducting cylinders, the inner one carrying a charge of σ coulombs per unit length and the outer one the negative of this charge. The equipotential surfaces surrounding a line charge on the axis are just such cylinders and this will give the potentials of the two conducting cylinders. The result is

$$V_1 - V_2 = \Delta V = - \frac{\sigma}{2\pi\epsilon_0} \log r_1 + \frac{\sigma}{2\pi\epsilon_0} \log r_2 = \frac{\sigma}{2\pi\epsilon_0} \log \frac{r_2}{r_1} \qquad (2)$$

The capacity per unit length is

$$C = \frac{\sigma}{\Delta V} = \frac{2\pi\epsilon_0}{\log r_2/r_1} \qquad (3)$$

where r_2 is the radius of the larger cylinder. By similar reasoning we can show that two concentric spheres have a capacity of

$$C = \frac{4\pi\epsilon_0}{1/r_1 - 1/r_2} \qquad (4)$$

It should be noted that this remains finite if r_2 goes to infinity. This is called the self-capacity of an isolated sphere.

The capacity per unit length of two parallel cylinders can be found by using images. In Figure 1.7a we have line charges $\pm\sigma$ at the image points. The potential on each of the cylinders of radius a is constant, as shown in Section 1.6. The potential of the left cylinder is

$$V_1 = \frac{-\sigma}{2\pi\epsilon_0} \log \frac{r_1}{r_2} = \frac{\sigma}{2\pi\epsilon_0} \log \frac{a}{d} \qquad (5)$$

and the potential of the right-hand cylinder is

$$V_2 = - \frac{\sigma}{2\pi\epsilon_0} \log \frac{a}{d} = -V_1 \qquad (6)$$

The capacity is then

$$C = \frac{\sigma}{V_1 - V_2} = \frac{\pi\epsilon_0}{\log{(a/d)}} = \frac{\pi\epsilon_0}{\log{(x/a)}} \qquad \text{farads/m} \qquad (7)$$

where the last part of (7) comes from the image relation $d/a = a/x$.

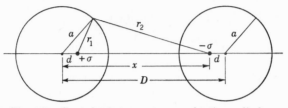

Fig. 1.7a. Capacity between two conducting cylinders.

It is more convenient to write (7) in terms of the separation of the centers of the cylinders:

$$\frac{D}{a} = \frac{x}{a} + \frac{d}{a} = \frac{x}{a} + \frac{a}{x} = e^{\pi\epsilon_0/C} + e^{-\pi\epsilon_0/C} = 2\cosh\frac{\pi\epsilon_0}{C} \qquad (8)$$

or

$$C = \frac{\pi\epsilon_0}{\cosh^{-1}{(D/2a)}} \qquad \text{farads/m} \qquad (9)$$

In actual engineering practice, (7) is often used as an approximation with $x \approx D$ if $a \ll D$.

1.8 Optimum Dimensions for a High-voltage Coaxial Line

Coaxial transmission lines are frequently used for transmitting power at very high voltages at direct current (in high voltage X-ray applications, for instance) and at both low and high frequencies. For a fixed outer radius there is clearly a best value for the radius of the inner conductor, because if it is too large the spacing between the two conductors becomes so small that for a given potential difference between the two the maximum E that the dielectric (usually air) can withstand is exceeded. On the other hand, a very small inner radius will result in a very high E at the surface of the inner conductor because of its small radius of curvature. In any case the maximum E, E_m, will be at the surface of the inner conductor.

The value of E, E_m, at the inner conductor is

$$E_m = \frac{\sigma}{2\pi\epsilon_0 b} \qquad (1)$$

where b is the radius of the inner conductor. We will take a to be the radius of the outer conductor. Using Equation (2), Section 1.7, to obtain the value of σ corresponding to a given difference of potential ΔV between the two cylindrical surfaces, we have instead of (1),

$$E_m = \frac{\Delta V}{b \log \dfrac{a}{b}} \tag{2}$$

If we now let $x = a/b$ and change Equation (2) so that only x and a (which is fixed) occur, we have

$$E_m = \frac{\Delta V}{a} \frac{x}{\log x} \tag{3}$$

The minimum value of (3) will then occur when dE_m/dx is zero,

$$\frac{dE_m}{dx} = \frac{\Delta V}{a} \left[\frac{1}{\log x} - \frac{1}{(\log x)^2} \right] = 0 \tag{4}$$

or when $\log x = 1$. This occurs when $x = a/b = e$, the base of the natural logarithm system. We shall find later that this corresponds to a 60-ohm transmission line.

PROBLEMS

1. A circular disk of radius R is charged to a uniform surface density σ. Find the electric field on the axis of the disk at a distance z from the center.

2. Two conducting concentric spheres of radius a and $b(a < b)$ are to have a potential difference V_0. What is the ratio of a to b for a minimum field intensity at the surface of a? Assume b to be fixed.

3. Four equal large conducting planes A, B, C, and D are fixed parallel to one another, with equal spacing "a." Planes A and D are grounded, B has total charge σ per unit area, and C has total charge σ' per unit area. Find V_B and V_C. Neglect fringing fields.

4. Consider an infinitely long cylindrical volume of radius a. The charge density ρ is constant inside this volume and is zero outside. What is $\mathbf{E}$ at all points?

5. In rectangular coordinates, the region from $z = 0$ to $z = a$ has a uniform charge density ρ_0. $\rho = 0$ outside this region. What is $\mathbf{E}$ at all points inside and outside this region?

6. Given a sphere filled with charge of constant density, prove that at points within the sphere, the field is directly proportional to the distance from the center.

7. A charge q is located a distance x meters from the center of an insulated conducting sphere of radius a. How much charge must be added to the sphere so that the force on the charge q is zero?

8. A sphere of radius a is in the presence of an external charge q at a distance x from its center. Show that if the sphere is grounded, the ratio of the charge on the part of the sphere visible from q to that on the rest is

$$\sqrt{\frac{(x + a)}{(x - a)}}$$

Hint: Use Gauss' theorem. The solid angle of the sphere as seen by the charge is

$$\Omega = 2\pi(1 - \cos \alpha) \qquad \text{where } \alpha = \sin^{-1}\left(\frac{a}{x}\right)$$

9. A charge q is placed within a hollow metal sphere a distance d from the center. Find the force attracting the charge to the inner surface of the sphere.

10. What is the least charge that must be carried by an insulated conducting sphere of radius a under the influence of a charge q at distance x from its center if the field is to be positive at all points on its surface?

11. Four equal charges are equally spaced around a conducting sphere of radius a in an equatorial plane. Each charge is at a distance x from the center of the sphere $(x > a)$. What is the change in force on one of the charges if the sphere, initially uncharged and insulated, is grounded?

12. Inside a hollow, infinitely long, grounded, conducting cylinder of radius R is placed a thin charged wire, carrying a charge σ per unit length. The wire is placed parallel to the axis of the cylinder, and distant by an amount d from the axis. Find the potential at points within the cylinder.

13. A spherical shell of radius a is placed inside of and concentric with a spherical shell of radius b. The outer sphere is grounded. A point charge is placed inside the inner sphere at a distance d from its center. What is the potential at all points inside the larger sphere?

14. Find the potential surfaces about two equal and opposite parallel-line charges. Show that they are circular cylinders.

2

Laplace's Equation

The methods of Chapter 1 are clearly restricted to quite simple problems. We shall now proceed to a more general method involving the use of partial differential equations. This method will in general have the less severe restriction that the boundary conditions of the problem should be expressible in a simple way in certain simple coordinate systems. We shall discuss in detail the solution of problems involving rectangular coordinates and to some extent problems involving spherical and cylindrical coordinates. The methods used in rectangular coordinates result in manipulation of simple, well-known functions such as trigonometric functions, exponentials, and hyperbolic sines and cosines; in addition, the usual methods of Fourier analysis shall be used.

Our understanding of problems involving rectangular coordinates shall not involve any mathematics presumably not already very well known to the reader. The methods developed apply directly to spherical and cylindrical coordinates, and in principle, problems can be solved just as easily in these coordinate systems. In practice, however, this is not the case, because less familiar functions such as Legendre polynomials and Bessel functions must be used and expansions of arbitrary functions must be made in terms of these functions. Several illustrative examples of spherical and cylindrical coordinates shall be given and some problems that do not involve complicated manipulation of advanced functions shall be solved in spherical and cylindrical coordinates.

2.1 Divergence Theorem and Poisson's Equation

We begin with a derivation of Poisson's equation which is based on the divergence theorem. This theorem states that for any vector field the surface integral of the normal component of a vector over a closed surface is equal to the volume integral of the divergence of this vector over the volume enclosed by the surface. Stated mathematically this means that for any vector field

$$\int_S \mathbf{F} \cdot \mathbf{n} \, da = \int_V \text{div } \mathbf{F} \, dv \tag{1}$$

This theorem is essentially an existence theorem. It says that there is a stated relation between the above surface integral and the volume integral of some unknown function of $\mathbf{F}$ which we will call div $\mathbf{F}$. If we can find that such a relation holds in rectangular coordinates, the theorem is proved and an expression for div $\mathbf{F}$ will be found for rectangular coordinates. Once Equation (1) is shown to be true, expressions for div $\mathbf{F}$ in other coordinate systems can easily be found by applying Equation (1) to a small volume. This is done in Appendix D.

We shall now derive an expression for div $\mathbf{F}$ in rectangular coordinates, thus proving Equation (1). $\mathbf{n}$ is the outer normal on the surface S. Consider a portion of the volume shown in Figure 2.1a, namely a rectangular prism parallel to the x axis. We have clearly

$$\int_{x_1}^{x_2} \frac{\partial F_x}{\partial x} \, dx = F_x \Big|_{x_1}^{x_2} \tag{2}$$

Now
$$-da_1 \, \mathbf{n}_1 \cdot \mathbf{i} = dy \, dz$$
$$da_2 \, \mathbf{n}_2 \cdot \mathbf{i} = dy \, dz \tag{3}$$

Thus $\left[\int_{x_1}^{x_2} \frac{\partial F_x}{\partial x} \, dx \right] dy \, dz = F_x(x_1)\mathbf{n}_1 \cdot \mathbf{i} \, da_1 + F_x(x_2)\mathbf{n}_2 \cdot \mathbf{i} \, da_2 \tag{4}$

Summing over all such elements in the volume, we have

$$\int_V \frac{\partial F_x}{\partial x} \, dv = \int_S F_x \mathbf{n} \cdot \mathbf{i} \, da = \int_S F_x \cos(n,x) \, da \tag{5}$$

Similar expressions hold for elements parallel to the y and z axes and we have

$$\int_V \left(\frac{\partial F_x}{\partial x} + \frac{\partial F_y}{\partial y} + \frac{\partial F_z}{\partial z} \right) dv = \int_S \mathbf{F} \cdot \mathbf{n} \, da \tag{6}$$

This is the divergence theorem; the integrand of the volume integral is called the divergence of $\mathbf{F}$:

$$\nabla \cdot \mathbf{F} = \text{div } \mathbf{F} = \frac{\partial F_x}{\partial x} + \frac{\partial F_y}{\partial y} + \frac{\partial F_z}{\partial z} \tag{7}$$

Expressions for div $\mathbf{F}$ in other coordinate systems are given in Appendix D.

A less rigorous derivation of the divergence theorem may be instructive. Consider a small rectangular volume as shown in Figure 2.1b.

The normal component of the flux of the vector **F** out through the left-hand face of this volume is $-F_x(x)\,dy\,dz$. The normal component of **F** through the right-hand side is $F_x(x + dx)\,dy\,dz$. If dx is

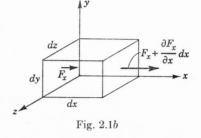

Fig. 2.1a. *(By permission from John C. Slater and Nathaniel H. Frank, "Electromagnetism," McGraw-Hill Book Company, Inc., New York, 1947.)*

Fig. 2.1b

small, $F_x(x + dx)$ is $F_x(x) + \dfrac{\partial F_x}{dx}\,dx$. The net flux through the two faces perpendicular to the x axis is then

$$\left[F_x(x) + \frac{\partial F_x}{dx}\,dx - F_x(x) \right] dy\,dz = \frac{\partial F_x}{dx}\,dx\,dy\,dz \qquad (8)$$

A corresponding argument also holds for the other faces, giving

$$\int_S \mathbf{F} \cdot \mathbf{n}\,da = \int_V \left(\frac{\partial F_x}{\partial x} + \frac{\partial F_y}{\partial y} + \frac{\partial F_z}{\partial z} \right) dx\,dy\,dz \qquad (9)$$

Thus we have proved the theorem for an elementary volume, where we define

$$\operatorname{div} \mathbf{F} = \frac{\partial F_x}{\partial x} + \frac{\partial F_y}{\partial y} + \frac{\partial F_z}{\partial z} \qquad (10)$$

in rectangular coordinates.

We see from the above that a physical picture of div **F** is as follows: It is the total outward flux of the vector per unit volume. A finite volume can be made up of a large number of elementary volumes as above. The outward flux of **F** on one face will be exactly cancelled by inward flux on the neighboring face for interior elementary volumes. At the surface of the finite volume, however, such cancellation does not occur and we have a sloppy proof of the divergence theorem. The weakness lies in the fact that an actual volume cannot be made up of an infinite number of rectangular volumes.

We now apply the divergence theorem to Gauss' law, which states that

$$\int_S \mathbf{E} \cdot \mathbf{n}\,da = \frac{\displaystyle\sum_n q_n}{\epsilon_0} \qquad (11)$$

If we consider a continuous distribution of charge of ρ coulombs per cubic meter, we can replace the right-hand side by $\int_V \rho/\epsilon_0 \, dv$, where ρ will in general be a function of position. We thus have

$$\int_S \mathbf{E} \cdot \mathbf{n} \, da = \int_V \frac{\rho}{\epsilon_0} \, dv \tag{12}$$

We can apply the divergence theorem to the left side of (12), giving

$$\int_S \mathbf{E} \cdot \mathbf{n} \, da = \int_V \text{div } \mathbf{E} \, dv = \int_V \frac{\rho}{\epsilon_0} \, dv \tag{13}$$

This is a general relation that must hold in any volume. For the last two volume integrals to be equal no matter what volume of integration is chosen, the integrands must be equal:

$$\text{div } \mathbf{E} = \frac{\rho}{\epsilon_0} \tag{14}$$

This is often referred to as the differential form of Gauss' law and (12) as the integral form of Gauss' law.

We wish now to change (14) into a form involving the potential. This is done by remembering that

$$\mathbf{E} = - \text{grad } \phi \tag{15}$$

which gives, on substitution into (14),

$$\text{div (grad } \phi) \equiv \nabla^2 \phi = \frac{-\rho}{\epsilon_0} \tag{16}$$

The operation div grad or, as it is often written, ∇^2 is called the Laplacian. In rectangular coordinates it is

$$\nabla^2 \phi = \frac{\partial^2 \phi}{\partial x^2} + \frac{\partial^2 \phi}{\partial y^2} + \frac{\partial^2 \phi}{\partial z^2} \tag{17}$$

The corresponding expressions in cylindrical and spherical coordinates are given in Appendix D. Equation (16) is called Poisson's equation. When ρ is taken to be zero, the equation becomes Laplace's equation:

$$\nabla^2 \phi = 0 \tag{18}$$

2.2 Some Special Solutions of Laplace's Equation in Rectangular Coordinates

Laplace's and Poisson's equations are partial differential equations and as such they are in general quite difficult to solve. There are an infinite number of solutions to such equations. The method of solving a problem is to select from this infinite number of solutions a suitable set that applies to the problem at hand. Such a set of solutions will often have an infinite number of terms in it.

We shall restrict ourselves to Laplace's equation for the present. This is a severe restriction but we are forced into it because of the difficulty of solving Poisson's equation. We thus at this time restrict ourselves to solving problems in regions where there is no space charge. There will of course be charges in the problem such as a few point or line charges and various conductors which will have fixed potentials. These, however, will be boundary conditions at the boundaries of the charge-free region where we are seeking solutions to Laplace's equation.

Before proceeding with a general solution to Laplace's equation it is well to mention that one special group of solutions can be written down by inspection. Clearly,

$$\phi = ax^2 + by^2 + cz^2 \tag{1}$$

is a solution, for on substitution in Equation (18), Section 2.1, we have

$$a + b + c = 0 \tag{2}$$

Not all of these constants can be positive, but any choice of a, b, and c which satisfies (2) will lead to a solution of Equation (18), Section 2.1. Such solutions are hyperboloids of one or two sheets. A similar solution is easily obtained in cylindrical coordinates for problems which have rotational symmetry.

A general solution of Laplace's equation in rectangular coordinates will now be obtained. This equation is

$$\frac{\partial^2 \phi}{\partial x^2} + \frac{\partial^2 \phi}{\partial y^2} + \frac{\partial^2 \phi}{\partial z^2} = 0 \tag{3}$$

The method of solution that we shall use is called "separation of variables." A solution of the form

$$\phi(x,y,z) = X(x)Y(y)Z(z) \tag{4}$$

is *assumed* and an attempt is made to find the functions X, Y, and Z. There is no guarantee that we shall succeed in this effort, but it has been found that such solutions do in fact exist for certain coordinate systems. Proceeding, we substitute (4) into (3), obtaining

$$YZ \frac{\partial^2 X}{\partial x^2} + XZ \frac{\partial^2 Y}{\partial y^2} + XY \frac{\partial^2 Z}{\partial z^2} = 0 \tag{5}$$

Dividing by XYZ we obtain

$$\frac{1}{X}\frac{\partial^2 X}{\partial x^2} + \frac{1}{Y}\frac{\partial^2 Y}{\partial y^2} + \frac{1}{Z}\frac{\partial^2 Z}{\partial z^2} = 0 \tag{6}$$

Thus the variables have been separated, for the first term is a function of x alone, the second a function of y alone, and the third a function of z alone. Now Equation (6) must hold no matter what value the variables x, y, and z have. This can only happen if each of the three terms is a constant. We can then write

$$\frac{1}{X}\frac{\partial^2 X}{\partial x^2} = a^2 \qquad \frac{1}{Y}\frac{\partial^2 Y}{\partial y^2} = b^2 \qquad \frac{1}{Z}\frac{\partial^2 Z}{\partial z^2} = c^2 \tag{7}$$

with the auxiliary condition

$$a^2 + b^2 + c^2 = 0 \tag{8}$$

Before proceeding with the easy solution of Equation (7) we must note that the restriction (8) means that the arbitrary constants a, b, and c cannot all be real or imaginary and still satisfy (8). Let us solve one of the equations of (7) and see just what this implies. Since only one variable is involved, we can replace the partial derivatives by total derivatives and get

$$\frac{1}{X}\frac{d^2 X}{dx^2} = a^2 \qquad \text{or} \qquad \frac{d^2 X}{dx^2} = a^2 X \tag{9}$$

If a is real and not zero, the solutions are

$$X = Ae^{ax} + Be^{-ax} \qquad \text{or} \qquad X = A \sinh ax + B \cosh ax \tag{10}$$

If a is imaginary, let $a = j\alpha$ and the equation becomes

$$\frac{d^2 X}{dx^2} = -\alpha^2 X \tag{11}$$

The potential itself must be real so we seek a real solution to (11). Such a solution is

$$X = A \sin \alpha x + B \cos \alpha x \tag{12}$$

The special case $a = 0$ results in the zero order or linear solution

$$X = A_0 x + B_0 \tag{13}$$

All the above solutions involve two arbitrary constants since we are solving a second-order differential equation. Similar solutions exist for Y and Z. We cannot choose any combination of these solutions, but must always choose the constants so as to satisfy (8). This means that if none of a, b, or c is zero, at least one of the solutions must *guthing a-term in (8)*

guthing a positive term in (8)

be trigonometric and at least one must be exponential, the third solution being of either kind. The values of the constants chosen must satisfy (8). If one of the constants is zero, one solution will be exponential, the other trigonometric, and the third a linear solution, as in (13).

Which solutions we choose depends on the problem to be solved. In general certain boundary conditions can be expressed in terms of trigonometric functions, as by a Fourier series, and this shall guide our choice of the type of solution to use. We shall not find it convenient to use the constants a, b, and c as above in solving an actual problem, but rather certain other constants k_x, k_y, and k_z. Thus if the desired solutions are of the form

$$\phi = \begin{Bmatrix} \sin \\ \cos \end{Bmatrix} k_x x \begin{Bmatrix} \sin \\ \cos \end{Bmatrix} k_y y \{e^{\pm k_z z}\} \tag{14}$$

the auxiliary condition (15) is expressed by

$$-k_x{}^2 - k_y{}^2 + k_z{}^2 = 0 \tag{15}$$

We use in (14) a special nomenclature of indicating a linear combination of two functions. Thus $\begin{Bmatrix} \sin \\ \cos \end{Bmatrix} k_x x$ means $A \sin k_x x + B \cos k_x x$, and $\{e^{\pm k_z z}\}$ means $A e^{k_z z} + B e^{-k_z z}$ where A and B are arbitrary constants.

We shall choose the type of solution wanted and then make up an auxiliary condition (15) from these chosen solutions. Trigonometric solutions will lead to negative contributions to the auxiliary equation, and exponentials to positive contributions. It is seen from (15) that only two of the arbitrary constants can be chosen at will, the third being determined by (15).

The use of the above solutions is best demonstrated by a number of examples. It should be noted that if the potential does not vary with a certain dimension the linear solution (13) must be used for this dimensional solution and the corresponding constant is (15) placed equal to zero.

2.3 Some Examples in Rectangular Coordinates : Fourier Series

Example 1. The potential in the xz plane is given by $V = V_0 \sin px$ and is independent of z. Find the potential at all points.

Solution. Since the problem is independent of z, $k_z = 0$ and $Z = A_0 z + B_0$ where we must choose $A_0 = 0$, and can set $B_0 = 1$.

The boundary condition at $y = 0$ suggests a trigonometric solution for X with $k_x = p$. The auxiliary condition then becomes

$$-k_x^2 + k_y^2 = -p^2 + k_y^2 = 0 \qquad (1)$$
or
$$k_y = \pm p \qquad (2)$$

The solution then is of the form

$$V = (A \sin px + B \cos px)(Ce^{py} + De^{-py}) \qquad (3)$$

It is clear that in the region of positive y the potential must become zero at large y. Therefore $C = 0$ for positive y. The boundary condition at $y = 0$ is then satisfied by taking $B = 0$ and $A = V_0$, giving the solution

$$V = V_0 e^{-py} \sin px \qquad y \geq 0 \qquad (4)$$

The solution for negative y is clearly

$$V = V_0 e^{+py} \sin px \qquad y \leq 0 \qquad (5)$$

To check this we note that the solution meets the boundary conditions at $y = 0$ and at $y = \pm \infty$ and that it is also a solution of Laplace's equation. Such a solution is unique and these are only conditions that the solution must satisfy, as shown in Appendix E.

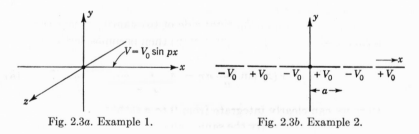

Fig. 2.3a. Example 1.   Fig. 2.3b. Example 2.

Example 2. Let the potential in the xz plane be given as a square wave in the x direction, each "wavelength" being of width $2a$ and amplitude V_0. The potential is independent of z.

Solution. Before proceeding with the solution proper, we must obtain the boundary condition in a suitable mathematical form. This is done by Fourier series. At $y = 0$ the potential is a square wave as in Figure 2.3c. In general this can be expressed as

$$V(x) = V(x) = \sum_{n=0}^{\infty} \left(A_n \sin \frac{\pi n x}{a} + B_n \cos \frac{\pi n x}{a} \right) \qquad (6)$$

Here the function is clearly odd, so only odd functions will appear in the expansion, making $B_n = 0$.   We can easily see that only odd n will appear.   The method of Fourier series is to multiply both sides of (6) by $\sin \dfrac{\pi p x}{a}$, where p is any integer, and integrate over the whole period, namely from $x = -a$ to $x = +a$.

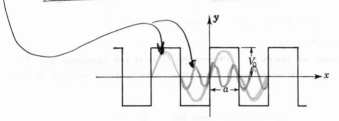

Fig. 2.3c. Potential for Example 2.

The following formulas apply:

$$\int_{-\pi}^{\pi} \sin nx \sin px\, dx = 0 \qquad \text{if } n \neq p$$

$$\int_{-\pi}^{\pi} \sin nx \cos px\, dx = 0 \qquad \text{in any case}$$

(7)

The result of this operation in view of (7) is that all the terms of the infinite sum on the right side of (6) vanish, except that one term for which $n = p$.   Equation (6) then becomes, letting $p = n$,

$$\int_{-a}^{+a} V(x) \sin \frac{\pi n x}{a}\, dx = A_n \int_{-a}^{+a} \sin^2 \frac{\pi n x}{a}\, dx \qquad (8)$$

Here we can clearly integrate from 0 to a rather than from $-a$ to $+a$ and will get exactly the same value of A_n.   The reason for this is that $V(x)$ is odd, as is $\sin \pi n x/a$ so that both integrands in (8) are even.   The contribution to the integrals from $-a$ to 0 is equal to that from 0 to a and hence only the integral from 0 to a need be computed.

A similar situation holds for an even function, where again only the integral over one of the symmetric half-periods need be computed.   If the function is neither even nor odd, the integration must be done over the full period.   For this problem we can replace (8) by

$$V_0 \int_{0}^{a} \sin \frac{\pi n x}{a}\, dx = A_n \int_{0}^{a} \sin^2 \frac{\pi n x}{a}\, dx \qquad (9)$$

These integrals are easily evaluated, the one on the right becoming

$$\int_0^a \sin^2 \frac{\pi n x}{a}\, dx = \frac{a}{\pi n} \int_0^{\pi n} \sin^2 \theta\, d\theta$$

$$= \frac{a}{\pi n} \left(\frac{\theta}{2} - \frac{1}{4} \sin 2\theta \right) \Big|_0^{\pi n} = \frac{a}{\pi n} \frac{\pi n}{2} = \frac{a}{2} \quad (10)$$

The left-hand integral of (9) becomes

$$\int_0^a \sin \frac{\pi n x}{a}\, dx = \frac{a}{\pi n} \int_0^{\pi n} \sin \theta\, d\theta = \frac{a}{\pi n} \left(- \cos \pi n + 1 \right)$$

$$= \frac{2a}{\pi n} \qquad \text{for } n \text{ odd} \quad (11)$$

$$= 0 \qquad \text{for } n \text{ even}$$

Equation (9) thus becomes, for n odd,

$$V_0 \frac{2a}{\pi n} = A_n \frac{a}{2} \qquad \text{or} \qquad A_n = \frac{4V_0}{\pi n} \quad (12)$$

Clearly $A_n = 0$ for n even. The boundary condition at $x = 0$ then is

$$V(x) = \sum_{\text{odd } n} \frac{4V_0}{\pi n} \sin \frac{\pi n x}{a} \quad (13)$$

We now proceed to choose the solutions of Laplace's equation that will fit this problem. As before, $Z = 1$ since the problem is independent of z. Equation (13) suggests that trigonometric solutions be used for X and this forces us to use exponential solutions for Y. The solution is of the form

due to auxiliary equation consideration

$$V = (Ae^{-ky} + Be^{+ky})(C \cos kx + D \sin kx) \quad (14)$$

We use the same k in the exponential solution as in the trigonometric solution because of the auxiliary condition

$$-k_x{}^2 + k_y{}^2 = 0 \qquad \text{or} \qquad k_x = \pm k_y = \text{say} \pm k \quad (15)$$

Since the potential must obviously vanish at $|y| = \infty$, we have $B = 0$ for positive y and $A = 0$ for negative y. To meet the boundary condition at $x = 0$, we must choose an infinite set of solutions such as (14) with $C = 0$ and also choose $k = \pi n/a$ where n will be odd only. The solution for positive y thus becomes

$$V = \sum_{\text{odd } n} A_n e^{-\pi n y/a} \sin \frac{\pi n x}{a} \quad (16)$$

Letting y become 0 and comparing with (13) we find that we must choose $A_n = 4V_0/\pi n$ and the answer becomes

$$V = \sum_{\text{odd } n} \frac{4V_0}{\pi n} e^{-\pi n y/a} \sin \frac{\pi n x}{a} \qquad (17)$$

For negative y the exponent must have a positive sign. This solution seems rather formal, but some useful information can be obtained from it. Consider values of y such that $\pi y/a$ is somewhat larger than 1. Then values of n greater than 1 will not contribute very much to V and the potential will be approximately

$$V = \frac{4V_0}{\pi} e^{-\pi y/a} \sin \frac{\pi x}{a} \qquad (18)$$

Thus the potential drops off as $e^{-\pi y/a}$, showing that the potential variation caused by alternating strips falls off very rapidly with distance beyond a distance about equal to a.

We can write the general exponential solution in several ways. The normal way would be

$$X = A_1 e^{kx} + B_1 e^{-kx} \qquad (19)$$

However, we can also write

$$X = A_2 \sinh kx + B_2 \cosh kx \qquad (20)$$

since the exponentials of (19) can be combined, using the formulas

$$\begin{aligned}
\sinh kx &= \frac{e^{kx} - e^{-kx}}{2} \\
\cosh kx &= \frac{e^{kx} + e^{-kx}}{2}
\end{aligned} \qquad (21)$$

Again, we can write the exponential solution as

$$X = A_3 \cosh k(b \pm x)$$

or

$$X = A_3 \sinh k(b \pm x) \qquad (22)$$

where b is another arbitrary constant. This is merely another form of (20) since

$$\begin{aligned}
\sinh k(b \pm x) &= \sinh kb \cosh kx \pm \cosh kb \sinh kx \\
\cosh k(b \pm x) &= \cosh kb \cosh kx \pm \sinh kb \sinh kx
\end{aligned} \qquad (23)$$

We shall find these forms useful in matching various boundary conditions.

Example 3. A square-wave potential in x is in the xz plane and the plane at $y = b$ is at zero potential. The problem is independent of z. Find the potential at all points between $y = 0$ and $y = b$.

Solution. Let the square-wave potential be that of Example 2. Then the boundary condition at $y = 0$ is

$$V = \sum_{\text{odd } n} \frac{4V_0}{\pi n} \sin \frac{\pi n x}{a} \tag{24}$$

A suitable potential to choose is

$$V = \sum_{\text{odd } n} A_n \sinh \frac{\pi n}{a} (b - y) \sin \frac{\pi n x}{a} \tag{25}$$

We choose the term $\sinh (\pi n/a)(b - y)$ since this is one form of the exponential solution that must be used for Y; in particular it

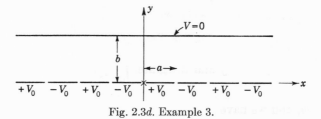

Fig. 2.3*d*. Example 3.

meets the boundary condition at $y = b$. To match the boundary condition at $y = 0$ we let $y = 0$ in (25) and compare with (24). This shows that we must choose

$$A_n \sinh \frac{\pi n b}{a} = \frac{4V_0}{\pi n}$$

or

$$A_n = \frac{4V_0}{\pi n} \frac{1}{\sinh \pi n b/ a} \tag{26}$$

The solution is thus

$$V = \sum_{\text{odd } n} \frac{4V_0}{\pi n} \frac{\sinh (\pi n/a)(b - y)}{\sinh \pi n b/a} \sin \frac{\pi n x}{a} \tag{27}$$

We could have used a solution of the form of (19) for Y but this would have involved a lot more work in determining A and B in (19) and the answer would not have been so neat.

Example 4. Find the potential at all points above an infinite checkerboard in the xy plane such that the black squares are at $+V_0$ and the white squares are at $-V_0$. Let the size of the squares be $a \times b$ and let the plane at $z = c$ be at zero potential.

Solution. Here the boundary condition in the xy plane is slightly more complicated than in Example 2. It is expressed by a double Fourier series:

$$V(z = 0) = \sum_{lm} A_{lm} \sin \frac{\pi l x}{a} \sin \frac{\pi m y}{b} \tag{28}$$

where we have chosen the origin at the corner of one of the black squares. Proceeding as in Example 2 we multiply through by

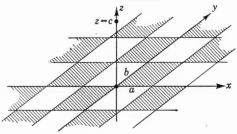

Fig. 2.3e. Example 4.

$\sin \dfrac{\pi p x}{a} \sin \dfrac{\pi q y}{b} \, dx \, dy$ and integrate $\displaystyle\int_0^b \int_0^a$. All the terms on the right side of (28) drop out except that one for which $p = l$ and $q = m$, and we have

$$\int_0^b \int_0^a V_0 \sin \frac{\pi l x}{a} \sin \frac{\pi m y}{b} \, dx \, dy$$

$$= A_{lm} \int_0^b \int_0^a \sin^2 \frac{\pi l x}{a} \sin^2 \frac{\pi m y}{b} \, dx \, dy \tag{29}$$

or

$$\frac{2a}{\pi l} \frac{2b}{\pi m} V_0 = A_{lm} \frac{ab}{4} \tag{30}$$

leading to

$$A_{lm} = \frac{16 V_0}{\pi^2 l m} \qquad \text{for } l \text{ and } m \text{ odd}$$

$$A_{lm} = 0 \qquad \text{for } l \text{ or } m \text{ even} \tag{31}$$

Equation (28) then becomes

$$V(z = 0) = \sum_{\text{odd } lm} \frac{16 V_0}{\pi^2 l m} \sin \frac{\pi l x}{a} \sin \frac{\pi m y}{b} \tag{32}$$

For the solution in z we choose

$$Z = \sinh k_z (c - z) \tag{33}$$

which will meet the boundary condition at $z = c$.

Consideration of (32) leads us to choose trigonometric solutions for X and Y, which forces us to choose an exponential solution such as (33) for Z. k_z is determined from the auxiliary condition

$$-k_x{}^2 - k_y{}^2 + k_z{}^2 = 0 \qquad (34)$$

Comparison with (32) shows that to match the boundary condition at $z = 0$ we must choose

$$k_x = \frac{\pi l}{a} \qquad k_y = \frac{\pi m}{b}$$

and hence

$$k_z = \sqrt{\left(\frac{\pi l}{a}\right)^2 + \left(\frac{\pi m}{b}\right)^2} \qquad (35)$$

The solution is then of the form

$$V = \sum_{lm} B_{lm} \sinh k_z(c - z) \sin \frac{\pi l x}{a} \sin \frac{\pi m y}{b} \qquad (36)$$

Comparison with (32) with $z = 0$ shows that we must choose

$$B_{lm} \sinh k_z c = \frac{16 V_0}{\pi^2 lm}$$

and the answer is

$$V = \sum_{\text{odd } lm} \frac{16 V_0}{\pi^2 lm} \frac{\sinh k_z(c - z)}{\sinh k_z c} \sin \frac{\pi l x}{a} \sin \frac{\pi m y}{b} \qquad (37)$$

where k_z is given by (35).

Inspection of the above problems will show that we have also solved several other problems which may be more interesting and useful than those we set out to solve. Consider Example 2 and its solution (17).

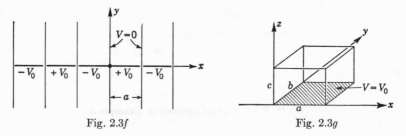

Fig. 2.3f   Fig. 2.3g

The plane $x = 0$ and the plane $x = a$ are clearly at zero potential; they can be replaced by grounded conducting surfaces. Thus the answer (17) is also the answer to the problem: Find the potential at all points if the planes $x = 0$ and $x = a$ are grounded and the region $y = 0$ between these two planes is at $+V_0$ volts. Everything, of course, is independent of z.

Similarly, in Example 4, the planes $x = 0$, $x = a$ and $y = 0$, $y = b$ are at zero potential and can be replaced by grounded conducting planes. Thus the answer (37) also applies to the problem of a conducting box $a \times b \times c$, having the top and sides grounded, but with the bottom of the box a conductor at $+V_0$ volts. Various details of Fourier analysis are hidden in the above, such as the fact that at a discontinuity in the function under analysis the Fourier series will converge to the average value of the function at the discontinuity. The Fourier series (28) will thus converge to the value 0 at the boundary between two squares on the checkerboard.

2.4 Superposition

Several examples of the same type can be superimposed to give the solutions to more complicated problems if the conditions are just right.

Example 5. Find the potential at all points between $y = 0$ and $y = b$ for Figure 2.4a.

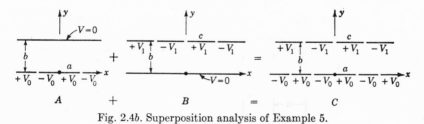

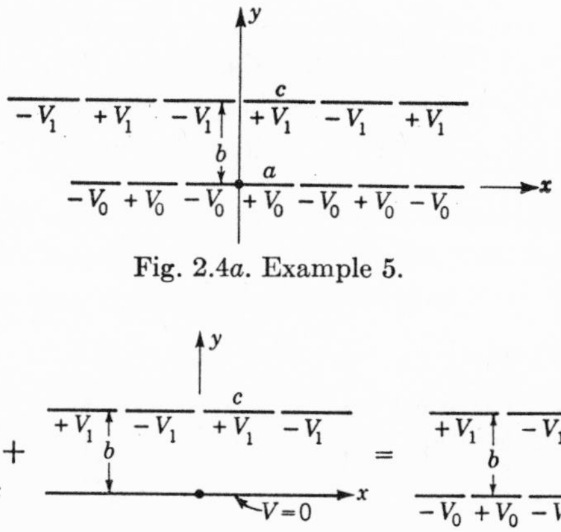

Fig. 2.4a. Example 5.

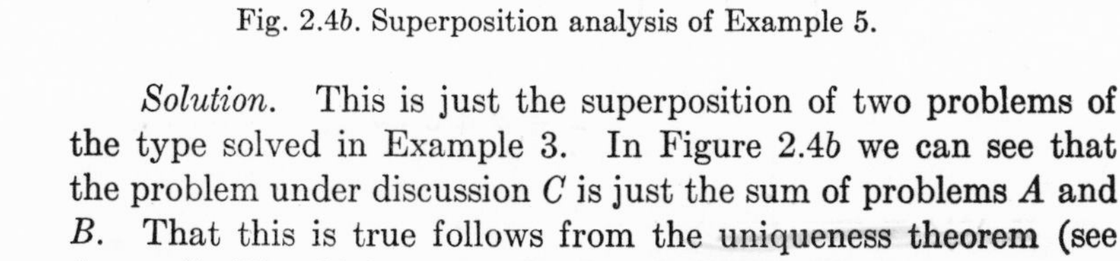

Fig. 2.4b. Superposition analysis of Example 5.

Solution. This is just the superposition of two problems of the type solved in Example 3. In Figure 2.4b we can see that the problem under discussion C is just the sum of problems A and B. That this is true follows from the uniqueness theorem (see Appendix E) which states that a solution to a problem is complete and unique if the solution is a solution of Laplace's equation and if it also satisfies all the boundary conditions. In the problem under consideration Problem A satisfies the boundary condition at $y = 0$ and makes no contribution to the potential at $y = b$. Problem B satisfies the boundary conditions at $y = b$ but makes no contribution at $y = 0$. Both solutions satisfy Laplace's equation and the boundary conditions are satisfied, so this is the solution of the problem. Problem A is solved by Equation (27), Section 2.3. The solution of Problem B can easily be shown to be

$$V_B = \sum_{\text{odd } n} \frac{4V_1}{\pi n} \frac{\sinh \pi n y/c}{\sinh \pi n b/c} \sin \frac{\pi n x}{c} \tag{1}$$

The whole solution is thus

$$V = \sum_{\text{odd } n} \frac{4V_0}{\pi n} \frac{\sinh (\pi n/a)(b - y)}{\sinh (\pi n b/a)} \sin \frac{\pi n x}{a}$$

$$+ \sum_{\text{odd } n} \frac{4V_1}{\pi n} \frac{\sinh \pi n y/c}{\sinh \pi n b/c} \sin \frac{\pi n x}{c} \tag{2}$$

Similar problems can be solved involving various sides of a conducting box at various potentials. Some of these problems have enough symmetry in them so that another plane at zero potential can be drawn to solve a problem having the cross section of a right triangle.

2.5   Gauss' Law and Series Solutions

Example 6.   Consider a grounded rectangular prism $a \times b$ in cross section with a line charge at $x = c$, $y = d$ of strength σ_0. Find the potential at all points inside the prism.

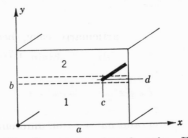

Fig. 2.5a. Line charge in a rectangular prism, Example 6.

Solution. Here we have the additional boundary condition of the line charge. We shall match this boundary condition by means of Gauss' law. We conveniently divide up the region of space into two regions, 1 and 2, as in Figure 2.5a, and expand the potential separately in these two regions. We write suitable expansions by inspection:

$$V_1 = \sum_n A_n \sinh \frac{\pi n y}{a} \sin \frac{\pi n x}{a}$$

$$V_2 = \sum_n B_n \sinh \frac{\pi n}{a} (b - y) \sin \frac{\pi n x}{a} \tag{1}$$

These two potentials must match everywhere along $y = d$. Thus at $y = d$ we must have $V_1 = V_2$, which requires that

$$A_n \sinh \frac{\pi n d}{a} = B_n \sinh \frac{\pi n}{a} (b - d)$$

or
$$B_n = \frac{A_n \sinh \pi n d / a}{\sinh (\pi n / a)(b - d)} \tag{2}$$

Equation (1) then becomes

$$V_1 = \sum_n A_n \sinh \frac{\pi n y}{a} \sin \frac{\pi n x}{a}$$

$$V_2 = \sum_n A_n \frac{\sinh (\pi n / a)(b - y)}{\sinh (\pi n / a)(b - d)} \sinh \frac{\pi n d}{a} \sin \frac{\pi n x}{a} \tag{3}$$

This matches the boundary condition $V_1 = V_2$ at $y = d$.

We now match the boundary condition concerning the line charge. The procedure is to expand the charge distribution $\sigma(x)$ at $y = d$ in a Fourier series in x.

$$\sigma(x) = \sum_n C_n \sin \frac{\pi n x}{a} \tag{4}$$

Here the expansion is particularly easy, because we multiply through by $\int_0^a \sin (\pi p x / a) \, dx$ and obtain, letting $p = n$,

$$\int_0^a \sigma(x) \sin \frac{\pi n x}{a} \, dx = C_n \frac{a}{2} \tag{5}$$

In this case the integrand has a value different from zero only at $x = c$, so we can take $\sin (\pi n c / a)$ out in front of the integral, and

$\int_0^a \sigma(x)\, dx$ just equals σ_0. Thus

$$C_n = \frac{2\sigma_0}{a} \sin \frac{\pi n c}{a} \tag{6}$$

We now apply Gauss' law to the "Gaussian volume" between the dotted lines in Figure 2.5a. At $y = d$ and at any x we have

[margin handwritten note: ∂ w.r.t. y is chosen since the y surface is the only one ⊥ to the E field. From line charge, the end caps (do at x=o,a) are differentially small, and contribute nothing to E·da]

$$\frac{\sigma(x)}{\epsilon_0} = -\frac{\partial V_2}{\partial y} + \frac{\partial V_1}{\partial y} \quad \text{\small per unit areas are assumed.} \tag{7}$$

The right side can be evaluated from (3) and the left side from the Fourier-series expansion of $\sigma(x)$ just completed. We then multiply through by $\int_0^a \sin \frac{\pi p x}{a}\, dx$ and readily obtain

$$\frac{2\sigma_0}{a\epsilon_0} \sin \frac{\pi n c}{a} \frac{a}{2} = A_n \frac{\pi n}{a} \frac{a}{2} \left[\cosh \frac{\pi n d}{a} + \frac{\cosh (\pi n/a)(b-d)}{\sinh (\pi n/a)(b-d)} \sinh \frac{\pi n d}{a} \right]$$

$$= A_n \frac{\pi n}{2} \frac{1}{\sinh \frac{\pi n}{a}(b-d)} \left[\sinh \frac{\pi n}{a}(b-d) \cosh \frac{\pi n d}{a} \right.$$

$$\left. + \cosh \frac{\pi n}{a}(b-d) \sinh \frac{\pi n d}{a} \right]$$

$$= A_n \frac{\pi n}{2} \frac{\sinh \pi n b/a}{\sinh (\pi n/a)(b-d)} \tag{8}$$

Finally we obtain the solution

$$A_n = \frac{2\sigma_0}{\epsilon_0 \pi n} \frac{\sin \pi n c/a \, \sinh (\pi n/a)(b-d)}{\sinh \pi n b/a}$$

$$\text{or} \quad V_1 = \sum_n \frac{2\sigma_0}{\epsilon_0 \pi n} \frac{\sin \pi n c/a}{\sinh \pi n b/a} \sinh \frac{\pi n}{a}(b-d) \sinh \frac{\pi n y}{a} \sin \frac{\pi n x}{a}$$

$$V_2 = \sum_n \frac{2\sigma_0}{\epsilon_0 \pi n} \frac{\sin \pi n c/a}{\sinh \pi n b/a} \sinh \frac{\pi n d}{a} \sinh \frac{\pi n}{a}(b-y) \sin \frac{\pi n x}{a} \tag{9}$$

If there had been some other charge distribution at $y = d$, the Fourier-series expansion of $\sigma(x)$ would have entailed some more work but the method would have been the same.

We shall now extend this problem to find the force on this line charge. The electric field that we can compute from (9) arises from both σ_0 itself, E_σ, as well as from charges induced on the walls E_w. We wish to compute just that part of E that is caused by the wall charges E_w. We shall calculate only E_y and rewrite (9) as

$$V_1 = \sum_n B_n \sinh \frac{\pi n}{a} (b - d) \sinh \frac{\pi n y}{a} \sin \frac{\pi n x}{a}$$

$$V_2 = \sum_n B_n \sinh \frac{\pi n d}{a} \sinh \frac{\pi n}{a} (b - y) \sin \frac{\pi n x}{a} \qquad (10)$$

where $\quad B_n = \dfrac{2\sigma_0}{\epsilon_0 \pi n} \dfrac{\sin \pi n c/a}{\sinh \pi n b/a}$

Close to σ_0 we have

$$E_{y1} = -E_{y\sigma} + E_{yw} \qquad \text{and} \qquad E_{y2} = E_{y\sigma} + E_{yw}$$

(see Figure 2.5b). Hence $E_{y2} + E_{y1} = 2E_{yw}$. At $x = c$, we

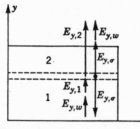

Fig. 2.5b. Forces on a line charge in a rectangular prism.

shall calculate E_{y2} at $y = d + \delta$ and E_{y1} at $y = d - \delta$, where δ is small.

$$E_{y2} = \sum_n B_n \frac{\pi n}{a} \sin \frac{\pi n c}{a} \sinh \frac{\pi n d}{a} \cosh \frac{\pi n}{a} (b - d - \delta)$$

$$E_{y1} = - \sum_n B_n \frac{\pi n}{a} \sin \frac{\pi n c}{a} \sinh \frac{\pi n}{a} (b - d) \cosh \frac{\pi n}{a} (d - \delta)$$

$$E_{y1} + E_{y2} = 2E_{yw} = \sum_n B_n \frac{\pi n}{a} \sin \frac{\pi n c}{a}$$

$$\left[\sinh \frac{\pi n d}{a} \cosh \frac{\pi n}{a} (b - d - \delta) - \cosh \frac{\pi n}{a} (d - \delta) \sinh \frac{\pi n}{a} (b - d) \right]$$

and as $\delta \to 0$ we obtain

$$E_{yw} = \frac{1}{2} \sum_n B_n \frac{\pi n}{a} \sin \frac{\pi n c}{a} \sinh \frac{\pi n}{a} (2d - b) \qquad (11)$$

As expected, $E_{yw} = 0$ when $d \to b/2$. E_{xw} can be obtained from the above interchanging a and b and also c and d.

It is somewhat more elegant to treat this problem differently at the start. For instance, (1) is

$$V_1 = \sum_n A_n \sinh \frac{\pi n y}{a} \sin \frac{\pi n x}{a}$$

$$V_2 = \sum_n B_n \sinh \frac{\pi n}{a} (b - y) \sin \frac{\pi n x}{a} \tag{12}$$

We have not yet determined A_n and B_n, so we can multiply the right-hand side of both of these equations by any function we choose which does not depend on x or y. We can choose these new functions by inspection so that $V_1 = V_2$ at $y = d$ and at the same time reduce the number of unknowns from two (A_n and B_n) to one (A'_n). Inspection shows that we should write

$$V_1 = \sum_n A'_n \sinh \frac{\pi n y}{a} \sin \frac{\pi n x}{a} \sinh \frac{\pi n}{a} (b - d)$$

$$V_2 = \sum_n B'_n \sinh \frac{\pi n}{a} (b - y) \sin \frac{\pi n x}{a} \sinh \frac{\pi n d}{a} \tag{13}$$

When $y = d$, $V_1 = V_2$ only if we choose $A'_n = B'_n$, giving

$$V_1 = \sum_n A'_n \sinh \frac{\pi n y}{a} \sin \frac{\pi n x}{a} \sinh \frac{\pi n}{a} (b - d)$$

$$V_2 = \sum_n A'_n \sinh \frac{\pi n}{a} (b - y) \sin \frac{\pi n x}{a} \sinh \frac{\pi n d}{a} \tag{14}$$

Using (14) instead of (3) we of course obtain (9) by the same method. In this case

$$A'_n = \frac{2\sigma_0}{\epsilon_0 \pi n} \sin \frac{\pi n c}{a} \frac{1}{\sinh (\pi n b / a)} \tag{15}$$

This method keeps the expressions for V_1 and V_2 more symmetric and reduces somewhat the algebraic work in obtaining the answer.

A different problem arises in the case of a grid of parallel wires terminating a uniform field.

Example 7. Find the potential distribution about a set of parallel-line charges each of strength σ_0, separated by a distance $2a$, that terminate a uniform electric field.

Solution. The Fourier-series expansion of the charge density at $y = 0$ will include a constant term here as the average charge density is not zero.   At $y = 0$ we have

$$\sigma(x) = C_0 + \sum_{n=1}^{\infty} C_n \cos \frac{\pi n x}{a} \tag{16}$$

In this case we shall integrate over the whole period from $x = -a$ to $x = +a$.   We obtain

$$\int_{-a}^{+a} \sigma(x) \, dx = C_0 \int_{-a}^{+a} dx \qquad \text{or} \qquad \sigma_0 = 2aC_0$$

and

$$\int_{-a}^{+a} \sigma(x) \cos \frac{\pi n x}{a} \, dx = C_n a = \sigma_0$$

Thus

$$\sigma(x) = \frac{\sigma_0}{2a} + \sum_{n=1}^{\infty} \frac{\sigma_0}{a} \cos \frac{\pi n x}{a} \tag{17}$$

Suitable potentials to use in each region are

$$V_1 = \sum_{n=1}^{\infty} A_n e^{-\pi n y/a} \cos \frac{\pi n x}{a} + A_0 y$$

$$\tag{18}$$

$$V_2 = \sum_{n=1}^{\infty} A_n e^{+\pi n y/a} \cos \frac{\pi n x}{a}$$

Note that $V_1 = V_2$ at $y = 0$ when the same coefficient is used in

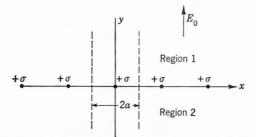

Fig. 2.5c. Line charges terminating a uniform field, Example 7.

both Fourier expansions.   At $y = 0$ we must have at every value of x

$$\frac{\sigma(x)}{\epsilon_0} = -\frac{\partial V_1}{\partial y} + \frac{\partial V_2}{\partial y} \tag{19}$$

Using (17) for $\sigma(x)$ and (18) for V_1 and V_2 we integrate (19) from $-a$ to $+a$:

$$\frac{\sigma_0}{2a\epsilon_0} = -A_0 \tag{20}$$

Multiplying both sides of (19) by $\cos \dfrac{\pi p x}{a} \, dx$ and integrating from $-a$ to $+a$ we have

$$\frac{\sigma_0}{a\epsilon_0} = \frac{2\pi n}{a} A_n \qquad \text{or} \qquad A_n = \frac{\sigma_0}{2\pi n \epsilon_0} \tag{21}$$

Finally we obtain

$$V_1 = \sum_{n=1}^{\infty} \frac{\sigma_0}{2\pi n \epsilon_0} e^{-\pi n y/a} \cos \frac{\pi n x}{a} - \frac{\sigma}{2a\epsilon_0} y$$

$$V_2 = \sum_{n=1}^{\infty} \frac{\sigma_0}{2\pi n \epsilon_0} e^{\pi n y/a} \cos \frac{\pi n x}{a} \tag{22}$$

If we now replace $\sigma_0/(2a\epsilon_0)$ by E_0, the uniform field at large y, we obtain

$$V_1 = \sum_{n=1}^{\infty} \frac{E_0 a}{\pi n} e^{-\pi n y/a} \cos \frac{\pi n x}{a} - E_0 y$$

$$V_2 = \sum_{n=1}^{\infty} \frac{E_0 a}{\pi n} e^{\pi n y/a} \cos \frac{\pi n x}{a} \tag{23}$$

Clearly (23) is the solution to the problem of an array of grounded thin wires terminating a uniform electric field E_0. Equation (23) shows that the leakage field at $y < -a$ is given approximately by

$$V = \frac{E_0 a}{\pi} e^{\pi y/a} \cos \frac{\pi x}{a} \tag{24}$$

The use of this expression to judge the quality of an electrostatic shield of this type is clear. The corresponding maximum E_y is

$$E_y = E_0 e^{\pi y/a} \tag{25}$$

This problem can also be solved by conformal transformation theory.

2.6 Laplace's Equation in Spherical Coordinates

We shall now discuss the solutions of Laplace's equation in spherical and cylindrical coordinates. We shall treat polar coordinates as a special case of cylindrical coordinates. The reader should have a clear understanding of these coordinate systems and of the expressions for grad, div, and div grad in these coordinate systems. This subject is discussed in the Appendix. We shall use the coordinates r, θ, and ϕ for spherical coordinates and r, θ, and z for cylindrical coordinates.

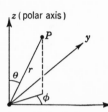

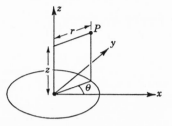

Fig. 2.6a. Spherical coordinates.   Fig. 2.6b. Cylindrical coordinates.

Laplace's equation in spherical coordinates is

$$\nabla^2 V = \frac{1}{r^2}\frac{\partial}{\partial r}\left(r^2\frac{\partial V}{\partial r}\right) + \frac{1}{r^2 \sin\theta}\frac{\partial}{\partial\theta}\left(\sin\theta\frac{\partial V}{\partial\theta}\right) + \frac{1}{r^2\sin^2\theta}\frac{\partial^2 V}{\partial\phi^2} = 0 \quad (1)$$

Solving this equation by the method of separation of variables, we substitute $V = R(r)\Theta(\theta)\Phi(\phi)$, and obtain, after dividing through by $R\Theta\Phi$,

$$\frac{1}{r^2 R}\frac{\partial}{\partial r}\left(r^2\frac{\partial R}{\partial r}\right) + \frac{1}{r^2\Theta\sin\theta}\frac{\partial}{\partial\theta}\left(\sin\theta\frac{\partial\Theta}{\partial\theta}\right) + \frac{1}{r^2\Phi\sin^2\theta}\frac{\partial^2\Phi}{\partial\phi^2} = 0 \quad (2)$$

Multiplying (2) by $r^2\sin^2\theta$ we obtain

$$\frac{\sin^2\theta}{R}\frac{\partial}{\partial r}\left(r^2\frac{\partial R}{\partial r}\right) + \frac{\sin\theta}{\Theta}\frac{\partial}{\partial\theta}\left(\sin\theta\frac{\partial\Theta}{\partial\theta}\right) + \frac{1}{\Phi}\frac{\partial^2\Phi}{\partial\phi^2} = 0 \quad (3)$$

The first two terms depend only on r and θ, and the last term depends only on ϕ. This is impossible unless the last term is a constant, as well as the sum of the first two terms. Putting the last term equal to $-m^2$, we have

$$\frac{d^2\Phi}{d\phi^2} + m^2\Phi = 0 \quad (4)$$

After dividing through by $\sin^2\theta$, (3) becomes

$$\frac{1}{R}\frac{d}{dr}\left(r^2\frac{dR}{dr}\right) + \frac{1}{\Theta\sin\theta}\frac{d}{d\theta}\left(\sin\theta\frac{d\Theta}{d\theta}\right) - \frac{m^2}{\sin^2\theta} = 0 \quad (5)$$

The first term of (5) is a function of r alone and the second two terms a function of θ alone. Let the first term be set equal to $l(l+1)$.

Equation (5) then becomes

$$\frac{d}{dr}\left(r^2\frac{dR}{dr}\right) - l(l+1)R = 0 \tag{6}$$

and

$$\frac{1}{\sin\theta}\frac{d}{d\theta}\left(\sin\theta\frac{d\Theta}{d\theta}\right) + \left[l(l+1) - \frac{m^2}{\sin^2\theta}\right]\Theta = 0 \tag{7}$$

The functions that we need are the solutions to equations (4), (6), and (7). Here we do not have an auxiliary condition as in rectangular coordinates since we have essentially eliminated it; as a result we have only two constants (m and l) which are now independent. We shall not investigate all the solutions to these equations, but shall limit ourselves to a few types that are most useful. Thus we shall choose m to be real, leading to the solution of (4):

$$\Phi = A\sin m\phi + B\cos m\phi \tag{8}$$

The solution to (6) is easily obtained by substituting $R = r^n$. We then find the two possible values of n to be $n = l$ or $n = -(l+1)$ leading to

$$R = a_l r^l + \frac{b_l}{r^{l+1}} \tag{9}$$

Equation (7) is known as Legendre's equation and the solutions are called Legendre functions. They are obtained by means of a complicated series expansion which we shall not present here. Wayland gives a detailed and excellent discussion (see Reference 12).*

If we restrict ourselves to a region in which ϕ can take on all possible values (this eliminates wedges in ϕ, for instance) only integer values of m are possible. This is because increasing ϕ by 2π returns us to the same point in space and the potential must then have the same value. This will occur for (8) only if m is an integer. Legendre functions are written $P_l^m(\cos\theta)$ or $P_l^m(\mu)$ where $\mu = \cos\theta$. Since this is the solution to a second order differential equation there must be another independent solution, and this is known as $Q_l^m(\mu)$. These functions, however, diverge for $\mu = \pm 1$ and are of use only when the polar axis is not in the region under consideration, as in cone problems. We shall not consider these functions further.

The $P_l^m(\mu)$ functions also diverge for $\mu = \pm 1$ unless l is also an integer. In this case the series expansion breaks off and we are left with a polynomial in μ. We shall consider only this case, and shall take both l and m to be integers. Further examination shows that $P_l^m(\mu)$ exists only for $l \geq m$. These polynomials are called associ-

* See Useful References at the end of the text.

ated Legendre polynomials; if $m = 0$, they are called Legendre polynomials and written $P_l(\mu)$.

The combination

$$Y_l^m(\mu,\phi) = P_l^m(\mu)(A \sin m\phi + B \cos m\phi) \qquad (10)$$

is called a spherical harmonic. This function is orthogonal in both μ and ϕ and is suitable for the expansion of arbitrary functions of μ and ϕ in spherical coordinates in just the same way that a double Fourier series is used to expand an arbitrary repetitive function in rectangular coordinates. In particular, these functions are used to express any reasonable function on the surface of a sphere. The integrations necessary for such an expression make considerable familiarity with the detailed properties of Legendre polynomials indispensable and are for this reason quite complicated. We shall use the following solution of Laplace's equation:

$$V = \sum_{lm} \left(a_l r^l + \frac{b_l}{r^{l+1}} \right) P_l^m(\mu)(A \sin m\phi + B \cos m\phi) \qquad (11)$$

We shall need the table of the properties of Legendre polynomials given in Appendix F. We shall now solve a simple example using spherical coordinates.

Example 8. Find the field at all points outside a conducting sphere of radius R situated in a uniform field.

Solution. Choose the potential of the sphere to be zero and let the uniform field be parallel to the polar axis. A uniform field is represented by choosing $m = 0$, $l = 1$ in (11), and letting $B = 1$, $A = 0$, $a_1 = -E_0$, $b_1 = 0$. Since $P_1(\mu) = \cos \theta$ this gives

$$V = -E_0 \, r \cos \theta$$

or, in rectangular coordinates,

$$V = -E_0 z \qquad (12)$$

In this problem there is clearly no dependence on ϕ, so we choose $m = 0$ and use the expansion

$$V = \sum_l \left(a_l r^l + \frac{b_l}{r^{l+1}} \right) P_l(\mu) \qquad (13)$$

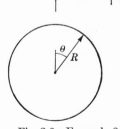

Fig. 2.6c. Example 8.

At large distances from the sphere, only the term $a_l r^l P_l(\mu)$ will be present and this must reduce to (12) since the effect of the sphere is limited. Thus we have only a_1 present, $a_l = 0$ for $l > 1$. Equation (13) then becomes

$$V = -E_0 r P_1(\mu) + \sum_l \frac{b_l}{r^{l+1}} P_l(\mu) \qquad (14)$$

This potential must meet the boundary condition $V = 0$ at $r = R$:

$$-E_0 R P_1(\mu) + \sum_l \frac{b_l}{R^{l+1}} P_l(\mu) = 0 \qquad (15)$$

We now use the orthogonal properties of the Legendre polynomials

$$\int_{-1}^{+1} P_l(\mu) P_n(\mu) \, d\mu = 0$$

unless $l = n$, when

$$\int_{-1}^{+1} [P_l(\mu)]^2 \, d\mu = \frac{2}{2l+1} \qquad (16)$$

Multiplying (15) by $P_n(\mu) \, d\mu$ and integrating over all possible values of μ, i.e., from -1 to $+1$, we have

$$E_0 R \int_{-1}^{+1} P_1(\mu) P_n(\mu) \, d\mu = \sum_l \frac{b_l}{R^{l+1}} \int_{-1}^{+1} P_l(\mu) P_n(\mu) \, d\mu \qquad (17)$$

Every term on the right is zero unless $l = n$. The term on the left is zero unless $n = 1$. Thus (17) shows that $b_l = 0$ for $l > 1$ and

$$E_0 R \frac{2}{3} = \frac{b_1}{R^2} \frac{2}{3}$$

or
$$b_1 = E_0 R^3 \qquad (18)$$

The solution then becomes

$$V = \left(-E_0 r + \frac{E_0 R^3}{r^2} \right) \cos \theta \qquad (19)$$

Inspection shows that this solution clearly meets the boundary condition at $r = R$ and $r = \infty$. It is a solution of Laplace's equation and is thus the only correct solution. This solution can also be obtained by image methods by considering the potential distribution about a conducting sphere in the field of two point charges of opposite polarity placed on opposite sides of the sphere. As these two charges are withdrawn to infinity and their charge increased as this is done, in the limit this will result in a uniform field far from the sphere, leaving two opposite image charges close together at the center of the sphere. Such a combination of charges is called a dipole and gives a field of the form $\cos\theta/r^2$ as in the second term of (19).

Example 9. A somewhat more difficult problem in spherical coordinates is the following: A spherical surface of radius R has $V = +V_0$ from $\theta = 0$ to $\theta = 90°$ and $V = -V_0$ from $\theta = 90°$ to $\theta = 180°$ (spherical coordinates). Find the potential at all points.

The answer to this problem is clearly

$$V_1 = \sum_l a_l \left(\frac{r}{R}\right)^l P_l(\mu)$$

$$V_2 = \sum_l a_l \left(\frac{R}{r}\right)^{l+1} P_l(\mu)$$

(20)

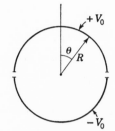

Fig. 2.6d. Example 9.

where V_1 is the potential for $r < R$ and V_2 for $r > R$. a_l is determined from

$$V(\mu) = V_0 \sum_l a_l P_l(\mu) \tag{21}$$

where $V(\mu) = +V_0$ for $1 > \mu > 0$ $(0° < \theta < 90°)$
         $V(\mu) = -V_0$ for $0 > \mu > -1$ $(90° < \theta < 180°)$

The potential distribution of this problem is seen to be quite similar to the square-wave potential in rectangular coordinates (Example 2). As in that problem, only odd l will occur here. Similarly, the expansion need only be carried from $\mu = 0$ to $\mu = 1$ since using odd l will then insure the correct potential for $0 > \mu > -1$. Multiplying both sides of (21) by $P_n(\mu)\,d\mu$ and integrating from 0 to 1, we have, using Equations (3) and (4), Appendix F,

$$\frac{a_l}{2l+1} = \int_0^1 P_l(\mu)\,d\mu = \frac{P_{l+1} - P_{l-1}}{2l+1}\bigg|_0^1 \tag{22}$$

Using Equations (9) to (12), Appendix F, we obtain

$$a_l = -\left[(-1)^{(l+1)/2}\frac{1\times3\times5\cdots l}{2\times4\times6\cdots(l+1)}\right.$$
$$\left. - (-1)^{(l-1)/2}\frac{1\times3\times5\cdots(l-2)}{2\times4\times6\cdots(l-1)}\right]$$
$$= -(-1)^{(l-1)/2}\frac{1\times3\times5\cdots(l-2)}{2\times4\times6\cdots(l-1)}\left[\frac{l}{l+1}\frac{(-1)^{(l+1)/2}}{(-1)^{(l-1)/2}} - 1\right]$$
$$= (-1)^{(l-1)/2}\frac{1\times3\times5\cdots(l-2)}{2\times4\times6\cdots(l+1)}(2l+1) \tag{23}$$

It should be noted that this example is in principle no more difficult than Example 2. The only actual difficulty is that involved in
performing the integration in (22), which is somewhat more arduous and
less familiar than computing $\int_0^a \sin \frac{\pi n x}{a}\, dx$ in Example 2.

2.7 Dipoles

We have already shown that one of the simple solutions of Equation (11), Section 2.6, is a uniform field in the direction of the polar
axis. If we choose $m = 0,\ l = 1$, the second term in r is of the form
$\cos \theta / r^2$ and is called the potential of a dipole. This potential distribution is just that arising from two equal and opposite charges very
close together, as is shown in Figure 2.7a. The potential at P is given
approximately by

$$V = \frac{q}{4\pi\epsilon_0}\left(\frac{1}{r - d/2\,\cos\theta} - \frac{1}{r + d/2\,\cos\theta}\right) \tag{1}$$

If $d \ll r$ this becomes

$$V \approx \frac{q}{4\pi\epsilon_0 r}\left(1 + \frac{d}{2r}\cos\theta - 1 + \frac{d}{2r}\cos\theta\right)$$

or $\qquad V = \frac{qd}{4\pi\epsilon_0 r^2}\cos\theta \tag{2}$

We now let d become small and q large in such a way that the product

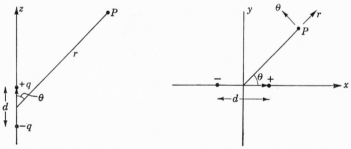

Fig. 2.7a. Spherical dipole.   Fig. 2.7b. Cylindrical dipole.

$qd \to m$ as a limit. m is called the dipole strength. The potential of
a dipole is thus

$$V = \frac{m}{4\pi\epsilon_0 r^2}\cos\theta \tag{3}$$

The field components are

$$E_r = \frac{2m}{4\pi\epsilon_0}\frac{\cos\theta}{r^3} \tag{4}$$

$$E_\theta = \frac{m}{4\pi\epsilon_0} \frac{\sin\theta}{r^3} \tag{5}$$

A similar expansion can be carried out for the case of two oppositely charged parallel line charges close together. If two line charges of strength $\pm\sigma$ are separated by a distance d as in Figure 2.7b, we easily obtain for $d \ll r$

$$
\begin{aligned}
V &= -\frac{\sigma}{2\pi\epsilon_0} \log\left(r - \frac{d}{2}\cos\theta\right) + \frac{\sigma}{2\pi\epsilon_0} \log\left(r + \frac{d}{2}\cos\theta\right) \\
&= \frac{\sigma}{2\pi\epsilon_0} \log\left[\frac{1 + d/2r\cos\theta}{1 - d/2r\cos\theta}\right] \\
&\approx \frac{\sigma}{2\pi\epsilon_0} \log\left(1 + \frac{d}{r}\cos\theta + \cdots\right) \approx \frac{\sigma d}{2\pi\epsilon_0}\frac{\cos\theta}{r}
\end{aligned} \tag{6}
$$

If we let σ increase and d decrease in such a fashion that the limit of σd approaches p, then

$$V = \frac{p}{2\pi\epsilon_0}\frac{\cos\theta}{r} \tag{7}$$

and p is called the strength of the linear dipole.

2.8 Laplace's Equation in Cylindrical Coordinates

We shall now consider the solutions of Laplace's equation in cylindrical coordinates. This equation is

$$\nabla^2 V = \frac{1}{r}\frac{\partial}{\partial r}\left(r\frac{\partial V}{\partial r}\right) + \frac{1}{r^2}\frac{\partial^2 V}{\partial\theta^2} + \frac{\partial^2 V}{\partial z^2} = 0 \tag{1}$$

We solve this by the method of separation of variables, letting

$$V = R\Theta Z$$

Substituting this and multiplying by r^2/V gives

$$\frac{r}{R}\frac{\partial}{\partial r}\left(r\frac{\partial R}{\partial r}\right) + \frac{1}{\Theta}\frac{\partial^2\Theta}{\partial\theta^2} + \frac{r^2}{Z}\frac{\partial^2 Z}{\partial z^2} = 0 \tag{2}$$

We let the second term be $-n^2$, multiply through by $1/r^2$, and obtain

$$\frac{1}{rR}\frac{\partial}{\partial r}\left(r\frac{\partial R}{\partial r}\right) - \frac{n^2}{r^2} + \frac{1}{Z}\frac{\partial^2 Z}{\partial z^2} = 0 \tag{3}$$

Letting the last term be k^2 and multiplying through by r^2R we obtain

$$r\frac{d}{dr}\left(r\frac{dR}{dr}\right) + (k^2r^2 - n^2)R = 0 \tag{4}$$

To put this equation into a simpler form we let $v = kr$, hence $\frac{\partial}{\partial r} = k\frac{\partial}{\partial v}$, and we obtain

$$\frac{1}{v}\frac{d}{dv}\left(v\frac{dR}{dv}\right) + \left(1 - \frac{n^2}{v^2}\right)R = 0 \tag{5}$$

This is Bessel's equation and has the solution

$$R_n(v) = A_n J_n(v) + B_n N_n(v) \tag{6}$$

or, in our case,

$$R_n(kr) = A_n J_n(kr) + B_n N_n(kr) \tag{7}$$

The J_n are similar to a sine wave of decreasing amplitude and slowly changing period. The N_n are $-\infty$ at the origin and hence are of use only when the origin is excluded from the problem. The equation for Θ is

$$\frac{d^2\Theta}{d\theta^2} = -n^2\Theta \tag{8}$$

leading to trigonometric solutions if n is real. The equation for Z is

$$\frac{d^2Z}{dz^2} = k^2 Z \tag{9}$$

which gives exponential solutions for real k. In general, useful solutions are obtained with real n, and k can be either real or imaginary depending on the problem at hand. The complete solution for real n and k is

$$V = [A_n J_n(kr) + B_n N_n(kr)]\begin{Bmatrix}\sin n\theta \\ \cos n\theta\end{Bmatrix}(e^{\pm kz}) \tag{10}$$

Example 10. A grounded conducting cylinder of radius a is closed off by a plate of radius a at potential V_0. Find the potential at all points.

Solution. Here there is clearly no dependence on θ, so we choose $n = 0$. The potential on the axis must not go to infinity, so $B_n = 0$. The potential at large z should drop to zero, so only e^{-kz} is used.

$$V = \sum_l A_l J_0(k_l r)e^{-k_l z} \tag{11}$$

At $z = 0$ this is

$$V = V_0 = \sum_l A_l J_0(k_l r) \qquad \text{for } r < a$$

$$V = 0 \qquad \text{at } r = a \tag{12}$$

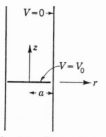

Fig. 2.8a. Example 10.

This must be zero at $r = a$, so we choose k_l such that $J_0(k_l a) = 0$ (i.e., $k_l a$ is the lth root of the zero order Bessel function J_0). We must now find A_l. Multiply both sides of (12) by $\int_0^a r J_0(k_s r)\, dr$. We obtain

$$V_0 \int_0^a r J_0(k_l r)\, dr = A_l \int_0^a r [J_0(k_l r)]^2\, dr \qquad (13)$$

by virtue of the orthogonality of the J_n functions, which states that $\int_0^a J_n(k_l r) J_n(k_s r) r\, dr = 0$ unless $l = s$, where $k_l a$ and $k_s a$ are roots of the J_n. In Appendix G the values of the integrals in (13) are given as

$$A_l \int_0^a r [J_0(k_l r)]^2\, dr = \frac{A_l}{2}\, [a J_1(k_l a)]^2 \qquad (14)$$

and
$$V_0 \int_0^a r J_0(k_l r)\, dr = V_0 \frac{a}{k_l} J_1(k_l a) \qquad (15)$$

Substituting these into (13) and solving for A_l we get

$$A_l = \frac{2 V_0}{[k_l a J_1(k_l a)]}$$

and the complete solution is

$$V = \sum_l \frac{2 V_0 e^{-k_l z} J_0(k_l r)}{(k_l a) J_1(k_l a)} \qquad (16)$$

where $k_l a$ is the lth root of $J_0(k_l a) = 0$.

The above is in principle no more difficult than the square wave in potential already treated in Cartesian coordinates. However, the mathematics involved in (14) and (15) and the general unfamiliarity with the expansion of functions in an infinite series of Bessel functions add many trees to the forest, making the latter somewhat invisible.

A much simpler solution to Laplace's equation in cylindrical coordinates is obtained by taking $k = 0$, giving

$$Z = A_0 z + B_0 \tag{17}$$

Then (4) becomes

$$r \frac{d}{dr}\left(r \frac{dR}{dr}\right) - n^2 R = 0 \tag{18}$$

We let $R = r^l$, substitute into (18), and find that the two possible values of l are $\pm n$, giving $R_n = a_n r^n + b_n r^{-n}$. Equation (8) still holds, and we have as the whole solution, when $k = 0$,

$$V = (a_n r^n + b_n r^{-n}) \begin{Bmatrix} \sin n\theta \\ \cos n\theta \end{Bmatrix} (A_0 z + B_0) \tag{19}$$

If $A_0 = 0$ this gives the solution when the potential does not depend on z, and the solutions (19) are called polar coordinate harmonics. The use of (19) is quite similar to that of Cartesian harmonics because we expand V at constant r in a Fourier series.

In some cases we must add to the solution of Laplace's equation the solution when both n and k are zero. We easily find this to be

$$V(n = k = 0) = (A_0 \log r + B_0)(C_0\theta + D_0)(E_0 z + F_0) \tag{20}$$

This is called a zero-order or logarithmic solution. If $E_0 = C_0 = 0$ this represents the potential of a line charge located on the axis.

Example 11. Consider two parallel line charges of unequal strength if of opposite sign. At some place on the plane containing these two line charges, the electric field from one line charge will exactly cancel that from the other line charge. In this two-dimensional problem this will occur along a line parallel to the line charges, and this line is called a neutral line. Describe the potential field near such a neutral line.

Solution. We take the z axis parallel to the two line charges. If we take the z axis to be anywhere except at the two line charges, the potential can be expanded as

$$V = \sum_n a_n r^n \cos n\theta \tag{21}$$

For r chosen sufficiently small, only the term with $n = 1$ in (21) will survive and, as expected, we obtain a uniform electric field arising from a potential near the origin of the form $V = a_1 r \cos\theta$. If we consider now a neutral line, choosing $\theta = 0$ to be in the plane containing the two line charges, we have

$$V = \Sigma a_n r^n \cos n\theta + C \tag{22}$$

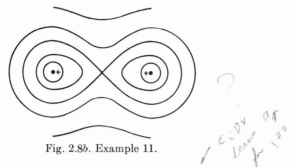

Fig. 2.8b. Example 11.

But E vanishes at a neutral line, so there can be no $n = 1$ term, implying $a_1 = 0$. The leading term of (22) must then be of the form

$$V = a_2 r^2 \cos 2\theta + C \qquad (23)$$

It is clear then that the potential surfaces $V = C$ cross at a neutral line, these two surfaces being (for $r \to 0$) the planes $\theta = \pm\pi/4$ and $\theta = \pm 3\pi/4$, where the first term in (23) vanishes. If there are more than two line charges of specified strength it is possible to have higher order neutral lines where more than two equipotential surfaces intersect.

Example 12. A grounded conducting cylinder of radius R is perpendicular to a uniform electric field E_0. Find the potential at all points.

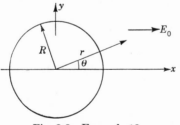

Fig. 2.8c. Example 12.

Solution. Since there is no z dependence here the general solution will be

$$V = \sum_n (a_n r^n + b_n r^{-n})(C_n \cos n\theta + D_n \sin n\theta) \qquad (24)$$

No zero-order solution such as (20) is needed here since there will be no net charge on the cylinder and no need for a line charge at the origin. Taking $\theta = 0$ to be in the direction of the external field, we choose $D_n = 0$ since the problem is even in θ. We can then choose $C_n = 1$, as the information in C_n can be contained in a_n and b_n.

The resultant solution will thus be

$$V = \sum_n (a_n r^n + b_n r^{-n}) \cos n\theta \tag{25}$$

n of course must be an integer, since the same potential must be obtained when θ is increased by 2π.

The boundary condition at large r is that we must have a uniform field E_0 in this region, since the effect of the cylinder is limited. If we take $\theta = 0$ to be in the x direction, a uniform field in the x direction is given by $V = -E_0 r \cos \theta$, since $r \cos \theta = x$. Inspection of (22) shows that at large r only the terms involving a_n will be important. We can see that $a_1 = -E_0$ and $a_n = 0$ for $n > 1$. This is so since any $a_n > 0$ for $n > 1$ will swamp $-E_0 r \cos \theta$ for r chosen sufficiently large, and this would violate the boundary condition at large r. Thus (25) becomes

$$V = -E_0 r \cos \theta + \sum_n b_n r^{-n} \cos n\theta \tag{26}$$

We determine b_n by the boundary condition that $V = 0$ at $r = R$. Using the normal methods of Fourier series, let us multiply both sides of (26) by $\cos m\theta$ and integrate from 0 to 2π. Every term of (26) is 0 unless $m = n = 1$. In this case we have

$$0 = -E_0 R \int_0^{2\pi} \cos^2 \theta \, d\theta + b_1 R^{-1} \int_0^{2\pi} \cos^2 \theta \, d\theta \tag{27}$$

giving $b_1 = E_0 R^2$. The solution to the problem is thus

$$V = \left(-E_0 r + \frac{E_0 R^2}{r} \right) \cos \theta \tag{28}$$

The form of the second term is called a linear dipole, and is the field arising from two parallel-line charges of opposite sign very close together as shown in Section 2.7.

We can easily work other problems of a similar nature. For instance, the field about a motor commutator, where alternate segments are at $\pm V_0$, is analogous to the square-wave potential problems in Cartesian coordinates. Likewise a line charge between two coaxial cylindrical surfaces can be solved in a way quite similar to that used for a line charge in a waveguide.

It should be noted that many of the problems that we have treated in this chapter can also be solved by conformal transformation theory.

The answers, however, appear in quite a different form and in any practical problem we should investigate both methods and determine which is more useful. Often the series method will lead to a more useful result if convergence is rapid and only the first term is needed in the region of interest. Image methods will also sometimes give a useful result.

PROBLEMS

1. If $V = r \sin \theta (A \sin \phi + B \cos \phi)$ (spherical coordinates), and $\mathbf{E} = -\nabla V$, evaluate $\nabla \cdot \mathbf{E}$.

2. If $V = r^2 \cos \theta \sin \phi$ (spherical coordinates) find ρ as a function of r, θ, ϕ by means of Poisson's equation.

3. In cylindrical coordinates the volume charge density is given by $\rho = \rho_0/r$, independent of θ and z. What is the potential at all points?

4. In rectangular coordinates, the plane $y = 0$ is at zero potential and the potential at $y = c$ is given by

$$V \equiv \sum_m B_m \sin \frac{\pi m x}{a}$$

What is the expression for B_m such that at $y = d(c > d > 0)$ the y component of the electric field will be given by

$$E_y = \sum_n C_n \sin \frac{\pi n x}{a}$$

5. Find the potential distribution arising from a set of conducting strips parallel to the z axis composed of flat strips of width a at $y = \pm b$. The potential of each plate increases with x and the potential difference between adjacent plates is V_0. Hint: A suitable linear solution must be used here.

6. Find the potential distribution at the gap of a cyclotron D. This system is one in which for x negative the two planes at $y = \pm a/2$ are at $-V_0/2$ volts and for x positive the two planes at $y = \pm a/2$ are at $+V_0/2$ volts.

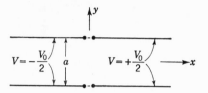

7. In rectangular coordinates, the planes $x = 0$ and $x = a$ are fixed at potential zero. At $(c,0)$ there is a line charge of strength σ. If $c < a$, what is the potential at all points between the two planes? Solve by using Cartesian harmonics.

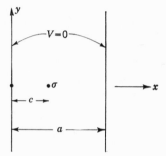

8. A point charge q is placed in a long waveguide $a \times b$ meters in cross section. If the coordinates of the point charge are $x = c$, $y = d$, $z = 0$, what is the potential at all points inside the guide?

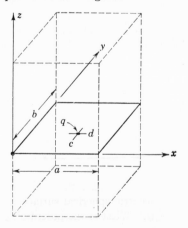

9. A grounded conducting box has sides a, b, and c meters long. If the origin is chosen at one corner and a point charge is placed at x_0, y_0, and z_0 inside the box, what is the potential at all points?

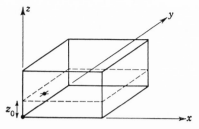

10. A grounded conducting box has dimensions $a \times b \times c$. The origin of a rectangular coordinate system is one corner such that each coordinate of every point inside the box is positive. A uniform sheet of surface charge, of strength σ_0 coulombs per square meter, is at $z = d$. Find the potential at all points inside the box.

11. Consider a box having dimensions $a \times b \times c$ in the x, y, and z directions respectively. Choose the center of the rectangular coordinate system to be at one corner of the box so that the coordinates of all points in the box are positive. The potential on the face of the box lying on the xy plane is given by

$$V_{xy0} = V_1 \sin \frac{\pi 2x}{a} \sin \frac{\pi 3y}{b}$$

The potential on the face of the box lying in the yz plane is given by

$$V_{0yz} = V_2 \sin \frac{\pi y}{b} \sin \frac{\pi 5z}{c}$$

The other four surfaces of the box are at zero potential. Find the potential at all points inside the box.

12. An infinite prism has as a cross section an isosceles right triangle. If the hypotenuse is at V_0 volts and the other two sides are grounded, find the potential at all points inside the prism.

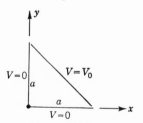

13. On a spherical surface of radius c the potential is given by $V_3 P_3(\mu)$, where $\mu = \cos \theta$. On a concentric spherical surface of radius $d(d > c)$ the potential is given by $V_5 P_5(\mu)$. What is the potential in the region between the two spheres?

14. Find the components of electric field resulting from a dipole in rectangular coordinates.

15. A linear dipole of strength p is at the center of a grounded conducting cylinder of radius R. Find the potential at all points such that $r < R$.

16. Find the potential distribution between a four-segment commutator of radius R_1 and a grounded concentric cylinder of radius R_2 $(R_2 > R_1)$. Alternate segments of the commutator are at $\pm V_0$ volts.

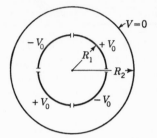

17. Solve the problem of a line charge of strength σ_0 located between two coaxial grounded conducting cylinders.

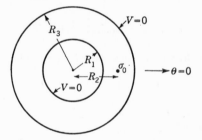

18. A cylindrical surface of radius R is centered on the z axis, and the potential on the surface of this cylinder is given as $V_5 \sin 5\theta$, where θ is the angle with the x axis (polar coordinates). There is also a uniform field parallel to the x axis. Find the potential at all points exterior to the cylinder.

19. Two grounded coaxial cylinders of radius R_1 and R_2 have a surface charge distribution between them at $r = R_3$. From $\theta = 0$ to $\theta = \pi, \sigma = +\sigma_0$, and from $\theta = \pi$ to $\theta = 2\pi, \sigma = -\sigma_0$. Find the potential at all points between the two cylinders.

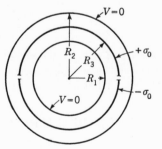

20. Solve the problem of a point charge located between two concentric grounded spherical surfaces.

21. A cylindrical can of radius R has its side grounded and the top and bottom ends at potential V_0. Find the potential at all points inside the can.

22. A grounded cylinder has as its surface the two concentric cylindrical surfaces $r = r_1$ and $r = r_3$ and the two planes $\theta = 0°$ and $\theta = \alpha$. A line charge of strength σ_0 is at $r = r_2$, $\theta = \beta$, where $r_1 < r_2 < r_3$ and $\alpha > \beta$. Find the potential at all points inside this cylinder.

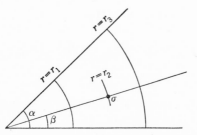

23. Sketch the field about two unequal point charges of opposite sign separated by a distance a. At some point along the line through the two charges the electric field will vanish. This is called a neutral point. Discuss the form of the equipotential surfaces near this neutral point. Show that the equipotential surfaces cross here and are circular cones of half-angle α, where $P_2(\alpha) = 0$, giving $\alpha = 55°$, $125°$ in spherical coordinates centered about the neutral point.

24. A rectangular box in the form of a cube has the pair of faces normal to the z axis at $+V_0$ volts and the other four faces at $-V_0/2$ volts. Choosing the origin at the center of the cube, find the potential at all points inside the box. Show that for regions near the origin this potential can be approximated by a potential of the form of Equation (1), Section 2.2, and determine the value of the coefficients.*

25. A square-wave potential in x is in the xz plane and the plane at $y = b$ is at V_1 volts. Find the potential at all points between $y = 0$ and $y = b$.

* *J. Appl. Phys.*, no. 30, p. 441, 1959.

3

Dielectric Phenomena

3.1 Dielectric Materials

It was shown in the last chapter that the potential of a dipole is given by

$$V = \frac{m}{4\pi\epsilon_0 r^2} \cos \theta \tag{1}$$

Experimental evidence shows that a large class of insulators such as glass, pure water, gases, etc., act as if they were composed of such dipoles when under the influence of an electric field. The most usual case is where the dipole moment per unit volume, called the polarization $\mathbf{P}$, is proportional to the electric field $\mathbf{E}$.

We shall consider the simple case where $\mathbf{P}$ is parallel to $\mathbf{E}$. This will not be true for crystalline materials where $\mathbf{P}$ is related to $\mathbf{E}$ by a tensor. We shall now proceed to obtain the potential arising from a volume distribution of polarized material. We shall consider two sources of potential—real charges and distributions of polarized material. This is done only for convenience since of course the potentials arise only from real charges and polarized material is composed of real charges arranged as dipoles.

3.2 Differentiation of Vectors. Potential of Polarized Material

The use of the gradient operator in forming the gradient from a scalar function of position is given by

$$\bar{E} = -\nabla V \qquad\qquad \nabla\phi = \frac{\partial\phi}{\partial x}\mathbf{i} + \frac{\partial\phi}{\partial y}\mathbf{j} + \frac{\partial\phi}{\partial z}\mathbf{k} \tag{1}$$

In some physical problems the gradient of a scalar depends on the distance between a source point (such as a charge or a dipole) and the

56

field point where the gradient is being computed. In such problems $\phi = \phi(r)$, where $r = \sqrt{(x - x')^2 + (y - y')^2 + (z - z')^2}$. Here x, y, and z are the coordinates of the field point and x', y', and z' the coordinates of the source point. $\mathbf{r}$ is presumed to point from the source point to the field point. Clearly another kind of gradient can be formed by differentiating with respect to the primed rather than the unprimed coordinates and this is written ∇':

$$\nabla'\phi \equiv \frac{\partial\phi}{\partial x'}\mathbf{i} + \frac{\partial\phi}{\partial y'}\mathbf{j} + \frac{\partial\phi}{\partial z'}\mathbf{k} \tag{2}$$

If $\phi = \phi(r)$ it is clear that

$$\nabla\phi(r) = -\nabla'\phi(r) \tag{3}$$

since $$\frac{\partial\phi}{\partial x} = \frac{\partial\phi}{\partial r}\frac{\partial r}{\partial x} \quad \text{and} \quad \frac{\partial\phi}{\partial x'} = \frac{\partial\phi}{\partial r}\frac{\partial r}{\partial x'} \tag{4}$$

and $$\frac{\partial r}{\partial x} = -\frac{\partial r}{\partial x'} \tag{5}$$

The change in potential for a given displacement of the field point, $d\mathbf{r}$ is clearly the negative of the change in potential if the field point were fixed and all the charges which gave rise to this potential were all moved a distance $d\mathbf{r}$. This is the meaning to be attached to (3). Formally one can extend the above use of ∇ and ∇' to the divergence and curl operations.

We shall now put Equation (1), Section 3.1, into vector form. Since

$$\nabla\left(\frac{1}{r}\right) = \frac{\partial}{\partial r}\left(\frac{1}{r}\right)\mathbf{e}_r = -\frac{\mathbf{r}}{r^3} \tag{6}$$

we can rewrite Equation (1), Section 3.1, as

$$V = \frac{-\mathbf{m}\cdot\nabla\left(\dfrac{1}{r}\right)}{4\pi\epsilon_0} \tag{7}$$

where we now write $\mathbf{m}$ for the vector dipole moment, a vector having the direction of the dipole (from the negative charge to the positive charge) and a length proportional to its strength. We can now use (3) to rewrite (7) as

$$V = \frac{1}{4\pi\epsilon_0}\mathbf{m}\cdot\nabla'\left(\frac{1}{r}\right) \tag{8}$$

The potential arising from a volume distribution of dipoles is thus

$$V = \frac{1}{4\pi\epsilon_0}\int_V \mathbf{P}\cdot\nabla'\left(\frac{1}{r}\right)dv \tag{9}$$

where **P** is the dipole moment per unit volume.   However, by a vector identity [see Equation (3), Appendix B],

$$\nabla' \cdot \left(\frac{\mathbf{P}}{r}\right) = \frac{1}{r}\left(\nabla' \cdot \mathbf{P}\right) + \mathbf{P} \cdot \nabla'\left(\frac{1}{r}\right) \tag{10}$$

Thus (9) becomes

$$V = \frac{1}{4\pi\epsilon_0}\left[\int_V \nabla' \cdot \left(\frac{\mathbf{P}}{r}\right) dv - \int_V \frac{1}{r}\nabla' \cdot \mathbf{P}\, dv\right] \tag{11}$$

The first integral becomes, by virtue of the divergence theorem, equal to

$$\int_S \frac{\mathbf{P} \cdot \mathbf{n}}{r}\, dS$$

The potential due to a polarized volume is thus the same as that due to a surface charge over the surface of the polarized volume of strength $\sigma_p = \mathbf{P} \cdot \mathbf{n} = P_n$ together with a volume charge density $\rho_p = -\nabla' \cdot \mathbf{P}$. Equation (11) becomes

$$V = \frac{1}{4\pi\epsilon_0}\left[\int_S \frac{\sigma_p}{r}\, dS + \int_V \frac{\rho_p}{r}\, dv\right] \tag{12}$$

where $\sigma_p = P_n$ and $\rho_p = -\nabla' \cdot \mathbf{P}$.

In what follows we shall drop the prime from $\nabla' \cdot \mathbf{P}$ since the differentiation is clearly of **P**, which is the source.   In a real problem there may also be a true charge density ρ.   Neglecting for the moment σ_p, we find that within a region containing a real charge density ρ and polarized material whose effects can be represented by a fictitious charge density ρ_p, the sources of potential are ρ and ρ_p.   The equation previously obtained for a vacuum $\nabla \cdot \mathbf{E} = \rho/\epsilon_0$ becomes in this case

$$\nabla \cdot \mathbf{E} = \frac{1}{\epsilon_0}\left(\rho + \rho_p\right)$$

or
$$\nabla \cdot (\epsilon_0\mathbf{E}) = \rho - \nabla \cdot \mathbf{P} \tag{13}$$

Rearranging (13) we get

$$\nabla \cdot (\epsilon_0\mathbf{E} + \mathbf{P}) = \rho \qquad \text{or} \qquad \nabla \cdot \mathbf{D} = \rho \tag{14}$$

The combination $\epsilon_0\mathbf{E} + \mathbf{P}$ occurs often and is called **D**, the electric displacement.   **D** is seen to be the electric vector that arises from real charges.   The vector **D** is thus defined to be

$$\mathbf{D} = \epsilon_0\mathbf{E} + \mathbf{P} \tag{15}$$

In many materials **P** is proportional to **E** and in the same direction. This can be written as $P = \epsilon_0\chi E$ and (15) becomes

$$\mathbf{D} = \epsilon_0(1 + \chi)\mathbf{E} \tag{16}$$

χ is called the electric susceptibility. If we place $K = 1 + \chi$ and call it the specific inductive capacity (often called dielectric constant), (16) becomes

$$\mathbf{D} = \epsilon_0 K \mathbf{E} = \epsilon \mathbf{E} \tag{17}$$

Just as in the previous chapter on electrostatics, we can apply the divergence theorem to (14), obtaining

$$\int_V \nabla \cdot \mathbf{D} \, dv = \int_S \mathbf{D} \cdot \mathbf{n} \, da = \int_V \rho \, dv$$

or
$$\int_S \mathbf{D} \cdot \mathbf{n} \, da = \int_V \rho \, dv \tag{18}$$

3.3   Boundary Conditions for Dielectric Materials

At the surface of a dielectric, we can construct a small Gaussian pillbox about a part of the surface small enough so that the surface element can be considered plane.   If the thickness of this pillbox is made very small and Equation (18), Section 3.2, is applied, we get

$$-\mathbf{D}_1 \cdot \mathbf{n} + \mathbf{D}_2 \cdot \mathbf{n} = \sigma \tag{1}$$

where σ is the real surface charge density.   For no *real* surface charge present at the surface, we obtain

$$D_{1n} = D_{2n} \tag{2}$$

or the normal component of $\mathbf{D}$ is continuous in crossing the boundary between two dielectrics.

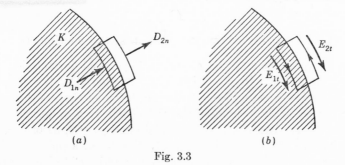

(a)   (b)

Fig. 3.3

We might ask what happened to the effects caused by σ_p in Equation (12), Section 3.2.   We can easily show that (2) is correct in any case.   One way to show this is to consider the polarization and hence the dielectric material as dropping off continuously in passing through the pillbox.   Then (2) is clearly correct, as there is no surface here.   There is, of course, a large value of $\nabla \cdot \mathbf{P}$ in this region.

Alternatively we can consider just the term containing σ_p in Equation (12), Section 3.2, ignoring the term in ρ_p as it disappears in the limit. The fields are thus caused by a fictitious charge $\sigma_p = P_n$ giving $-E_{1n} + E_{2n} = \sigma_p/\epsilon_0$ or, since $\sigma_p = P_n$,

$$\epsilon_0 E_{2n} = P_n + \epsilon_0 E_{1n} = \epsilon_0 K E_{1n} \tag{3}$$

Noting Equation (15), Section 3.2, this is the same as (2).

We have obtained one boundary condition, (2). Another can be obtained by applying Equation (5), Section 1.3, $\nabla \times \mathbf{E} = 0$. By Stokes' law this can be transformed to

$$\iint_S (\nabla \times \mathbf{E}) \cdot \mathbf{n}\, da = \oint \mathbf{E} \cdot d\mathbf{l} = 0 \tag{4}$$

Applying this to the path shown in Figure 3.3b, we have $lE_{1t} - lE_{2t} = 0$ or

$$E_{1t} = E_{2t} \tag{5}$$

Here the sides perpendicular to the boundary have been made infinitesimally small. The tangential components of $\mathbf{E}$ are thus continuous. It is clear that the potential is also continuous in crossing through the boundary of a dielectric, because, from Equation (12), Section 3.2, the potential difference between the two regions is just the work done in passing through a surface charge σ_p which gives rise to a finite E. If the path length is made very small this potential difference becomes negligible. The two boundary conditions that apply at the uncharged surface of a dielectric are thus

$$\text{Normal } D \text{ is continuous} \tag{6}$$
$$\text{The potential is continuous (tangential } E \text{ is continuous)} \tag{7}$$

The physics behind the above mathematical formulation now becomes apparent. In Equation (12), Section 3.2, the fictitious charges ρ_p arise from an incomplete cancellation of charges that make up the dipoles in the volume of the dielectric. In a uniformly polarized medium the cancellation is complete and $\rho_p = 0$, as of course it must, since $\nabla \cdot \mathbf{P} = 0$ as $\mathbf{P}$ is constant. However, a point charge at the center of a spherical ball of dielectric material will give rise to an $\mathbf{E}$ that falls off with radius. The polarization also falls off with radius and hence there is an incomplete cancellation of the $+$ and $-$ charges that make up the dipoles. This will give a net charge density ρ_p in the sphere. Likewise near the surface of a uniformly polarized dielectric all the charges in the dipoles will cancel except right at the surface, where there will be an apparent surface charge σ_p.

3.4 Some Problems Involving Dielectrics

We shall now apply the above knowledge to the solution of a certain class of problems. This class of problems will have adjacent regions where the dielectric constant K is uniform. We shall find solutions to Laplace's equation in each region and choose the correct solutions by applying Equations (6) and (7), Section 3.3, at the boundary between different regions.

If in a certain region K is constant, Equation (14), Section 3.2, becomes

$$\nabla \cdot \mathbf{D} = \nabla \cdot (\epsilon_0 K \mathbf{E}) = \rho \tag{1}$$

and if there is no real space charge ρ in the region, this results in $\nabla \cdot \mathbf{E} = 0$. Just as in Chapter 2, this leads to Laplace's equation $\nabla^2 V = 0$. The solutions that we shall use in each region are thus those already discussed in Chapter 2.

A typical problem is that of a dielectric cylinder of radius R and dielectric constant K in a uniform electric field. This is quite similar to Example 2 in Section 2.8. Many of the same considerations will apply in the region outside the cylinder (region 1). Thus in region 1 the solution that we shall use is

$$V_1 = -E_0 r \cos \theta + \sum_n b_n r^{-n} \cos n\theta \tag{2}$$

The region inside the dielectric cylinder (region 2) will have

$$V_2 = \sum_n c_n r^n \cos n\theta \tag{3}$$

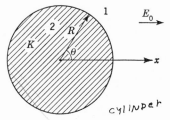

Fig. 3.4a. Dielectric sphere in a uniform field.

No terms involving $\log r$ or r^{-n} occur in (3) because they go to infinity at the origin, and there are no line charges or higher multipoles given at the origin that would cause this. We are thus faced with the problem of determining b_n and c_n from Equations (6) and (7), Section 3.3. Applying Equation (6), Section 3.3, we have, at $r = R$,

$$\frac{\partial V_1}{\partial r} = K \frac{\partial V_2}{\partial r}$$

or $-E_0 \cos \theta + \sum_n b_n(-n)R^{-(n+1)} \cos n\theta = K \sum_n c_n n R^{n-1} \cos n\theta$ (4)

Multiplying through by $\cos m\theta \, d\theta$ and integrating from 0 to 2π, we get

$$-E_0 - b_1 R^{-2} = Kc_1 \qquad \text{for } n = 1 \tag{5}$$

and $-nb_n R^{-(n+1)} = Kc_n n R^{n-1} \qquad \text{for } n > 1$ (6)

Applying the same procedure to Equation (7), Section 3.3, we get

$$-E_0R + b_1R^{-1} = c_1R \qquad \text{for } n = 1 \tag{7}$$

and
$$b_nR^{-n} = c_nR^n \qquad \text{for } n > 1 \tag{8}$$

The last four equations must be solved simultaneously to yield values of the unknowns b_n and c_n. Equations (6) and (8) are of the form

$$ax + by = 0 \qquad cx + dy = 0 \tag{9}$$

These are the equations of straight lines through the origin. The simultaneous solution of the two equations in (9) is clearly $x = y = 0$ since these lines cannot be parallel. Likewise the solution of (6) and (8) is $b_n = c_n = 0$ for $n > 1$. The solution of (5) and (7) is

$$b_1 = \frac{K-1}{K+1} E_0R^2 \qquad c_1 = -\frac{2E_0}{K+1} \tag{10}$$

This gives the final solution

$$V_1 = \left(-E_0r + \frac{E_0R^2}{r}\frac{K-1}{K+1}\right)\cos\theta$$

and
$$V_2 = -\frac{2E_0}{K+1} r \cos\theta \tag{11}$$

This solution can be checked by observing the behavior at $K = 1$ and $K = \infty$. At $K = 1$, $V_1 = V_2 = -E_0r \cos\theta$, a uniform field as it should be. At $K = \infty$ we should reduce to Equation (25), Section 2.8, for V_1, and this is seen to be true. The field is seen to be a uniform field inside the cylinder, and to be a uniform field plus a linear dipole field outside the cylinder. The problem of a dielectric sphere in a uniform field leads to quite similar results. We could have observed or guessed somewhat earlier in this problem that only $n = 1$ terms would occur.

In a very similar fashion we can solve the problem of a dielectric sphere immersed in a uniform electric field E_0. Since we shall have occasion later to refer to the answer to this problem we shall give it here.

$$V_1 = \left(-E_0r + \frac{K-1}{K+2}\frac{E_0R^3}{r^2}\right)\cos\theta \qquad \text{outside the sphere}$$

$$V_2 = \frac{-3E_0}{K+2} r \cos\theta \qquad\qquad \text{inside the sphere} \tag{12}$$

A somewhat more difficult problem is that of a conducting rectangular prism $a \times b$ in cross section, partially filled with a dielectric to a height c and with the bottom face at V_0 volts, the other faces being grounded. We divide the prism into two regions, region 1 being filled with the dielectric and region 2 above it, as in Figure 3.4b. The potentials must be of the form

$$V_1 = \sum_n \left(A_n \sinh \frac{\pi n y}{a} + B_n \cosh \frac{\pi n y}{a} \right) \sin \frac{\pi n x}{a}$$

$$V_2 = \sum_n C_n \sinh \frac{\pi n}{a} (b - y) \sin \frac{\pi n x}{a} \tag{13}$$

Here we need three constants and so must use the more general form for V_1, since we have one boundary condition to meet at $y = 0$ and two (normal D and tangential E to be continuous) at $y = c$. The other boundary conditions of $V = 0$ at the other walls are already met by (13). Applying the boundary conditions we have $V = V_0$ at $y = 0$, giving

$$B_n = \frac{4V_0}{\pi n} \qquad \text{odd } n \ (= 0 \text{ for even } n)$$

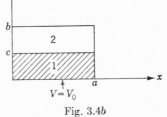

Fig. 3.4b

$$\tag{14}$$

At $y = c$ we must have $V_1 = V_2$ or

$$A_n \sinh \frac{\pi n c}{a} + B_n \cosh \frac{\pi n c}{a} = C_n \sinh \frac{\pi n}{a} (b - c) \tag{15}$$

Normal D is continuous at $y = c$, giving

$$K \left(A_n \cosh \frac{\pi n c}{a} + B_n \sinh \frac{\pi n c}{a} \right) = -C_n \cosh \frac{\pi n}{a} (b - c) \tag{16}$$

Here we have three linear equations (14), (15), and (16) in the three unknowns A_n, B_n, and C_n. These equations can easily be solved for the unknowns. Only odd n will appear in this problem.

3.5 An Image Problem with Dielectrics

It happens that some problems involving dielectrics can be solved by image methods similar to those used in Chapter 1. Let a charge q be at a distance a from a plane dielectric surface having a dielectric constant K. The image system that we shall attempt to use here is to presume that the solution in region 1 can arise from the original charge q and an image charge q' at the image point, the dielectric not being present. In region 2 we presume that the field is that arising from a charge q'' at the original source point, all of space being filled with dielectric material of dielectric constant K. We must now match the boundary condition given in Equations (6) and (7), Section 3.3. The potentials in the two regions are

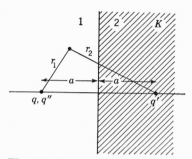

$$V_1 = \frac{1}{4\pi\epsilon_0}\left(\frac{q}{r_1} + \frac{q'}{r_2}\right) \qquad (1)$$

$$V_2 = \frac{1}{4\pi\epsilon_0 K}\frac{q''}{r_1} \qquad (2)$$

At the boundary $r_1 = r_2$ and Equations (6) and (7), Section 3.3, give

Fig. 3.5a. Image solution of a point charge in front of a dielectric half-space.

$$q - q' = q'' \qquad (3)$$

$$q + q' = \frac{q''}{K} \qquad (4)$$

The solution of (3) and (4) for q' and q'' is

$$q' = \frac{1 - K}{1 + K}q \qquad q'' = \frac{2K}{1 + K}q \qquad (5)$$

It is easily seen that if $K = 1$ (i.e., no dielectric material present) the field is just that of the original charge q, as it should be. If $K = \infty$, the electric field in 1 is just that of q and an image $-q$ at the image point, the field in region 2 vanishing. This is just what we would get for a conductor in place of a dielectric. A dielectric of infinite dielectric constant is quite similar to a conductor—in fact, it can be easily shown that $\mathbf{E}$ is perpendicular to the surface of such a material.

A similar image problem can be worked out for a line charge parallel to a plane dielectric material. This in turn is a special case of an image problem concerning a line charge parallel to a dielectric cylinder.

PROBLEMS

1. A charge q is at a distance r from a polarizable dipole whose moment is α times the field in which it is located, where α is the polarizability. Find the force of attraction between the charge and the dipole.

2. A condenser is formed of two parallel plates, the lower at zero potential, a distance h apart. The space between the plates is filled with a dielectric whose inductive capacity K increases uniformly from K_1 to K_2, K_1 being at the lower plate and K_2 at the upper plate. Find the capacity per unit area.

3. A dielectric cylinder of inductive capacity K and radius R is placed in a uniform field E_0 with its axis perpendicular to this field. A linear dipole of strength m, pointing in the same direction as E_0, is placed on the axis of the cylinder. What is the potential at all points?

4. A dielectric sphere of radius R is situated in a uniform electric field E_0. Find the potential at all points.

5. Four equal conducting plates A, B, C, and D, each of area 1 square meter, are fixed parallel to each other with equal spacing a. Plates A and D are grounded and the space between plates B and C is filled with a material of inductive capacity K. A charge σ_1 is placed on plate B and a charge σ_2 is placed on plate C. What is the potential of plates B and C?

6. A conducting sphere of radius b is at a potential V_0. A smaller dielectric sphere of inductive capacity K and radius a is at a large distance r from the center of the conducting sphere. Making approximations suitable for $r \gg b$, find the force between the dielectric sphere and the conducting sphere.

7. Two spherical cavities of radius small compared with their separation are cut out of an infinite rigid medium of dielectric constant K. Point charges q_1 and q_2 are placed in each cavity. Find approximately the force between the two charges.

8. A dielectric sphere of radius r_1 and dielectric constant ϵ is placed inside of and concentric with a spherical surface of radius r_2. The potential at $r = r_2$ is given to be $V = V_5 P_5(\mu)$. What is the potential at all points such that $r < r_2$?

9. A small cavity of radius b is cut out of a semi-infinite dielectric slab of material of dielectric constant ϵ at a distance a from the surface of the dielectric material. If $b \ll a$, find the force on a charge q placed inside the cavity.

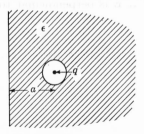

10. Show that for any vector $\mathbf{A}$

$$\int_V \nabla' \cdot \mathbf{A}\, dv' = \int_V \nabla \cdot \mathbf{A}\, dv = \int_S \mathbf{A} \cdot \mathbf{n}\, da$$

4

Magnetism

We shall now discuss the subject of magnetostatics, which has to do with phenomena involving the interaction between steady currents. We shall follow the same type of development that occurred in electrostatics, first discussing phenomena in a vacuum and introducing polarized materials later.

4.1 The Law of Biot and Savart: Units

Instead of Coulomb's law, in magnetostatics we have as the basic experimental law the law of Biot and Savart. This states that if a charge q is moving with a velocity $\mathbf{v}$, then at a distance $\mathbf{r}$ away from this charge ($\mathbf{r}$ is a vector from q to the field point) the magnetic field $\mathbf{B}$ is given by

Fig. 4.1a

$$B = \frac{\mu_0 q(\mathbf{v} \times \mathbf{r})}{4\pi r^3} \tag{1}$$

The name of the vector $\mathbf{B}$ is "magnetic induction." In the next chapter we shall describe another magnetic field vector $\mathbf{H}$, which is called the "magnetic intensity." These names are usually used in textbooks, but in actual engineering practice the term "magnetic field" is often used to refer to either vector; which vector is meant being immediately evident by reference to the usually accompanying equation. In conversation it is almost universal practice to merely pronounce the letters "B" or "H" when referring to these two field vectors. In this text we shall seldom use the definite names "magnetic induction" and "magnetic intensity," but shall usually use the terms "the magnetic field B" or "the magnetic field H."

The experimental measurement of **B** is made by measuring the force on a moving charge at the field point in accordance with the experimental law, Equation (1), Section 1.1, which is in this case

$$\mathbf{F} = q(\mathbf{v} \times \mathbf{B}) \tag{2}$$

The units of B are webers per square meter (one weber per square meter is equal to ten thousand gauss). μ_0 is a constant of proportionality and has the value

$$\mu_0 = 4\pi \times 10^{-7} \quad \text{henry/m} \tag{3}$$

The units of μ_0 will be justified when we discuss inductance. We see that **B** is a vector perpendicular to **v** and **r**, having an absolute magnitude

$$B = \frac{\mu_0}{4\pi} \frac{qv \sin\theta}{r^2} \tag{4}$$

where θ is the angle between **v** and **r**.

In magnetostatics we are more interested in the magnetic field caused by an element of current than that of a single moving charge. We shall now relate qv, referring to a moving charge, to a length of wire ds carrying a current i. If the cross section of the wire is A, and a charge density ρ is moving with a velocity v, the charge crossing any cross section per second is ρvA. But this is just the current i, measured in amperes, where one ampere is one coulomb per second. Thus

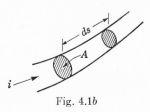

Fig. 4.1b

we have $qv = \rho vA \; ds = i \; ds$ which is the total charge contained in an element of wire times its velocity. We can make this into a vector equation by writing

$$q\mathbf{v} = i \, d\mathbf{s} \tag{5}$$

The magnetic field $d\mathbf{B}$ resulting from a length of wire ds carrying a current i is then

$$d\mathbf{B} = \frac{\mu_0 i}{4\pi} \frac{d\mathbf{s} \times \mathbf{r}}{r^3} = \frac{\mu_0}{4\pi} \frac{\mathbf{J} \times \mathbf{r}}{r^3} \, dv \tag{6}$$

where we define **J**, the current density, by $\mathbf{J} \, dv = i \, d\mathbf{s}$.

Using Equation (2) we can find the force between two elements of current $i_1 \, d\mathbf{s}_1$ and $i_2 \, d\mathbf{s}_2$:

$$d\mathbf{F} = \frac{\mu_0 i_1 i_2}{4\pi} \left\{ \frac{d\mathbf{s}_1 \times (d\mathbf{s}_2 \times \mathbf{r})}{r^3} \right\} \tag{7}$$

Equation (7) permits us to define the ampere. If we take two equal current elements, each of unit length and unit distance apart and so oriented that the expression in braces in (7) is unity, then the currents are defined to be an ampere if the resulting force is 10^{-7} newton. Thus (3) ($\mu_0 = 4\pi \times 10^{-7}$) is seen to be the result of definition rather than experiment. This is not the case with ϵ_0 in Coulomb's law in Chapter 1. Here we define the unit of current from (7). This fixes the value of the coulomb, which is an ampere second. Therefore we cannot define ϵ_0 but must measure it by an experiment. The experiment leads to $\epsilon_0 = 8.85 \times 10^{-12}$ farad per meter. This course of reasoning leads to a value of **B** in Equation (6) to which we attach the units "webers per square meter."

The whole system of units in electricity and magnetism as introduced in this text works backward from (7). This is why a suitable discussion of units has had to be deferred until this point, since the unit of charge is here really defined in terms of the magnetic effects of an ampere of current. With this definition of the ampere we should refer to our system of units as mksa.

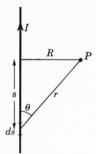

Fig. 4.2a. Current in a straight infinite wire.

4.2   Vector Integration for Solving Problems

Just as in Chapter 1, we can use the vector expression for **B** found in Equation (6), Section 4.1, to calculate **B** in several simple cases. We consider first the field of an infinite straight wire carrying a current I. In Figure 4.2a we see that the direction of **B** at the field point is into the paper for all current elements. Thus

$$B_\theta = \int_{-\infty}^{+\infty} dB = \frac{\mu_0 I}{4\pi} \int_{-\infty}^{+\infty} \frac{R\,ds}{(R^2 + s^2)^{3/2}} = \frac{\mu_0 I}{2\pi R} \qquad (1)$$

The direction of **B** is of course in circles surrounding the wire.

4.3   Useful Techniques

Just as in electrostatics, we wish to find more suitable ways to compute **B**. It will turn out that a scalar potential can be formed, but this potential is useful only in regions where there is no current density. A more general approach leads to the vector potential. We shall emphasize the vector potential here for several reasons. First, a good working knowledge of the use of $\nabla^2\mathbf{F}$ is necessary for the later discussion of wave propagation; and second, the vector potential is often used in the advanced treatment of electricity and in quantum mechanics.

4.4 The Divergence of B

We begin by computing the divergence of **B**. We expect this to be zero, since the field lines close on themselves and do not have source points. We shall prove this for an element of current and by an obvious extension this will hold for the field of a complete circuit. In Appendix A it is shown that

$$\text{div} (\mathbf{a} \times \mathbf{b}) = \mathbf{b} \cdot \text{curl } \mathbf{a} - \mathbf{a} \cdot \text{curl } \mathbf{b} \tag{1}$$

Applying this to Equation (6), Section 4.1, we have for a current element $i\,d\mathbf{s}$:

$$\text{div} (d\mathbf{B}) = \frac{\mu_0 i}{4\pi} \left[\frac{\mathbf{r}}{r^3} \cdot \text{curl } d\mathbf{s} - d\mathbf{s} \cdot \text{curl} \left(\frac{\mathbf{r}}{r^3} \right) \right] \tag{2}$$

The first term is zero, since $d\mathbf{s}$ is a constant vector. Since $\mathbf{r}/r^3 = \nabla(1/r)$ the second term contains the factor curl grad $(1/r)$, which is zero since the curl of any gradient is zero. We have thus shown that

$$\text{div} (d\mathbf{B}) = 0 \tag{3}$$

for a current element; this is true for the sum of many current elements and hence for a complete circuit. Thus we have in general

$$\text{div } \mathbf{B} = 0 \tag{4}$$

4.5 Curl of B

We shall now discuss the curl of **B**. We shall first show that B can be derived from a scalar potential if there is no current density at the field point. Since curl grad of any vector is zero [see Equation (8), Appendix B] curl **B** = 0 under these restrictive conditions. Consider the

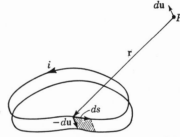

Fig. 4.5a. (*By permission from John C. Slater and Nathaniel H. Frank, "Electromagnetism," McGraw-Hill Book Company, Inc., New York, 1947.*)

field of a steady current flowing in a closed loop of wire as shown in Figure 4.5a. If we displace the field point by $d\mathbf{u}$ the solid angle subtended by the loop will change by $d\Omega$. This is the same as moving the circuit by $-d\mathbf{u}$, leaving the field point P fixed. $d\Omega$ is the sum of the changes in the solid angles subtended by the areas made up of $-d\mathbf{u} \times d\mathbf{s}$. The projection of this area $(-d\mathbf{u} \times d\mathbf{s})$ on the radius vector **r** is $-d\mathbf{u} \times d\mathbf{s} \cdot \mathbf{r}/r$ and the increment in $d\Omega$ is

$$-d\mathbf{u} \times d\mathbf{s} \cdot \frac{\mathbf{r}}{r^3} = -d\mathbf{u} \cdot \frac{d\mathbf{s} \times \mathbf{r}}{r^3} \tag{1}$$

Integrating over the loop, we have

$$d\Omega = -d\mathbf{u} \cdot \oint \frac{d\mathbf{s} \times \mathbf{r}}{r^3} \tag{2}$$

However, the change in Ω due to a displacement $d\mathbf{u}$ is the scalar product of the gradient of Ω and $d\mathbf{u}$:

$$d\Omega = d\mathbf{u} \cdot \operatorname{grad} \Omega \tag{3}$$

Comparing (2) and (3) we see that

$$-\operatorname{grad} \Omega = \oint \frac{d\mathbf{s} \times \mathbf{r}}{r^3} \tag{4}$$

Comparing this with Equation (6), Section 4.1, we have

$$\mathbf{B} = -\frac{\mu_0 i}{4\pi} \operatorname{grad} \Omega \tag{5}$$

Thus $(\mu_0 i / 4\pi)\Omega$ is a scalar potential, the negative gradient of which will generate $\mathbf{B}$. This shows that curl $\mathbf{B} = 0$ in the case where there is no current density at the field point for any problem that can be made up by superimposing current loops of the kind just discussed. It does not follow in general that the line integral of $\mathbf{B} \cdot d\mathbf{l}$ is zero. This would be true only if $\nabla \times \mathbf{B} = 0$ everywhere inside the contour around which the line integral is taken, and this would occur only when no current links this contour.

Let us now compute such a line integral from (3) and (5)

$$\oint \mathbf{B} \cdot d\mathbf{l} = -\oint \operatorname{grad} \left(\frac{\mu_0 i}{4\pi} \Omega \right) \cdot d\mathbf{l} = -\frac{\mu_0 i}{4\pi} \oint d\Omega \tag{6}$$

If the path of integration is such that it does not enclose the current-carrying conductor, $\oint d\Omega$ is zero for a closed loop and $\oint \mathbf{B} \cdot d\mathbf{l} = 0$. Suppose, however, that the path of integration does include the wire, as in Figure 4.5b. Starting in the plane of the loop the solid angle is 2π. We presume that Ω is positive when we are above the plane of the loop and negative when we are below this plane. Halfway around the contour of integration this solid angle drops to zero and then becomes -2π. Thus $\oint d\Omega = -4\pi$ and (6) becomes

$$\oint \mathbf{B} \cdot d\mathbf{l} = -\frac{\mu_0 i}{4\pi} \oint d\Omega = \mu_0 i \tag{7}$$

Thus the integral of the tangential component of **B** about a closed contour is μ_0 times the current in the loop. In general, many loops can be present and, treating each separately, we have

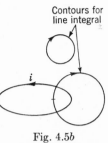

Contours for
line integral

$$\oint \mathbf{B} \cdot d\mathbf{l} = \mu_0 \sum_n i_n \qquad (8)$$

where $\sum_n i_n$ represents the total current traversing

a surface bounded by the contour of integration. Equation (8) is called the integral form of Ampere's law.

Fig. 4.5*b*

We can express (8) in another way by applying Stokes' theorem, which is discussed in Appendix C. This states that for any vector

$$\oint \mathbf{A} \cdot d\mathbf{l} = \int_S \operatorname{curl} \mathbf{A} \cdot \mathbf{n} \, da \qquad (9)$$

The right side of (8) represents the total current passing through the contour of integration. If we represent the current flowing at any point by a vector **J** times the area, where **J** is the current density in amperes per square meter, then the whole current through the contour is $\int_S \mathbf{J} \cdot \mathbf{n} \, da$. Thus (8) becomes

$$\oint \mathbf{B} \cdot d\mathbf{l} = \mu_0 \int_S \mathbf{J} \cdot \mathbf{n} \, da = \int_S \operatorname{curl} \mathbf{B} \cdot \mathbf{n} \, da \qquad (10)$$

The two surface integrals are equal no matter what surface is selected and thus the integrands must be equal at all points. This gives

$$\operatorname{curl} \mathbf{B} = \mu_0 \mathbf{J} \qquad (11)$$

This is called the differential form of Ampere's law. If $\mathbf{J} = 0$, curl **B** $= 0$ and a scalar potential exists. If $\mathbf{J} \neq 0$ at the field point, no scalar potential exists and we must use some other type of potential. We wish to choose this new type of potential so that Equation (4), Section 4.4, (div **B** $= 0$) is automatically satisfied. Such a choice is the vector potential **A** where **B** is derived from **A** by

$$\mathbf{B} = \operatorname{curl} \mathbf{A} \qquad (12)$$

This automatically satisfies Equation (4), Section 4.4, since the divergence of any curl is identically zero, and taking the divergence of both sides of (12) leads to Equation (4), Section 4.4.

We can now arrive at an equation similar to Poisson's equation in electrostatics. Equations (11) and (12) lead to

$$\operatorname{curl} \operatorname{curl} \mathbf{A} = \mu_0 \mathbf{J} \qquad (13)$$

But $\nabla \times \nabla \times \mathbf{A} = \text{grad div } \mathbf{A} - \nabla^2\mathbf{A}$. It is shown in complete treatments of vector analysis (for instance, in Phillips, see Reference 8) that if a vector is defined as being the curl of another vector, as $\mathbf{B} = \text{curl } \mathbf{A}$, then div $\mathbf{A}$ can be chosen arbitrarily without affecting the value of $\mathbf{B}$. Choosing div $\mathbf{A} = 0$, we get

$$\nabla^2\mathbf{A} = -\mu_0\mathbf{J} \tag{14}$$

This does not limit our use of $\mathbf{A}$ to any extent, since the real use of $\mathbf{A}$ results from (12). Thus only curl $\mathbf{A}$ is of importance to us, and we can fix div $\mathbf{A}$ to be anything that we choose.

We can solve (14) in rectangular coordinates. Consider only the x component of (14). This is

$$(\nabla^2\mathbf{A})_x = \frac{\partial^2 A_x}{\partial x^2} + \frac{\partial^2 A_x}{\partial y^2} + \frac{\partial^2 A_x}{\partial z^2} = -\mu_0 J_x \tag{15}$$

The known solution of this from electrostatics is

$$A_x = \frac{\mu_0}{4\pi} \int_V \frac{J_x}{r} dv \tag{16}$$

This follows from the known but not very useful solution of Poisson's equation

$$\nabla^2\phi = -\frac{\rho}{\epsilon_0} \qquad \phi = \int_V \frac{\rho \, dv}{4\pi\epsilon_0 r} \tag{17}$$

Similar solutions are had for A_y and A_z; adding such solutions, we get

$$\mathbf{A} = \frac{\mu_0}{4\pi} \int \frac{\mathbf{J}}{r} dv \tag{18}$$

If we are considering a single circuit carrying a current i, (18) becomes

$$\mathbf{A} = \frac{\mu_0 i}{4\pi} \oint \frac{d\mathbf{s}}{r} \tag{19}$$

4.6   Another Derivation of Ampere's Law

The above derivation of Ampere's law from the law of Biot and Savart is quite graphical but not very rigorous. We shall now make a more formal derivation. The law of Biot and Savart is the experimental foundation of magnetostatics. For our purposes here it is convenient to write it as

$$\mathbf{B} = \frac{\mu_0}{4\pi} \int \frac{\mathbf{J} \times \mathbf{r}}{r^3} dv \tag{1}$$

We wish to show first that **B** can be derived from a vector potential.
Since $-\nabla \left(\dfrac{1}{r}\right) = \mathbf{r}/r^3$ we can rewrite (1) as

$$\mathbf{B} = -\frac{\mu_0}{4\pi} \int \mathbf{J} \times \nabla \left(\frac{1}{r}\right) dv \tag{2}$$

However, by a vector identity [see Equation (4), Appendix B(4)],

$$\nabla \times \left(\frac{\mathbf{J}}{r}\right) = \frac{1}{r}\nabla \times \mathbf{J} - \mathbf{J} \times \nabla \left(\frac{1}{r}\right) \tag{3}$$

Here ∇ operates on the field point, which depends on r but not on the source point **J**. The first term on the right is therefore zero. Equation (2) then becomes

$$\mathbf{B} = \frac{\mu_0}{4\pi} \int \left(\nabla \times \frac{\mathbf{J}}{r}\right) dv \tag{4}$$

Since $\nabla \times$ does not affect the integration process here, (4) can be written as

$$\mathbf{B} = \nabla \times \left[\frac{\mu_0}{4\pi} \int \frac{\mathbf{J}}{r} dv\right] \tag{5}$$

If we now define the vector potential **A** to be

$$\mathbf{A} = \frac{\mu_0}{4\pi} \int \frac{\mathbf{J}}{r} dv \tag{6}$$

we have
$$\mathbf{B} = \operatorname{curl} \mathbf{A} \tag{7}$$

We have immediately $\nabla \cdot \mathbf{B} = 0$, since the divergence of any curl vanishes identically.

We must now compute $\nabla \cdot \mathbf{A}$ and $\nabla \times \mathbf{B}$ as well as find a differential equation for **A**. We first take the divergence of both sides of (6). Since the operation $\nabla \cdot$ does not interfere with the integration, we can take $\nabla \cdot$ inside the integral, obtaining

$$\nabla \cdot \mathbf{A} = \frac{\mu_0}{4\pi} \int \nabla \cdot \frac{\mathbf{J}}{r} dv \tag{8}$$

Equation (8) can be rewritten

$$\nabla \cdot \mathbf{A} = \frac{\mu_0}{4\pi} \int_V \nabla \cdot \frac{\mathbf{J}}{r} dv = \frac{\mu_0}{4\pi} \int_S \frac{\mathbf{J}}{r} \cdot \mathbf{n} \, da \tag{9}$$

where the last equation results from the divergence theorem. If now the surface over which this last integral is taken is a sphere of infinite radius, r is constant and we have

$$\nabla \cdot \mathbf{A} = 0 \qquad \text{if A is defined as above in (6)} \tag{10}$$

This results from the fact that $\mathbf{J}$ is a solenoidal vector; i.e., as much $\mathbf{J}$ flows in as out of a volume in the steady state. To obtain the differential equation for $\mathbf{A}$ we take the x component of (6)

$$A_x = \frac{\mu_0}{4\pi} \int \frac{J_x}{r}\, dv \tag{11}$$

Comparing this with the solution of Poisson's equation,

$$\nabla^2 \phi = -\frac{\rho}{\epsilon_0} \qquad \phi = \frac{1}{4\pi\epsilon_0} \int \frac{\rho\, dv}{r} \tag{12}$$

the differential equation for A_x is clearly

$$\nabla^2 A_x = -\mu_0 J_x \tag{13}$$

Similar equations exist for A_y and A_z; adding these three equations together we have

$$\nabla^2 \mathbf{A} = -\mu_0 \mathbf{J} \tag{14}$$

since $\nabla^2 \mathbf{A} = \mathbf{i}\nabla^2 A_x + \mathbf{j}\nabla^2 A_y + \mathbf{k}\nabla^2 A_z$. This is the equation for $\mathbf{A}$ which we sought.

It is shown in the appendix that $\nabla \times \nabla \times \mathbf{A} = \nabla(\nabla \cdot \mathbf{A}) - \nabla^2 \mathbf{A}$. Here, of course, $\nabla \cdot \mathbf{A} = 0$ by (10), so (14) can be written

$$\nabla \times \nabla \times \mathbf{A} = \mu_0 \mathbf{J} \tag{15}$$

Since $\mathbf{B} = \nabla \times \mathbf{A}$, (15) becomes the differential form of Ampere's law

$$\nabla \times \mathbf{B} = \mu_0 \mathbf{J} \tag{16}$$

This is the differential equation for $\mathbf{B}$ that we wished to obtain from the law of Biot and Savart. The above discussion is limited to $\nabla \cdot \mathbf{A} = 0$. Since we are only interested in $\nabla \times \mathbf{A}$, however, it turns out that $\nabla \cdot \mathbf{A}$ can be chosen at will, since it can be shown that the divergence of $\mathbf{A}$ can be arbitrarily chosen without affecting the value of $\nabla \times \mathbf{A}$. Likewise we can add to $\mathbf{A}$ the gradient of any scalar without affecting $\nabla \times \mathbf{A}$.

4.7   Field from a Loop of Wire

We shall now demonstrate the use of the above treatment in the solution of some typical problems. A simple one is the field from a circular loop of wire carrying a current i at distances from the loop large compared to its radius. If the loop has an area A, and we set up a spherical coordinate system at the center of the loop such that the normal to the loop is in the direction of the polar axis, we can apply Equation (5), Section 4.5, to find **B**. The solid angle subtended by the loop is $A \cos \theta / r^2$, so that the scalar potential is

$$V = \frac{\mu_0 i}{4\pi} \frac{A \cos \theta}{r^2} \tag{1}$$

The form of this scalar potential is similar to that of Equation (3), Section 2.7, which is the scalar potential of an electric dipole. If we

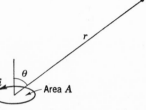

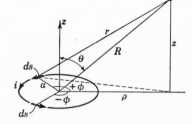

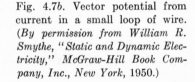

Fig. 4.7a. Scalar potential from current in a small loop of wire.

Fig. 4.7b. Vector potential from current in a small loop of wire. (*By permission from William R. Smythe, "Static and Dynamic Electricity," McGraw-Hill Book Company, Inc., New York, 1950.*)

let $iA = m$, and call a small loop of current a magnetic dipole, we have the scalar potential

$$V = \frac{\mu_0 m}{4\pi} \frac{\cos \theta}{r^2} \tag{2}$$

We can approach this same problem from the vector potential viewpoint. Using the same coordinate system as above, we let the field point be at $\phi = 0$. We can pair off current elements at equal $\pm \phi$ as in Figure 4.7b. The resultant contribution to **A** at P is, from Equation (19), Section 4.5, in the ϕ direction only. Thus **A** has only one component, A_ϕ. Let ds_ϕ be the component of ds in the ϕ direction. Then

$$A_\phi = \frac{\mu_0 i}{4\pi} \oint \frac{ds_\phi}{r} \tag{3}$$

From Figure 4.7b we have $ds_\phi = a \cos \phi \, d\phi$ and $r^2 = a^2 + \rho^2 - 2a\rho \cos \phi + z^2$. This leads to

$$A_\phi = \frac{\mu_0 i}{2\pi} \int_0^\pi \frac{a \cos \phi \, d\phi}{(a^2 + \rho^2 + z^2 - 2a\rho \cos \phi)^{1/2}} \tag{4}$$

If $a \ll R$, the denominator is approximately $(R^2 - 2a\rho \cos \phi)^{1/2}$.

Here $2a\rho \ll R^2$, and we can expand as follows

$$\frac{1}{(R^2 - 2a\rho \cos \phi)^{\frac{1}{2}}} = \frac{1}{R\left(1 - \frac{2a\rho}{R^2} \cos \phi\right)^{\frac{1}{2}}} \approx \frac{1}{R}\left(1 + \frac{a\rho}{R^2} \cos \phi\right) \quad (5)$$

Equation (4) thus becomes

$$A_\phi \approx \frac{\mu_0 i}{2\pi} \int_0^\pi \frac{a \cos \phi}{R}\left(1 + \frac{a\rho \cos \phi}{R^2}\right) d\phi$$

$$= \frac{\mu_0 i}{2\pi} \frac{a^2\rho}{R^3} \frac{\pi}{2} = \frac{\mu_0 i a^2 \rho}{4R^3} = \frac{a^2 \mu_0 i \sin \theta}{4R^2} \quad (6)$$

If we let $\pi a^2 i = iA = m$,

$$A_\phi = \frac{\mu_0 m}{4\pi} \frac{\sin \theta}{R^2} \quad (7)$$

We can also let m be a vector **m** having the stated value and with a direction perpendicular to the loop. Then (7) can be written

$$\mathbf{A} = \frac{\mu_0}{4\pi} \frac{\mathbf{m} \times \mathbf{r}}{r^3} \quad (8)$$

It can easily be shown that the components of **B** obtained by taking the curl of (7) are the same as those generated by taking the gradient of (1).

We would expect that the solution (7) would show up as a simple solution of Equation (14), Section 4.5, just as the scalar potential of an electric dipole showed up as a simple solution of Laplace's equation in Chapter 2. This occurs when we inspect the value of $\nabla^2 \mathbf{A}$ given in Appendix D. In this case, Equation (14), Section 4.5, becomes

$$\nabla^2 \mathbf{A} = 0 \quad (9)$$

and the problem consists of restricting **A** to only a ϕ component that is itself independent of ϕ. The only terms in (9) are thus

$$\nabla^2 A_\phi - \frac{A_\phi}{r^2 \sin^2 \theta} = 0 \quad (10)$$

Reference to Section 2.6 shows that a solution of (10) is easily obtained by the method of separation of variables. There will be no dependence on ϕ of course; the R solution will be Equation (9), Section 2.6, and the equation for θ will be Equation (7), Section 2.6, where we must choose $m = 1$ because of the extra term in (10) above. The θ solution is thus $P_l^1(\mu)$ and the general solution of (10) is

$$A_\phi = \sum_l \left(a_l r^l + \frac{b_l}{r^{l+1}}\right) P_l^1(\mu) \quad (11)$$

It is clear, letting $a_1 = 0$ and $b_1 = \mu_0 m/4\pi (l = 1$ only$)$, that this is identical with (7), since $P_1{}^1(\mu) = \sin \theta$. Other values of l give higher magnetic multipoles at the origin that do not depend on ϕ.

4.8 Boundary Conditions

We shall now consider problems in which there are several separated regions but where no current flows inside the various regions. The equation governing $\mathbf{A}$ is $\nabla^2 \mathbf{A} = 0$ in each region. Currents may flow in the form of current sheets (having a strength $\mathbf{J}_s$, measured in amperes per meter) along the boundaries of the regions under consideration. If $\mathbf{J} = 0$ in the regions of interest, then curl $\mathbf{B} = 0$ and

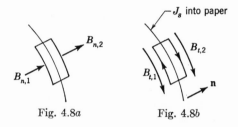

Fig. 4.8a   Fig. 4.8b

the problem can be solved by the use of a scalar potential. In any case, we are faced with the problem of the boundary conditions that apply at the boundary between two regions where there is a current sheet $\mathbf{J}_s$. Using div $\mathbf{B} = 0$ and applying the same arguments used in Chapter 3, it is clear that normal B is continuous, as shown in Figure 4.8a. This follows from the application of the divergence theorem to a "Gaussian pillbox" of vanishingly small height. We thus have

$$B_{n1} = B_{n2} \tag{1}$$

We now consider the effect of Ampere's law, curl $\mathbf{B} = \mu_0 \mathbf{J}$. We apply Stokes' law and obtain

$$\oint \mathbf{B} \cdot d\mathbf{l} = \iint_S \text{curl } \mathbf{B} \cdot \mathbf{n} \, da = \mu_0 \iint_S \mathbf{J} \cdot \mathbf{n} \, da \tag{2}$$

Applying this to Figure 4.8b, the expression on the right is the total current crossing the surface bounded by the path of integration. If $\mathbf{J}_s$ is going into the paper in Figure 4.8b this is $J_s \, dl$ for a small contour. If the length of the path of integration that is perpendicular to the boundary is made very small,

$$\oint \mathbf{B} \cdot d\mathbf{l} = (B_{t2} - B_{t1}) \, dl = \mu_0 J_s \, dl$$

and we have in general

$$\mathbf{e}_t(B_{t2} - B_{t1}) = \mu_0 \mathbf{J}_s \times \mathbf{n} \tag{3}$$

where $\mathbf{e}_t$ is a unit vector in the surface normal to $\mathbf{J}_s$ and where $\mathbf{n}$ is perpendicular to the boundary surface. Thus tangential B is discontinuous by an amount given by (3). Equations (1) and (3) are the boundary conditions that we need.

4.9 Some Problems

We shall apply these boundary conditions to several problems using the vector potential rather than the scalar potential. We first consider the field caused by an infinite solenoid. Here we approximate the solenoid by a current sheet in which current flow is only in the θ direction (cylindrical coordinates). From the previous discussion of the field from a loop it is obvious that here there will be only an A_θ which will be independent of θ and z. Thus $\nabla^2 \mathbf{A} = 0$ becomes

$$\nabla^2 A_\theta - \frac{A_\theta}{r^2} = 0 \tag{1}$$

which is in this case

$$\frac{1}{r} \frac{d}{dr} \left(r \frac{dA_\theta}{dr} \right) - \frac{A_\theta}{r^2} = 0 \tag{2}$$

Letting $A_\theta = B_n r^n$ and substituting into (2), we get

$$n^2 - 1 = 0 \qquad \text{or} \qquad n = \pm 1 \tag{3}$$

This gives

$$A_\theta = Cr + \frac{D}{r} \tag{4}$$

To get $\mathbf{B}$, we have $\mathbf{B} = \text{curl } \mathbf{A}$ or

$$B_z = \frac{1}{r} \frac{d}{dr} (rA_\theta) = 2C, \text{ a constant} \qquad B_\theta = B_r = 0 \tag{5}$$

The solution (5) applies both inside and outside the infinite solenoid, where the constant $2C$ of course will be different in the two regions. Applying Equation (3), Section 4.8, we have

$$B_{zi} - B_{z0} = \mu_0 J_s \tag{6}$$

where B_{zi} and B_{z0} are constants inside and outside the solenoid. This result is easily obtained without the use of the vector potential.

A calculation of the magnetic field of a finite solenoid along the axis can be made directly by the use of the law of Biot and Savart.

This shows that a long thin solenoid will have only one-half the B at one end that it has in the middle. Since the solenoid is made very long, the returning flux outside the solenoid will be spread over an increasingly large area. The flux density outside the solenoid will tend to zero, and (6) becomes

$$B_{zi} = \mu_0 J_s \tag{7}$$

A somewhat more difficult problem is a plane current sheet in the yz plane having $\mathbf{J}_z$ only, where J_z can be expressed by a Fourier series,

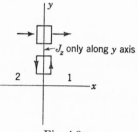

J_z only along y axis

Fig. 4.9a

as in Figure 4.9a. Let

$$J_z = \sum_n F_n \sin \frac{\pi n y}{a} \qquad \text{at } x = 0 \tag{8}$$

What is $\mathbf{B}$ at all points? Here we have only $\mathbf{J}_z$, independent of z, and it is obvious that only A_z which is also independent of z will occur. Thus $\nabla^2 A_z = 0$ in rectangular coordinates.

The solution of this equation, discussed in Chapter 2, is

$$A_z = \sum_m (A_m e^{k_m x} + B_m e^{-k_m x}) \sin k_m y$$

Since A_z must not go to infinity at large x, we choose for solutions in regions 1 and 2,

$$\begin{aligned} A_{z1} &= \sum_m A_m e^{-k_m x} \sin k_m y \\ A_{z2} &= \sum_m B_m e^{k_m x} \sin k_m y \end{aligned} \tag{9}$$

Normal B is continuous across the current sheet, so $B_{x1} = B_{x2}$ at $x = 0$. But $B_x = \partial A_z / \partial y$ here and we have, from (9),

$$A_m = B_m \tag{10}$$

Equation (9) then becomes

$$A_{z1} = \sum_m A_m e^{-k_m x} \sin k_m y$$
$$A_{z2} = \sum_m A_m e^{k_m x} \sin k_m y \tag{11}$$

The other boundary condition is

$$B_{y1} - B_{y2} = \mu_0 J_z \qquad \text{at } x = 0 \tag{12}$$

or, since $B_y = -\partial A_z / \partial x$,

$$-\frac{\partial A_{z1}}{\partial x} + \frac{\partial A_{z2}}{\partial x} = \mu_0 J_z \tag{13}$$

From (11) and (8) we now obtain

$$\sum_m A_m 2k_m \sin k_m y = \mu_0 \sum_n F_n \sin \frac{\pi n y}{a} \tag{14}$$

The members of the two series are equal term by term, so we must choose $k_m = \pi n/a$ and $A_m = \mu_0 F_n a/2\pi n$. This gives

$$A_{z1} = \sum_n \frac{\mu_0 F_n a}{2\pi n} \sin \frac{\pi n y}{a} e^{-\pi n x/a} \tag{15}$$

$$B_{y1} = -\frac{\partial A_{z1}}{\partial x} = \sum_n \frac{\mu_0}{2} F_n e^{-\pi n x/a} \sin \frac{\pi n y}{a} \tag{16}$$

$$B_{x1} = \frac{\partial A_{z1}}{\partial y} = \sum_n \frac{\mu_0}{2} F_n e^{-\pi n x/a} \cos \frac{\pi n y}{a}$$

If the current sheet is like a square wave, made of bands of current of strength J_0 and of width a in alternately opposite directions,

$$F_n = \frac{4J_0}{\pi n} \quad \text{for } n \text{ odd} \qquad F_n = 0 \quad \text{for } n \text{ even} \tag{17}$$

A problem involving spherical geometry can be solved in a somewhat similar manner. Consider a spherical current sheet of radius R, in which current flows only in the ϕ direction. Suppose that the surface current density can be expanded as

$$J_\phi = \sum_n \frac{C_n}{R} P_n^1(\mu) \tag{18}$$

Clearly there is only an A_ϕ which is independent of ϕ. The discussion in Section 4.7 applies directly to this problem and the general solution

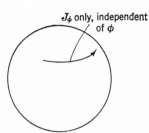

Fig. 4.9b. Equatorial currents on the surface of a sphere.

is Equation (11), Section 4.7.   Here we seek solutions inside and outside the spherical current sheet. A_ϕ should not go to infinity either
at $r = 0$ or $r = \infty$, so we choose

$$A_{\phi i} = \sum_l a_l \left(\frac{r}{R}\right)^l P_l^1(\mu)$$

$$A_{\phi 0} = \sum_l b_l \left(\frac{R}{r}\right)^{l+1} P_l^1(\mu)$$

(19)

Div **B** $= 0$ gives $B_{ri} = B_{r0}$; but $B_r = \text{curl}_r$ **A** or

$$B_r = \frac{\cos\theta}{r\sin\theta} A_\phi + \frac{1}{r}\frac{\partial A_\phi}{\partial\theta}$$

(20)

Substituting (19) we have the boundary condition, at $r = R$,

$$a_l[\cot\theta P_l^1 + (P_l^1)'] = b_l[\cot\theta P_l^1 + (P_l^1)']$$

(21)

This leads to $a_l = b_l$ in (19).   Since there clearly can be no B_ϕ in this
problem, the only tangential component of **B** is

$$B_\theta = -\frac{1}{r}\frac{\partial}{\partial r}(rA_\phi) = -\frac{A_\phi}{r} - \frac{\partial A_\phi}{\partial r}$$

The boundary condition $B_\theta^0 - B_\theta^i = \mu_0 J_\phi$ at $r = R$ leads to

$$-\sum_l a_l P_l^1 \frac{1}{R} - a_l(l+1)\frac{1}{R}P_l^1 - a_l P_l^1 \frac{1}{R} - a_l l\frac{1}{R}P_l^1 = \mu_0 J_\phi$$

(22)

which simplifies to

$$\sum_l a_l(2l+1)\frac{1}{R}P_l^1 = \sum_l \frac{\mu_0 C_l}{R}P_l^1 \qquad \text{letting } n = l$$

(23)

This shows that the solution is

$$a_l = \frac{\mu_0 C_l}{2l+1}$$

(24)

Suppose that $C_1 = J_1$, $C_l = 0$ for $l > 1$.   Then

$$A_{\phi i} = \frac{\mu_0 J_1}{3R} r \sin \theta \qquad A_{\phi 0} = \frac{\mu_0 J_1 R^2}{3} \frac{\sin \theta}{r^2} \tag{25}$$

The field outside the sphere is the same as that arising from a dipole at the origin and the field inside is

$$B_r = \frac{2\mu_0 J_1}{3R} \cos \theta \qquad B_\theta = - \frac{2\mu_0 J_1}{3R} \sin \theta$$

or $\qquad\qquad B_z = \frac{2\mu_0 J_1}{3R}$

$$\tag{26}$$

This is clearly a uniform field in the direction of the polar axis.   The current sheet that corresponds to this case is one which can be closely

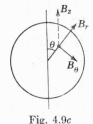

Fig. 4.9c

approximated by winding a layer of wire of constant thickness perpendicular to the polar axis so that the coil window is that formed by two equal circles which are not quite concentric.   This method is sometimes used to produce a uniform field in a restricted region.   A very similar solution exists for an ellipsoidal current sheet, and physicists use this method to obtain a uniform field inside an ellipsoid for beta-ray spectrometers.

4.10   The Quasi-stationary State and the Relation between Electrostatic and Magnetostatic Problems

We shall show later on in this book that under certain conditions the magnetic field caused by an alternating current is essentially the same as the d-c magnetic field; it will, of course, vary with time in the same way that the current does.   The condition under which this will occur is that the frequency be not too high.   In particular, the wavelength that we compute from the frequency ($\lambda f = c = 3 \times 10^8 m/\text{sec}$) must be much larger than the dimensions of the circuit under consideration.   This situation is called the quasi-stationary state.   We shall also show that at frequencies much above 60 cycles the current will flow in a very thin surface layer of thickness δ ($\delta = 0.3$ in. at 60 cycles and 0.0004 in. at 40 mc in copper).

Under these conditions there is a close connection between some problems in two dimensions in electrostatics and similar magnetic problems. We consider a two-dimensional problem in which unit surface-current density is flowing in the z direction on one conductor and returning on another. Here we shall have only a z component of the vector potential $\mathbf{A} = A\mathbf{k}$. The solution for A can be written

$$A = \frac{\mu}{4\pi} \int \frac{1}{r} \, dv \tag{1}$$

and $\mathbf{B}$ can be computed from

$$\mathbf{B} = \text{curl } \mathbf{A} = A \text{ curl } \mathbf{k} + (\text{grad } A) \times \mathbf{k} = (\text{grad } A) \times \mathbf{k} \tag{2}$$

since $\mathbf{k}$ is a constant vector. If we had unit surface charge density per unit length instead of unit current, the solution for $\mathbf{E}$ would be

$$\mathbf{E} = - \text{ grad } \phi \tag{3}$$

where

$$\phi = \frac{1}{4\pi\epsilon_0} \int \frac{1}{r} \, dv \tag{4}$$

Comparing (1) and (4) we have

$$\mathbf{E} = - \frac{1}{\epsilon_0\mu_0} \text{ grad } A \tag{5}$$

or

$$\mathbf{B} = -\epsilon_0\mu_0 \mathbf{E} \times \mathbf{k} = \epsilon_0\mu_0(\mathbf{k} \times \mathbf{E}) \tag{6}$$

Thus $\mathbf{B}$ is normal to $\mathbf{E}$ and proportional to it. This of course means that lines of $\mathbf{B}$ in the magnetic problem are equipotentials in the electrostatic problem. The restriction to the quasi-stationary case is necessary, for then the current flows only on the surface of the conductors where the charge would be in the electrostatic case. We can now solve the problem of a line current flowing inside of a rectangular waveguide and returning as a thin surface current on the inside surface of this waveguide.

PROBLEMS

1. A current i flows in a wire circle of radius a. Find $\mathbf{B}$ along a line normal to the circle and through its center.

2. Find **B** along the axis of a finite solenoid of radius R, length L, having ni ampere-turns per meter.

3. Current flows in sheets as in the figure. The current flows only in the z direction. Find **B** at all points.

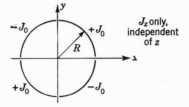

4. In cylindrical coordinates there is only A_θ independent of θ. If $J = 0$ in the region of interest, show that

$$A_\theta = \sum_l A_l J_1(k_l r) e^{\pm k_l z}$$

5. If there is only A_z, and $J = 0$ in the region of interest, find the general solution for A_z in cylindrical coordinates.

6. Find the magnetic field arising from a high-frequency alternating current flowing down a thin wire inside a rectangular waveguide.

7. If there is a volume current flow of J_0 amperes per meter flowing only in the x direction from $y = -a$ to $y = +a$ and no currents flowing anywhere else (including infinity), find an expression for the vector potential **A** everywhere.

5

Magnetic Materials

5.1 Types of Magnetic Materials

There are three types of magnetic materials: diamagnetic, para-magnetic, and ferromagnetic. A diamagnetic material contains no permanent dipoles, but dipoles can be induced in such material by an external field. These dipoles (a magnetic dipole is a circulating cur-rent) are the result of changes in the motion of electrons around the core of an atom caused by a magnetic field. The field of these dipoles opposes that of the generating field. Diamagnetism is usually very weak and is normally smaller than paramagnetism.

Paramagnetism occurs in substances that do contain permanent dipoles. These dipoles are the result of rotation of electrons about an atom and also result from the permanent magnetic moment of the electron which arises from the classical model of a sphere of charge which is rotating. Paramagnetism occurs when an external magnetic field lines up these permanent dipoles; this lining-up process is opposed by the random thermal motion of the atoms. Both paramagnetism and diamagnetism give effects which are usually proportional to the external field.

Ferromagnetism is an advanced stage of paramagnetism. In this case quantum mechanical effects cause the magnetic moments of many electrons to line up parallel to each other even in the absence of an external field. This occurs over a region called a domain, which includes a large number of atoms. The magnetic moments of these domains can be lined up by an external magnetic field with great ease, resulting in very large magnetic fields from the domains. At low magnetic fields a domain may merely reverse its direction of magnet-ization so as to aid the external field along an axis preferred by the domain. In addition the boundaries of the domains may change so as

85

to increase the volume of favorably oriented domains. At higher fields the direction of magnetization of the domain will change until it is parallel to the external magnetic field. When all the domains are magnetized in the direction of the external field, further increase in the external field can cause no further alignment of the dipoles. This is called saturation and generally occurs near 20,000 gauss (2 webers per square meter) for iron.

Ferromagnetism is not linear with the external field and usually exhibits a hysteresis effect since the dipoles when once lined up tend to remain that way and thus show a sort of "memory" of the previous magnetic history of the material. We shall simplify the above by dividing magnetic materials into two classes: soft magnetic materials that show effects which are linear with the external field and have no hysteresis; and hard magnetic materials that are nonlinear and show hysteresis.

5.2   Potential of Magnetized Materials : B and H

A substance which has a certain number of magnetic dipoles per unit volume is said to have a magnetization **M**, where **M** is the vector sum of the dipole moments per unit volume. In a soft magnetic material **M** will be proportional to **B** and in a hard magnetic material the relation between **M** and **B** is usually given by a graph. We shall consider only such cases where **M** and **B** are parallel.

We wish now to find the effect of magnetized material. The existence of magnetized material implies the existence of currents. These are the result of incomplete cancellation of the atomic circulating currents caused by changes of **M** with position in the media. We shall replace the magnetization by an equivalent current distribution, and this fictitious current distribution will be added to the real currents present when computing the actual magnetic field. The situation is similar to what was done for dielectrics, where we replaced a variable polarization by a fictitious charge distribution and then calculated the electric fields from the sum of the real charges and the fictitious or polarization charges.

The vector potential of a single dipole is

$$\mathbf{A} = \frac{\mu_0}{4\pi} \frac{\mathbf{m} \times \mathbf{r}}{r^3} \tag{1}$$

and for a continuous distribution of magnetization we have

$$\mathbf{A} = \frac{\mu_0}{4\pi} \int \frac{\mathbf{M} \times \mathbf{r}}{r^3} \, dv \tag{2}$$

In (1) and (2) the vector $\mathbf{r}$ is directed from the dipole to the field point. It is more convenient here to consider $\mathbf{r}$ to go from the field point to the source point at the dipole, thus reversing the sign of (2). With this new definition of $\mathbf{r}$ we then have

$$A = - \frac{\mu_0}{4\pi} \int \frac{\mathbf{M} \times \mathbf{r}}{r^3} \, dv \tag{3}$$

Since $\mathbf{r}/r^3 = -\nabla(1/r)$ we have

$$A = \frac{\mu_0}{4\pi} \int \mathbf{M} \times \nabla \left(\frac{1}{r} \right) dv \tag{4}$$

By a vector identity, Appendix B, Equation (4),

$$\nabla \times \left(\frac{\mathbf{M}}{r} \right) = \frac{1}{r} \nabla \times \mathbf{M} + \nabla \left(\frac{1}{r} \right) \times \mathbf{M} \tag{5}$$

Equation (4) then becomes

$$A = \frac{\mu_0}{4\pi} \int_V \frac{\nabla \times \mathbf{M}}{r} \, dv - \frac{\mu_0}{4\pi} \int_V \nabla \times \left(\frac{\mathbf{M}}{r} \right) dv \tag{6}$$

We wish now to change the second volume integral in (6) to a surface integral. To do this we shall prove the following theorem for any vector $\mathbf{F}$:

$$\int_S \mathbf{n} \times \mathbf{F} \, da = \int_V \nabla \times \mathbf{F} \, dv \tag{7}$$

To prove (7) we expand

$$\int_V \nabla \cdot (\mathbf{F} \times \mathbf{a}) \, dv = \int_V (\mathbf{a} \cdot \nabla \times \mathbf{F} - \mathbf{F} \cdot \nabla \times \mathbf{a}) \, dv \tag{8}$$

where $\mathbf{a}$ is any arbitrary constant vector. Since $\mathbf{a}$ is a constant the second term in the integrand on the right is zero and we have, by the divergence theorem,

$$\int_V \nabla \cdot (\mathbf{F} \times \mathbf{a}) \, dv = \int_S (\mathbf{F} \times \mathbf{a}) \cdot \mathbf{n} \, da = \int_V \mathbf{a} \cdot \nabla \times \mathbf{F} \, dv \tag{9}$$

Here $(\mathbf{F} \times \mathbf{a}) \cdot \mathbf{n} = \mathbf{a} \cdot (\mathbf{n} \times \mathbf{F})$ by Appendix B, and $\mathbf{a}$ can then be taken outside the integral sign, giving

$$\mathbf{a} \cdot \int_S \mathbf{n} \times \mathbf{F} \, da = \mathbf{a} \cdot \int \nabla \times \mathbf{F} \, dv \tag{10}$$

Since this is true for any arbitrary vector $\mathbf{a}$ the two integrals must be equal and we have proved the theorem (7).

Using this theorem in (6), we have

$$A = \frac{\mu_0}{4\pi} \int_V \frac{\operatorname{curl} \mathbf{M}}{r} \, dv + \frac{\mu_0}{4\pi} \int_S \frac{\mathbf{M} \times \mathbf{n}}{r} \, da \tag{11}$$

We see that the effects of magnetized material can be calculated by replacing the magnetized material by some fictitious currents. From (11) these are: a current density throughout the volume of integration

$$\mathbf{J}' = \text{curl } \mathbf{M} \tag{12}$$

together with a surface current

$$\mathbf{J}'_s = \mathbf{M} \times \mathbf{n} \tag{13}$$

over the surface of the volume of integration. As in the case of $P_n = \sigma_p$ in the discussion of dielectrics we can ignore $\mathbf{J}'_s$ unless we are specifically interested in its effects. If instead of having a sharp discontinuity in $\mathbf{M}$ at the surface of a magnetized body we have a rapid but finite change in $\mathbf{M}$ near the surface then curl $\mathbf{M}$ and hence $\mathbf{J}'$ will have a large value in this region and we can dispense with (13). With this reservation we see that magnetized material can be replaced by a fictitious current distribution $\mathbf{J}' = \text{curl } \mathbf{M}$. This current $\mathbf{J}'$ is just as effective as real current $\mathbf{J}$ in producing a magnetic field $\mathbf{B}$. Ampere's law thus becomes

$$\text{curl } \mathbf{B} = \mu_0(\mathbf{J} + \mathbf{J}') = \mu_0(\mathbf{J} + \text{curl } \mathbf{M}) \tag{14}$$

This can be written as

$$\text{curl} \left(\frac{\mathbf{B}}{\mu_0} - \mathbf{M} \right) = \mathbf{J} \quad \text{or} \quad \text{curl } \mathbf{H} = \mathbf{J} \tag{15}$$

The quantity $\left(\dfrac{\mathbf{B}}{\mu_0} - \mathbf{M} \right)$ occurs often and is called $\mathbf{H}$. In a vacuum $\mathbf{M} = 0$ and $\mathbf{B} = \mu_0\mathbf{H}$. In soft magnetic material $\mathbf{M}$ is proportional to $\mathbf{B}$ and we can write

$$\mathbf{B} = \mu_0 K_m \mathbf{H} \tag{16}$$

where K_m is a dimensionless quantity called the permeability.

Since
$$\mathbf{B} = \mu_0(\mathbf{H} + \mathbf{M}) \tag{17}$$
and div $\mathbf{B} = 0$, we have

$$\text{div } \mathbf{H} = - \text{div } \mathbf{M} \tag{18}$$

Thus $\mathbf{H}$ is a vector which does have a divergence arising from sources alone in the absence of a current density. These sources are the ordinary north and south poles of permanent magnets which are made of hard magnetic material so that there can be $\mathbf{M}$ without any real current flowing anywhere.

Consideration of a long uniformly magnetized iron bar shows that the external field $\mathbf{H}$ arises from the large value of div $\mathbf{M}$ at the ends, in the same way that the electric field from a uniformly polarized dielectric rod arises from the polarization charges on the ends. If the ends

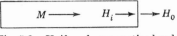

Fig. 5.2a. Uniformly magnetized rod

of the rod are separated by a distance large compared with the diameter, the effect of one end of the rod on the other can be neglected, and by symmetry we must have

$$H_0 = -H_i \tag{19}$$

at one end. However, by (18) and the divergence theorem, we have

$$H_0 - H_i = M \qquad \text{or} \qquad H_i = -\frac{M}{2} \tag{20}$$

B inside the rod near one end becomes

$$B_i = \mu_0(H_i + M) = \frac{\mu_0 M}{2} \tag{21}$$

5.3 Boundary Conditions for Magnetic Materials: Some Problems

A large group of problems concerning magnetized media can be solved using the above theory. We shall first consider problems where there are various regions of space, each region being of homogeneous soft magnetic material. No real currents flow in the interior of the various regions but surface currents may flow on the boundaries between the regions. Since div $\mathbf{B} = 0$, normal B is continuous at any boundary. Considerations exactly similar to those in Section 4.5, but using Equation (15), Section 5.2, instead of Equation (11), Section 4.5, show that in the case of magnetic materials tangential H is discontinuous by an amount J_s. The boundary conditions in this case become

$$B_{n1} = B_{n2} \tag{1}$$
$$H_{t1} - H_{t2} = J_s \tag{2}$$

where J_s flows in a direction normal to H_t. Since $\mathbf{J} = 0$ in the various regions curl $\mathbf{H} = 0$ and $\mathbf{H}$ can be derived from a scalar potential. Since div $\mathbf{B} = 0$ is the same as div $(\mu_0 K_m \mathbf{H}) = 0$ where $\mu_0 K_m$ is a constant, we have div $\mathbf{H} = 0$. If we let $\mathbf{H} = -$ grad V, then in each region $\nabla^2 V = 0$, and the boundary conditions (1) and (2) apply.

We shall apply this method to the solution of the problem of a soft magnetic sphere of radius R and permeability K_m in a uniform external magnetic field $\mathbf{H}_0$. Let the polar axis be chosen in the direction of $\mathbf{H}_0$. Using spherical coordinates, the proper solutions of $\nabla^2 V = 0$ that we must use are

$$V_0 = \left(-H_0 r + \frac{a}{r^2}\right) P_1(\mu) \quad \text{and} \quad V_i = br P_1(\mu) \tag{3}$$

This choice of solutions and the restriction to $l = 1$ is based on the same considerations as obtain in the case of the dielectric sphere in a uniform

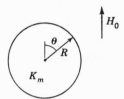

Fig. 5.3a. Sphere of constant permeability in a uniform magnetic field.

electric field. Normal B is continuous so $\partial V_0/\partial r = K_m \partial V_i/\partial r$ at $r = R$. This gives

$$-H_0 - \frac{2a}{R^3} = K_m b \tag{4}$$

Continuity of tangential H ($J_s = 0$ here) yields

$$-H_0 R + \frac{a}{R^2} = bR \tag{5}$$

Simultaneous solution of (4) and (5) for the unknowns a and b gives

$$a = \frac{K_m - 1}{K_m + 2} H_0 R^3 \quad \text{and} \quad b = \frac{-3}{K_m + 2} H_0 \tag{6}$$

Thus
$$V_0 = \left[-H_0 r + \frac{(K_m - 1)H_0 R^3}{(K_m + 2)r^2}\right] \cos \theta$$
$$V_i = \frac{-3H_0}{K_m + 2} r \cos \theta \tag{7}$$

We take the negative gradient of these scalar potentials to get the field $\mathbf{H}$. Clearly this will give on the outside the original uniform magnetic field plus the field of a dipole. The field inside is a uniform field in the direction of H_0 and of magnitude $H_i = 3H_0/(K_m + 2)$. Since this solution is for a "soft" material, $\mathbf{B}$ inside and outside the sphere can easily be obtained.

The case of a "hard" magnetic sphere in a uniform external field can also be solved. We make the simplifying assumption that the sphere has only been magnetized in the past along the polar axis. Then we can use the same analysis as above, except that the equation $B_i = \mu_0 K_m H_i$ merely gives the relation between B_i and H_i under the conditions of the experiment and does not imply any linearity between

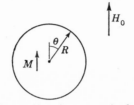

Fig. 5.3b. Uniformly magnetized sphere.

B_i and H_i. It is instructive to solve this problem in a slightly different way. We assume that the form of the solution is the same as (7), i.e.,

$$V_0 = \left(-H_0 r + \frac{a}{r^2} \right) \cos \theta$$
$$V_i = br \cos \theta \tag{8}$$

We also assume that B_i, H_i, and M_i are all in the same direction and uniform. The boundary condition that normal B is continuous can be obtained from

$$B_{r0} = -\mu_0 \frac{\partial V_0}{\partial r}$$

and $\qquad B_{ri} = \mu_0 (H_{ri} + M_r) = \mu_0 \left(-\frac{\partial V_i}{\partial r} + M_r \right) \tag{9}$

This leads to

$$-\frac{\partial V_0}{\partial r} = -\frac{\partial V_i}{\partial r} + M \cos \theta \tag{10}$$

or $\qquad H_0 + \frac{2a}{R^3} = -b + M \tag{11}$

Continuity of tangential H leads to

$$-H_0 R + \frac{a}{R^2} = bR \tag{12}$$

The simultaneous solution of (11) and (12) gives

$$a = \frac{R^3 M}{3} \qquad b = \frac{M}{3} - H_0 \tag{13}$$

The answer then is

$$V_0 = \left(-H_0 r + \frac{R^3 M}{3r^2}\right) \cos \theta$$

$$V_i = \left(\frac{M}{3} - H_0\right) r \cos \theta \qquad (14)$$

The field outside is a uniform field plus the field of a dipole and the field inside is

$$H_i = H_0 - \frac{M}{3} \qquad (15)$$

The problem we have just solved is that of a sphere having any magnetization $\mathbf{M}$ in a uniform external field. The factor multiplying M in this expression is called the demagnetization factor L, and in general for other geometries we have

$$H_i = H_0 - LM \qquad (16)$$

We find B_i from

$$\frac{B_i}{\mu_0} = H_i + M = 3H_0 - 2H_i \qquad (17)$$

This equation gives B_i as a function of H_i for given H_0. This can be plotted as a straight line of slope -2. Another relation between B_i and H_i exists and is related to the previous history of the iron. It is called a hysteresis curve. Figure 5.3c shows how these two curves

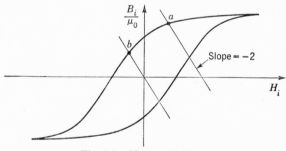

Fig. 5.3c. Hysteresis loop.

intersect at a point which gives B_i and H_i. Point a is the intersection used after returning to low fields from a high field. Point b is $(B_i/\mu_0, H_i)$ for no external field after returning from a high field.

5.4 Magnet Design

The design of simple magnets is accomplished using the above theory. Consider a simple magnet as shown in Figure 5.4a. We have

$$\oint \mathbf{H} \cdot d\mathbf{l} = ni \tag{1}$$

Assuming that **H** will be essentially uniform in the gap and the iron, (1) becomes

$$H_i l_i + H_g l_g = ni \tag{2}$$

Since normal B is continuous in going from the gap to the iron, and $H_g = B_g/\mu_0$, (2) becomes

$$H_i l_i + l_g \frac{B_i}{\mu_0} = ni \tag{3}$$

This is a linear relation between H_i and B_i, leading in particular to $B_i/\mu_0 = (-l_i/l_g)H_i$ at $ni = 0$. This, in conjunction with the BH curve for the iron used, gives B and H in the iron after an excursion to high fields, as shown in Figure 5.4b, and permits the design of permanent magnets. Actually, we have neglected any leakage flux in the above calculation. This will depend on details at the pole tips and often will increase B in the iron by a factor of two or more.

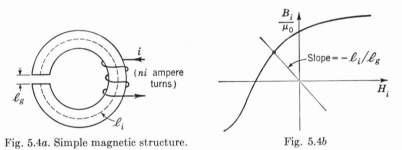

Fig. 5.4a. Simple magnetic structure.   Fig. 5.4b

To design a permanent magnet we must know the desired B in the air gap, guess the leakage factor which will permit computation of the B in the iron, and then by (3) fix H_i and l_i. It will be shown later that the material of a permanent magnet is most efficiently used if the product $B_i H_i$ is a maximum, which will fix both B_i and H_i. The desired B_g is then obtained by using suitable pole tips.

The design of an electromagnet is quite similar to the design of a permanent magnet. Soft iron is usually used and the hysteresis loop is quite narrow. This means that H in the iron is quite small and usually can be neglected in a first design. Equation (3) then becomes

$$B_g l_g = \mu_0(ni) \qquad \text{or} \qquad H_g l_g = ni \tag{4}$$

The units of H are clear from (4); they are amperes per meter (sometimes called ampere turns per meter). Sufficient cross section of the iron path should always be used so that the assumption of low H in the iron is obtained. This usually means not exceeding flux densities of 15,000 or 20,000 gauss. Knowing the leakage fields is quite important at this point.

PROBLEMS

1. An infinite slab of hard magnetic material is of thickness t. Outside one face of the material the field is a constant equal to H_0 and directed perpendicular to the slab face. Find B and H inside the magnetic material. $M = M_0$ in the iron. All vector-field quantities are normal to the slab.

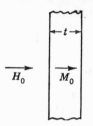

2. A thin circular disk of radius a and thickness t_0 ($t_0 \ll a$) is uniformly magnetized in a direction parallel to the axis of the disk. Find B at a distance d from the center of the disk on the axis of the disk. The magnetization of the disk is M.

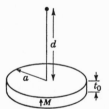

3. A long cylinder parallel to the z axis has an inner radius a and an outer radius b. This cylinder is uniformly magnetized in the z direction with a magnetization M. Find the magnetic field along the axis.

4. A long cylinder of radius R is made of a "hard" magnetic material. This cylinder is immersed in a uniform magnetic field H_0 so that its axis is normal to H_0. Find the magnetic field at all points.

6

Maxwell's Equations

We have discussed classical phenomena having to do with electric charges at rest (electrostatics) and electric charges moving with a constant velocity in steady currents (magnetostatics). We shall now discuss the new ideas that must be considered when electric and magnetic fields change with time.

6.1 Faraday's Law

The experimental law that describes phenomena connected with a changing magnetic field was discovered by Michael Faraday. Since currents could cause magnetic effects, he hoped to show that magnetic effects could cause currents. He wound two coils close together but insulated from each other, hoping that a large current through the first coil would cause continuous current to flow in the second coil, since the first coil caused a magnetic flux to link the second coil. The experiment was a failure as no steady current was observed in the second coil. However Faraday was a good experimenter: he observed that when the current in the first coil was originally turned on there was a momentary flow of current in the second coil, and when the current was broken there was a transient current in the second coil in the opposite direction. He made more refined measurements and found that the current in the second coil was proportional—not to the magnetic field linking the second coil—but to the time rate of change of this quantity.

This experimental work led to Faraday's law, which is best stated in terms of the emf which arises in a circuit when the magnetic flux through this circuit changes with time, rather than in terms of the current that flows. Emf (electromotive force) is defined as the work done by electric, magnetic, or other forces such as the chemical processes involved in batteries, in carrying unit charge around a circuit, i.e., it is the agency that makes electric charges move around a circuit. In the case of changing magnetic fields this law states that the line integral of **E** around the circuit is equal to the negative of the time rate of change of the total flux through the circuit. We thus have

$$\text{emf} \equiv \oint \mathbf{E} \cdot d\mathbf{l} = -\frac{d}{dt} \int_S \mathbf{B} \cdot \mathbf{n} \, da = -\frac{d\Phi}{dt} \tag{1}$$

The term on the right is the time rate of change of the flux through any surface bounded by the line integral. Since div **B** = 0, any such surface will give the same value of the surface integral.

We shall see later that the following discussion is correct only if we consider the magnetic fields everywhere in the circuit to be strictly proportional to the current flowing. This implies that the magnetic fields associated with a given current distribution change immediately when the current distribution changes. Actually this is not so—magnetic and electric fields propagate with the speed of light $(3 \times 10^8$ m/ sec). At present we shall restrict our treatment to circuits of such size and such rates of change of current in the circuit that the electromagnetic disturbance has propagated over most of the useful parts of the circuit before the current has changed very much. Under such conditions, known as the "quasi-stationary state," the magnetic fields at any instant are considered to be those that would occur if a steady current equal to the current actually existing at that instant were flowing.

An example of the quasi-stationary state is that in which the current in the circuit will not have changed by more than a few per cent in the time required for a signal traveling at the velocity of light to travel over a distance of, for instance, five times the maximum dimension of the circuit under consideration. Under these conditions the usual concepts of lumped parameters such as capacity and inductance are useful. Larger circuits or faster rates of current change require more advanced treatment and lead to such concepts as cavities, waveguides, antennas, and the propagation of electromagnetic waves. These subjects are treated in later chapters.

Equation (1) is the integral form of Faraday's law. The flux through the circuit can change with time in several ways. The circuit itself may change position while the magnetic field does not change, or the circuit may remain fixed while **B** changes. Under this last condition the derivative with respect to time in (1) does not depend on the contour of integration and the time derivative can be taken inside. It then operates only on the time-dependent parts of **B** and becomes a partial derivative. We have

$$\text{emf} = \oint \mathbf{E} \cdot d\mathbf{l} = - \int_S \frac{\partial \mathbf{B}}{\partial t} \cdot \mathbf{n} \, da \tag{2}$$

The line integral can be transformed by Stokes' law to

$$\text{emf} = \oint \mathbf{E} \cdot d\mathbf{l} = \int_S \text{curl } \mathbf{E} \cdot \mathbf{n} \, da = - \int_S \frac{\partial \mathbf{B}}{\partial t} \cdot \mathbf{n} \, da \tag{3}$$

Since the two surface integrals are equal for any surface of integration, the integrands must be equal, leading to

$$\text{curl } \mathbf{E} = - \frac{\partial \mathbf{B}}{\partial t} \tag{4}$$

This is Faraday's law expressed in differential form.

6.2 Inductance

Under quasi-stationary conditions the time rate of change of $\mathbf{B}$ at any point will be proportional to the time rate of change of the current causing this $\mathbf{B}$. The emf around the circuit will thus be proportional to di/dt:

$$\text{emf} = - \frac{d}{dt} \int_S \mathbf{B} \cdot \mathbf{n} \, da = -L \frac{di}{dt} \tag{1}$$

L is a factor of proportionality and is called the self-inductance of the circuit. We can obtain a general expression for the inductance of a circuit by the use of the vector potential. Using Stokes' law we have

$$\int_S \mathbf{B} \cdot \mathbf{n} \, da = \int_S \text{curl } \mathbf{A} \cdot \mathbf{n} \, da = \oint \mathbf{A} \cdot d\mathbf{l} \tag{2}$$

Integration of (1) with respect to time shows that the inductance is the total flux linking a circuit divided by the current flowing or the flux linkages per ampere.

$$L = \frac{\int_S \mathbf{B} \cdot \mathbf{n} \, da}{i} = \frac{n\Phi}{i} \tag{3}$$

The right-hand side of (3) refers to a coil of n turns rather than one turn. Substitution of (2) into (3) gives

$$L = \frac{\oint \mathbf{A} \cdot d\mathbf{l}}{i} \tag{4}$$

However, from Equation (18), Section 4.5, we have

$$\mathbf{A} = \frac{\mu_0 i}{4\pi} \oint \frac{d\mathbf{l}'}{r} \tag{5}$$

Substituting into (5) we have

$$L = \frac{\mu_0}{4\pi} \oint\oint \frac{d\mathbf{l} \cdot d\mathbf{l}'}{r} \tag{6}$$

Here $d\mathbf{l}$ and $d\mathbf{l}'$ are two different elements of length in the circuit and r the absolute value of the distance between them. The double-line integral means that we fix $d\mathbf{l}$, integrate $d\mathbf{l}'$ over the circuit, and then integrate this result over the circuit again. Considerable care must be exercised in using this formula, for r can go to zero, making L go to infinity. What has happened is that we have assumed that the current is contained in an infinitely thin filament. Such an unrealistic circuit will have infinite inductance and some changes in the formulation of the integral must be made to take into account the fact that the current is distributed over a wire of finite cross section. This integration is usually quite difficult to perform, but many such integrals have been evaluated and are available in Circular 74 of the National Bureau of Standards and in Terman's "Radio Engineering Handbook" (Reference 14).

Another type of inductance is called mutual inductance and is defined as the emf induced in one circuit due to a current change in another circuit. The mutual inductance M is defined by

$$\text{emf}_2 = -M \frac{di_1}{dt} \tag{7}$$

A discussion similar to that for self-inductance leads to

$$M = \frac{\mu_0}{4\pi} \oint\oint \frac{d\mathbf{l}_1 \cdot d\mathbf{l}_2}{r} \qquad \text{or} \qquad M = \frac{n\Phi_1}{i_2} \tag{8}$$

where $d\mathbf{l}_1$ is an element of the first circuit, $d\mathbf{l}_2$ an element of the second circuit, and r the distance between them. It is clear from the symmetry of (8) that the mutual inductance is the same if we have current in the second circuit rather than the first circuit and measure the emf in the first circuit.

It is generally easier to compute the inductance using (3) rather than (6) if the circuit under discussion is one in which we know the magnetic field over a surface bounded by the circuit. Calculation of inductance will not be treated extensively here. The unit of inductance is the henry, and is that inductance which gives a back emf of one volt if the current is changing at a rate of one ampere per second.

H inside of an infinite solenoid carrying a surface current of J_s amperes per meter is clearly J_s. The units of H are thus amperes per meter or, as is more often used in magnet design, ampere-turns per meter. Mks units in magnetism are usually not used in engineering practice, which usually uses the cgs system. The cgs system expresses B in terms of gauss, which is one line per square centimeter. The mks system of units uses the weber per square meter which corresponds to ten thousand gauss. In the cgs system of units, B is numerically equal to H in empty space; the units of H are oersteds in the cgs system. Thus ten thousand oersteds corresponds to an H of one weber per square meter divided by $4\pi \times 10^{-7}$ or $10^7/4\pi$ amperes per meter. One oersted thus is $10^3/4\pi$ amperes per meter or about 80 amperes per meter. In English units this amounts to about 2 ampere-turns per inch. The unit of flux in the mks system is the weber—a flux changing at the rate of one weber per second induces an emf of 1 volt. A weber per square meter corresponds to ten thousand gauss and one gauss is a line per square centimeter. Thus a weber is 10^8 lines and 1 volt is the emf generated by a changing flux of 10^8 lines per second.

The expression for inductance will always turn out to be of the form

$$L = C\mu_0 n^2(l) \qquad h \tag{9}$$

where n is the number of turns and (l) an expression having the dimensions of a length. Thus it is clear that the units of μ_0 are henries per meter.

6.3 Energy Storage in Electric and Magnetic Fields

We shall now discuss the energy of a system of charged particles, computing first the work done in assembling such a system and then considering this energy to be stored in the electric field in the space between the particles. A similar calculation can be done for the magnetic case. In these cases we shall consider only the static case where there is no time dependence. The potential energy of two particles is

$$V_{12} = \frac{q_1 q_2}{4\pi\epsilon_0 r_{12}} \tag{1}$$

The potential energy of an assemblage of such particles will have an energy which is the sum of expressions like (1) over all possible pairs. This will be

$$V = \frac{1}{2} \sum_i q_i \sum_j \frac{q_j}{4\pi\epsilon_0 r_{ij}} \qquad i \neq j \tag{2}$$

The factor of $\frac{1}{2}$ arises from the fact that each pair is counted twice, $V_{ij} = V_{ji}$, and each should be counted only once. Equation (2) can be written as

$$V = \frac{1}{2} \sum_i q_i \phi_i \tag{3}$$

In the limit of a continuous distribution of charges, we have

$$V = \frac{1}{2} \int_V \rho \phi \, dv \tag{4}$$

This is the potential energy in terms of the charges and potentials. Using the relations

$$\mathbf{E} = - \text{grad } \phi \qquad \text{and} \qquad \text{div } \mathbf{D} = \rho = - \text{div } (\epsilon \text{ grad } \phi) \tag{5}$$

together with the vector identity

$$\text{div } (\epsilon\phi \text{ grad } \phi) = \phi \text{ div } (\epsilon \text{ grad } \phi) + \epsilon(\text{grad } \phi)^2 \tag{6}$$

(4) becomes, after using the divergence theorem,

$$V = \frac{1}{2} \int_V \epsilon E^2 \, dv + \frac{1}{2} \int_S \epsilon\phi \mathbf{E} \cdot \mathbf{n} \, da \tag{7}$$

The second integral of (7) varies as $1/r$, since $\phi \sim 1/r$, $E \sim 1/r^2$, and $da \sim r^2$ if we integrate over a large sphere. If we integrate over all space out to infinity the second integral vanishes and we have

$$V = \frac{1}{2} \int_V \epsilon E^2 \, dv = \int_V \frac{\mathbf{D} \cdot \mathbf{E}}{2} \, dv \tag{8}$$

Thus in any region of space we can attribute an electrostatic energy density $\mathbf{E} \cdot \mathbf{D}/2$ to a volume element. It is easy to show from this that the energy stored in a capacitor is $\frac{1}{2}CV^2$. We find the forces on an object in an electrostatic field by finding the change in energy for a small displacement of the object. We shall not pursue this subject further.

We can also make a similar calculation concerning the energy stored in a magnetic field. However, magnetic materials are often nonlinear and we shall use a somewhat different approach. Consider an infinite solenoid filled with a magnetic material. If the current through this solenoid starts from zero and increases with time the voltage across 1 meter of this solenoid at any time is

$$E = n \frac{d\Phi}{dt} = nA \frac{dB}{dt} \tag{9}$$

where n is the number of turns per meter and A is the cross-sectional area. The current in the solenoid is related to H by

$$I = \frac{H}{n} \tag{10}$$

The energy stored at the end of a time T is then

$$\int_0^T EI\,dt = \int_0^{B_{max}} \mathbf{H} \cdot d\mathbf{B} \cdot A \tag{11}$$

or the energy stored per unit volume is

$$W/\text{vol} = \int_0^{B_{max}} \mathbf{H} \cdot d\mathbf{B} \tag{12}$$

If B and H are linearly related the energy density is

$$W/\text{vol} = \frac{\mathbf{B} \cdot \mathbf{H}}{2} \tag{13}$$

Here we neglect any loss of energy due to ohmic losses in the solenoid

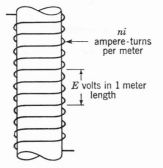

ni
ampere-turns
per meter

E volts in 1 meter
length

Fig. 6.3a. Infinite solenoid filled with magnetic material.

or eddy currents in the iron.   From this it is clear that the energy lost in traversing a hysteresis loop is

$$W/\text{vol} = \oint \mathbf{H} \cdot d\mathbf{B} = \text{area of loop} \tag{14}$$

If linear magnetic materials are used we can obtain an expression for the energy stored in an inductance. A changing current in an inductance will have a back emf of $-L\,di/dt$. The work done by a current i flowing against this emf for a time dt is $iL\left(\dfrac{di}{dt}\right)dt$ or $Li\,di$. The total work done to obtain a current I in an inductance L is thus

$$W = \int_0^I Li\,di = \tfrac{1}{2}LI^2 \tag{15}$$

We can now attribute a magnetostatic energy density of $\mathbf{B} \cdot \mathbf{H}/2$ to any element of space if linear magnetic materials are present.   Combining (13) and (15) we have

$$T = \tfrac{1}{2}Li^2 = \int_V \frac{\mathbf{B} \cdot \mathbf{H}}{2}\,dv \tag{16}$$

This is a very convenient way to compute the inductance of a circuit where B and H are known everywhere.

6.4   Displacement Current

We now have completed our discussion of electrostatics, magneto-statics, and the effects of changing magnetic fields.   We must now con-sider an effect that has to do with changing electric fields.   This results in the concept of the displacement current, and this is the great con-tribution made by Maxwell.   Consider first

$$\text{curl } \mathbf{H} = \mathbf{J} \tag{1}$$

If we take the divergence of both sides we have

$$\text{div curl } \mathbf{H} = \text{div } \mathbf{J} = 0 \tag{2}$$

since the divergence of any curl is zero.   Equation (1) is, of course, correct for steady currents in the absence of changing electric fields—namely in magnetostatics.   In the general case, however, when chang-ing electric fields are present (2) cannot be true.   This is a consequence of the equation of continuity which we shall now discuss.

The equation of continuity is based on the conservation of charge, i.e., charges are neither created nor destroyed but flow from one region to another by the usual phenomena of current flow.   The charge inside a volume can leave this volume only by current flow across the bound-ing surface.   Thus we have

$$\int_S \mathbf{J} \cdot \mathbf{n} \, da = -\frac{\partial}{\partial t} \int_V \rho \, dv \tag{3}$$

If we keep the volume fixed and apply the divergence theorem we can rewrite (3) as

$$\int_S \mathbf{J} \cdot \mathbf{n} \, da = \int_V \text{div } \mathbf{J} \, dv = \int_V \left(-\frac{\partial \rho}{\partial t} \right) dv \tag{4}$$

Since the last two integrals must be equal no matter what volume is used, the integrands must be equal, or

$$\text{div } \mathbf{J} = -\frac{\partial \rho}{\partial t} \tag{5}$$

This clearly contradicts (2).   Maxwell *assumed* that we must add something to $\mathbf{J}$ in (1) so that the divergence of $\mathbf{J}$ plus this something is zero.   Since we know that

$$\text{div } \mathbf{D} = \rho \tag{6}$$

we can rewrite (5) as

$$\text{div}\left(\mathbf{J} + \frac{\partial \mathbf{D}}{\partial t}\right) = 0 \tag{7}$$

Thus if we add $\partial \mathbf{D}/\partial t$ to (1), (2) becomes

$$\text{div curl }\mathbf{H} = \text{div}\left(\mathbf{J} + \frac{\partial \mathbf{D}}{\partial t}\right) = 0 \tag{8}$$

and the continuity equation, (5) is still valid. Maxwell's assumption then is that we must add to the real current $\mathbf{J}$ a displacement current $\partial \mathbf{D}/\partial t$ which will be just as effective as $\mathbf{J}$ in producing magnetic fields. Maxwell thus replaced (1) by

$$\text{curl }\mathbf{H} = \mathbf{J} + \frac{\partial \mathbf{D}}{\partial t} \tag{9}$$

The above ideas may be made clearer by an example. Consider a charged condenser which is then discharged through a resistor, as in Figure 6.4a. Real current is leaving the dotted volume through the wire. Div $\mathbf{J}$ is not zero, since $\int_S \mathbf{J} \cdot \mathbf{n}\, da$ is equal to I, the current flowing through the wire. This current results from the diminishing charge inside the volume, and hence $\int_S \mathbf{J} \cdot \mathbf{n}\, da = -\frac{\partial}{\partial t}\int_V \rho\, dv$. However, $\mathbf{D}$ in the condenser is just equal to σ; hence $-\partial\sigma/\partial t$ is equal to $-\partial \mathbf{D}/\partial t$, where σ is the charge per unit area on the condenser plate.

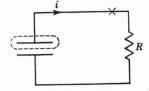

Fig. 6.4a. Condenser discharging.

Thus there is a displacement current density $\partial \mathbf{D}/\partial t$ entering the dotted volume in the region of the condenser plates, and the integral of this displacement current is just equal to the real current leaving through the wire. The divergence of $(\mathbf{J} + \partial \mathbf{D}/\partial t)$ is thus zero, and Maxwell's assumption is made plausible.

The justification of (9) is that it is plausible and if the displacement currents are large enough their magnetic effects can be easily measured. This occurs in microwave apparatus where $\partial \mathbf{D}/\partial t$ may be very large and also in propagating waves. The electromagnetic explanation of radio and light waves depends solely on the existence of the displacement current and their existence is sufficient justification of (9).

6.5 Maxwell's Equations

We can now collect all our present knowledge of electromagnetic phenomena into a small number of equations. These are called Maxwell's equations and should be memorized. They are

$$\text{curl } \mathbf{E} = -\frac{\partial \mathbf{B}}{\partial t} \tag{1}$$

$$\text{curl } \mathbf{H} = \mathbf{J} + \frac{\partial \mathbf{D}}{\partial t} \tag{2}$$

$$\text{div } \mathbf{B} = 0 \tag{3}$$

$$\text{div } \mathbf{D} = \rho \tag{4}$$

To these should be added the "constitutive equations"

$$\mathbf{B} = \mu \mathbf{H} \tag{5}$$

$$\mathbf{D} = \epsilon \mathbf{E} \tag{6}$$

where we write $\mu = \mu_0 K_m$, $\epsilon = \epsilon_0 K$ for generality. There is often added to these an equation based on Ohm's law. In a large class of conductors over a very large range of current densities it is experimentally observed that the voltage drop in a material is linearly related to the current density. This equation will be written as

$$\mathbf{J} = \sigma \mathbf{E} \tag{7}$$

where σ is the conductivity in mhos per meter (a mho is an inverse ohm). For copper, $\sigma = 5.7 \times 10^7$ mhos per meter. A complete description of an electromagnetic experiment may also require the use of the Lorentz equation

$$\mathbf{F} = \rho \mathbf{E} + \mathbf{J} \times \mathbf{B} \tag{8}$$

These equations, together with Newton's laws, are sufficient to explain any classical electromagnetic phenomena. Equations (1) through (4) are called Maxwell's equations, to which the three constitutive equations are often added. The rest of this book will be devoted to a discussion of the consequence of these equations. Some advanced treatments of electromagnetism begin by assuming Maxwell's equations as a basis and develop the consequences of this assumption.

6.6 The Wave Equation

Under conditions where time-varying phenomena occur we cannot use a scalar potential for either $\mathbf{B}$ or $\mathbf{E}$ in general, since Maxwell's equations give a finite value for curl **B** and curl **E**. It turns out that we can still derive **B** from a vector potential **A** by

$$\mathbf{B} = \text{curl } \mathbf{A} \tag{1}$$

and that **E** can be derived from

$$\mathbf{E} = -\text{ grad } \phi - \frac{\partial \mathbf{A}}{\partial t} \tag{2}$$

Since div curl of any vector is zero, (1) leads to div **B** = 0, which is Equation (3), Section 6.5. If **B** is constant in time we have $\partial \mathbf{A}/\partial t = 0$ in (2) and **E** can be derived from a scalar potential in the electrostatic case. If we take the curl of (2) we get Equation (1), Section 6.5, since curl grad of any scalar function is identically zero. Thus (1) and (2) are consistent with Maxwell's equations.

We wish now to find the equations for **A** and ϕ. Here we shall use the constitutive equations (5) and (6), Section 6.5, where we shall assume that ϵ and μ are constants over the regions considered. Applying (1) and (2) to Equation (2), Section 6.5, we get

$$\nabla \times (\nabla \times \mathbf{A}) = \mu \mathbf{J} - \epsilon\mu \text{ grad } \frac{\partial \phi}{\partial t} - \epsilon\mu \frac{\partial^2 \mathbf{A}}{\partial t^2} \tag{3}$$

However, $\nabla \times \nabla \times \mathbf{A} = \text{grad div } \mathbf{A} - \nabla^2 \mathbf{A}$ and we get

$$\nabla^2 \mathbf{A} - \epsilon\mu \frac{\partial^2 \mathbf{A}}{\partial t^2} - \text{grad} \left(\text{div } \mathbf{A} + \epsilon\mu \frac{\partial \phi}{\partial t} \right) = -\mu \mathbf{J} \tag{4}$$

A similar equation can be obtained for ϕ

$$\nabla^2 \phi - \epsilon\mu \frac{\partial^2 \phi}{\partial t^2} + \frac{\partial}{\partial t} \left(\text{div } \mathbf{A} + \epsilon\mu \frac{\partial \phi}{\partial t} \right) = \frac{-\rho}{\epsilon} \tag{5}$$

It can be shown that div **A** can be chosen to have any value we choose without affecting the value of curl **A**. Thus we can choose

$$\text{div } \mathbf{A} + \epsilon\mu \frac{\partial \phi}{\partial t} = 0 \tag{6}$$

and (4) and (5) become

$$\nabla^2 \mathbf{A} - \epsilon\mu \frac{\partial^2 \mathbf{A}}{\partial t^2} = -\mu \mathbf{J} \qquad \nabla^2 \phi - \epsilon\mu \frac{\partial^2 \phi}{\partial t^2} = \frac{-\rho}{\epsilon} \tag{7}$$

Thus both potentials obey the same differential equation. At this point some advanced treatments of electromagnetism form a "four-vector" which is a sort of vector potential having four components, namely the three components of **A** and ϕ. This four-vector obeys an equation of the form of (7).

If **J** and ρ are zero (7) becomes what is known as the wave equation since the solutions represent waves traveling at a velocity $(\epsilon\mu)^{-\frac{1}{2}}$. If $\rho = 0$ and **J** obeys Ohm's law, Equation (7), Section 6.5, we find that if instead of (6) we use

$$\text{div }\mathbf{A} + \sigma\mu\phi + \epsilon\mu\frac{\partial\phi}{\partial t} = 0 \tag{8}$$

we then shall get

$$\nabla^2\mathbf{A} - \sigma\mu\frac{\partial\mathbf{A}}{\partial t} - \epsilon\mu\frac{\partial^2\mathbf{A}}{\partial t^2} = 0$$

$$\nabla^2\phi - \sigma\mu\frac{\partial\phi}{\partial t} - \epsilon\mu\frac{\partial^2\phi}{\partial t^2} = 0 \tag{9}$$

The solutions of (9) represent damped propagating waves propagating in a lossy conducting material.

We shall not compute **E** and **B** from (1), (2), and (9), but shall solve for the components of **E** and **B** directly. **A** and ϕ or more complicated vector potentials such as the Hertz vector and the four-vector, are of great use when discussing general questions concerned with electromagnetism such as arise in the quantum mechanical description of the interaction of matter with an electromagnetic field. For engineering purposes, however, a simpler understanding of what goes on can be obtained by solving Maxwell's equations directly for the field components. This is done in the next chapter.

PROBLEMS

1. Compute the mutual inductance between a long straight wire and a rectangular loop of wire of length a and width b. The long straight wire lies in the plane of the loop and is parallel to one of its edges, and is c meters distant from the nearest wire in the loop.

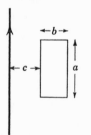

2. Calculate the mutual inductance between two concentric and coplanar circular loops of wire of radii a and b. Assume $a \ll b$.

3. Two small coils of a size small compared with their separation are at a distance d apart. It is desired that the axes of these two coils be parallel.

Find the angle between the coils and the line joining them so that the mutual inductance between them is zero.

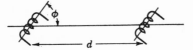

4. Two parallel conducting strips of width w, distance of separation d (where $d \ll w$), infinitely long, carry current in opposite directions so as to form the two conductors of an electric circuit. Find the self-inductance of such a circuit per unit length. Use a suitable approximation.

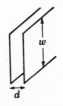

5. Two concentric thin-walled hollow conducting cylinders of radii r_1 and r_2 carry current in opposite directions. Find the self-inductance per unit length. Find how the result is changed if the inner conductor is a solid conducting rod carrying current uniformly distributed through its interior.

6. The outer conductor of a coaxial line as in Problem 5 is a thin-walled cylinder of radius a and thickness t. Show that the contribution to the inductance per unit length of the line arising from the magnetic field in this conductor is given very nearly by $(\mu_0/6\pi)(t/a)$, where $t/a \ll 1$.

7. Compute the inductance per unit length of a parallel-wire transmission line, where the wires have radius a and the wires are separated by a distance d. Neglect any contribution to the inductance of any flux inside the wires.

8. Starting with the equation of continuity and assuming Ohm's law, show that the charge density in a conductor obeys the equation

$$\frac{\sigma}{\epsilon}\, \rho + \frac{\partial \rho}{\partial t} = 0$$

Show that any existing charge distribution within a conductor will be damped off exponentially, and find the time required for it to be reduced to $1/e$ of its initial value. Insert numerical values for copper and find the value of this time, the relaxation time. Similarly find the relaxation time for a good insulator such as quartz.

9. An iron-core inductance with an air gap is constructed by winding 1,000 turns of wire about a C-shaped laminated iron core. The area of the air gap is 10×20 cm and the gap length is 1 cm. Assuming the permeability of the iron to be very large and neglecting fringing fields, compute the inductance. At what current will the magnetic field be 10,000 gauss?

7

Electromagnetic Waves

7.1 Wave Equations for E and H

We consider now the wave equations for the field components when the real charge density in the medium under consideration is zero. It is conventional to use the field components $\mathbf{E}$ and $\mathbf{H}$ in connection with electromagnetic waves, obtaining $\mathbf{D}$ and $\mathbf{B}$ from the constitutive equations. Maxwell's equations then become

$$\nabla \times \mathbf{E} = -\mu \frac{\partial \mathbf{H}}{\partial t} \tag{1}$$

$$\operatorname{div} \mathbf{H} = 0 \tag{2}$$

$$\nabla \times \mathbf{H} = \sigma \mathbf{E} + \epsilon \frac{\partial \mathbf{E}}{\partial t} \tag{3}$$

$$\operatorname{div} \mathbf{E} = 0 \tag{4}$$

Here we assume that the medium is homogeneous (μ, ϵ, σ constant over the region) and that Ohm's law applies. Let us take the curl of (3) and substitute (1) for curl $\mathbf{E}$. We obtain

$$\nabla \times \nabla \times \mathbf{H} = -\sigma\mu \frac{\partial \mathbf{H}}{\partial t} - \epsilon\mu \frac{\partial^2 \mathbf{H}}{\partial t^2} \tag{5}$$

Since $\nabla \times \nabla \times \mathbf{A} = \operatorname{grad} \operatorname{div} \mathbf{A} - \nabla^2 \mathbf{A}$ where $\mathbf{A}$ is any vector, we have, since div $\mathbf{H}$ is zero,

$$\nabla^2 \mathbf{H} - \sigma\mu \frac{\partial \mathbf{H}}{\partial t} - \epsilon\mu \frac{\partial^2 \mathbf{H}}{\partial t^2} = 0 \tag{6}$$

A similar calculation for $\mathbf{E}$ yields

$$\nabla^2 \mathbf{E} - \sigma\mu \frac{\partial \mathbf{E}}{\partial t} - \epsilon\mu \frac{\partial^2 \mathbf{E}}{\partial t^2} = 0 \tag{7}$$

An equation of the form of (6) is called a wave equation. If $\sigma = 0$ we have the wave equation for propagation in a nondissipative medium.

7.2 Plane Waves

We shall first discuss the solution of Equations (6) and (7), Section 7.1, for a uniform plane wave. This means that we seek solutions of the wave equation such that propagation takes place in one direction (we will choose the z direction) but no variation of the field components occurs in any direction transverse to the direction of propagation (x and y directions here). We shall restrict our problems to those in which the frequency is fixed. This is what actually happens when we consider the fields about an antenna or waveguide which is driven at constant frequency by a transmitter. The time dependence of all the field vectors will be chosen to be $e^{j\omega t}$. Thus we have $\mathbf{E}' = \mathbf{E}e^{j\omega t}$ and $\mathbf{H}' = \mathbf{H}e^{j\omega t}$ where $\mathbf{E}$ and $\mathbf{H}$ are vectors that vary with space but not time. We can now write Maxwell's equations without the time variation explicitly stated as

$$\nabla \times \mathbf{E} = -j\omega\mu\mathbf{H} \tag{1}$$
$$\nabla \cdot \mathbf{E} = 0 \tag{2}$$
$$\nabla \cdot \mathbf{H} = 0 \tag{3}$$
$$\nabla \times \mathbf{H} = \sigma\mathbf{E} + j\omega\epsilon\mathbf{E} \tag{4}$$

The wave equation without the time dependence explicitly stated is

$$\nabla^2\mathbf{E} - j\omega\mu\sigma\mathbf{E} + \epsilon\mu\omega^2\mathbf{E} = 0 \tag{5}$$

and there is a similar equation for $\mathbf{H}$.

Equation (2), when written out in rectangular coordinates, is

$$\frac{\partial E_x}{\partial x} + \frac{\partial E_y}{\partial y} + \frac{\partial E_z}{\partial z} = 0 \tag{6}$$

Since in a plane wave there must be no variation of the field components with x or y, (6) becomes

$$\frac{\partial E_z}{\partial z} = 0 \tag{7}$$

Thus E_z is at most a constant in space with no variation with x, y, or z. Such a solution is trivial as it does not constitute a wave. An exactly similar argument holds for $\mathbf{H}$ and we can say that the plane wave solution of Maxwell's equations must have $E_z = H_z = 0$ if propagation takes place in the z direction. The components of $\mathbf{H}$ and $\mathbf{E}$ are thus transverse to the direction of propagation. Such waves are called **TEM** waves, meaning transverse electric and magnetic fields.

We shall now look for solutions of (5) in which a propagating wave results; i.e., we shall assume that the z dependence of the vectors is $e^{\gamma z}$, where propagation will take place if γ is imaginary. For simplicity we shall assume that $\sigma = 0$ in (5) and presume that the x axis is oriented so that it coincides with the $\mathbf{E}$ vector. Equation (5) then becomes

$$\frac{\partial^2 E_x}{\partial z^2} + \epsilon\mu\omega^2 E_x = 0 \tag{8}$$

Since E_x is a function only of z we get $\gamma^2 + \epsilon\mu\omega^2 = 0$ or $\gamma = \pm j\omega/c$ where $c = 1/\sqrt{\epsilon\mu}$.

Equation (5) is an example of what is called a wave equation. More generally we can write such an equation as

$$\frac{\partial^2 f}{\partial z^2} = \frac{1}{c^2}\frac{\partial^2 f}{\partial t^2} \tag{9}$$

A general solution to the partial differential equation (9) must contain two independent solutions. By inspection such a solution is

$$f = f_1(z + ct) + f_2(z - ct) \tag{10}$$

where f_1 and f_2 are arbitrary functions. Let us consider the solution $f_2(z - ct)$. If z increases by an amount z_0 and t increases by an amount $t_0 = z_0/c$, we return to the same value of the argument of f_2 and hence the same value of f_2. Thus the same value of f_2 propagates in the positive z direction with a velocity c. c is called the phase velocity. The function $f_1(z + ct)$ represents a wave traveling in the $-z$ direction.

In the solution of (8) if we choose $\gamma = -j\omega/c$ the solution for E_x *including* the time is

$$E_x = E_0 e^{j(\omega t - \omega z/c)} = E_0 e^{j\omega(t - z/c)} \tag{11}$$

Comparison of (11) and (10) shows that here also we have a wave propagating in the $+z$ direction with the velocity c, where $c^2 = 1/\epsilon\mu$.

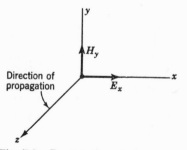

Fig. 7.2a. Propagation of plane wave.

Without the time dependence explicitly stated we have

$$E_x = E_0 e^{-j\omega z/c} \tag{12}$$

We can now calculate **H** from (1). $\nabla \times$ **E** will have only a y component and we get

$$\frac{\partial E_x}{\partial z} = -j\omega\mu H_y = -j\frac{\omega}{c}E_x \tag{13}$$

or

$$\frac{E_x}{H_y} = \mu c = \frac{\mu}{\sqrt{\epsilon\mu}} = \sqrt{\frac{\mu}{\epsilon}} = Z_0 \tag{14}$$

In (14) E_x/H_y has the dimensions of volts per meter divided by amperes per meter, which is the same as ohms. We thus call Z_0 the impedance of the medium. In empty space this is $\sqrt{\mu_0/\epsilon_0} = 120\pi = 377$ ohms.

The solution just obtained is called a plane polarized wave, for **E** is in the x direction only and remains there. A more generalized type of wave can be obtained by adding to the above wave another in which **E** is just in the y direction but has a different amplitude and phase from the original wave. This added **E** can be written as

$$E_y = E_1 e^{j[\omega(t-z/c)+\delta]} \tag{15}$$

where δ is an arbitrary phase angle. It can be shown that this results in an **E** vector that rotates with time and distance, its tip tracing out an ellipse in general. Such a wave is an elliptically polarized wave, with circular polarization being a special case.

A solution to (5) where σ is not zero can easily be obtained. We shall assume plane polarized waves to be the solution, and, as above, the equation to solve is

$$\frac{\partial^2 E_x}{\partial z^2} + \left(\frac{\omega^2}{c^2} - j\omega\mu\sigma\right)E_x = 0 \tag{16}$$

Assuming a solution of the form $E_x = E_0 e^{\gamma z}$ we obtain

$$\gamma = \pm\sqrt{j\omega\mu\sigma - \frac{\omega^2}{c^2}} = \pm j\frac{\omega}{c}\sqrt{1 - j\frac{\sigma}{\epsilon\omega}} \tag{17}$$

γ is thus a complex number, which we write as

$$\gamma = \pm(\alpha + j\beta) \tag{18}$$

The square root in (17) is of a complex number in the second quadrant. α and β are thus both positive, as the square root lies in the first quadrant. We have as a solution

$$E_x = E e^{-\gamma z} = E e^{-\alpha z}e^{-j\beta z} \tag{19}$$

where we have chosen the minus sign in (17) and (18) so as to obtain a wave traveling in the $+z$ direction.   It is seen that this represents a plane wave which is attenuated as the wave progresses in the $+z$ direction. H_y is determined from (1) which gives

$$\frac{E_x}{H_y} = \frac{j\omega\mu}{\gamma} = \frac{j\omega\mu}{\alpha + j\beta} = Z_0 \qquad (20)$$

The characteristic impedance of the medium is seen to be complex when losses are present.   If the conductivity is very large, $\alpha \gg \beta$ and the ratio of E_x to H_y becomes very small.   If $\sigma = 0$, we obtain the earlier solution $\beta = \omega/c$.   The velocity of propagation (phase velocity) is given by

$$v = \frac{\omega}{\beta}$$

In addition to the attenuation, the phase velocity is reduced by the presence of conductivity in the media.

In wave phenomena we often talk of the wavelength rather than the frequency.   The connection is given by

$$\lambda f = v \qquad \text{or} \qquad \frac{\lambda}{2\pi}\omega = v \qquad (21)$$

where v is the phase velocity.   Thus instead of ω/v we can write $2\pi/\lambda$, and the solution with time is

$$E_x = E_0 e^{j(\omega t - 2\pi z/\lambda)} \qquad (22)$$

The wavelength λ is the distance we must go along z to obtain the same value of E_x and $\partial E_x/\partial z$ if time is frozen.

7.3   Poynting's Theorem

We shall now discuss the flow of electromagnetic energy out of a closed surface.   A vector identity shows that

$$\text{div} (\mathbf{E} \times \mathbf{H}) = \mathbf{H} \cdot \text{curl } \mathbf{E} - \mathbf{E} \cdot \text{curl } \mathbf{H} \qquad (1)$$

However $\nabla \times \mathbf{E} = -\partial \mathbf{B}/\partial t$ and $\nabla \times \mathbf{H} = \mathbf{J} + \partial \mathbf{D}/\partial t$.   Thus (1) becomes

$$\text{div} (\mathbf{E} \times \mathbf{H}) = -\mathbf{H} \cdot \frac{\partial \mathbf{B}}{\partial t} - \mathbf{E} \cdot \frac{\partial \mathbf{D}}{\partial t} - \mathbf{E} \cdot \mathbf{J} \qquad (2)$$

Applying the divergence theorem to a volume, and letting

$$\mathbf{S} = \mathbf{E} \times \mathbf{H} \qquad (3)$$

(2) becomes

$$\int_S \mathbf{S} \cdot \mathbf{n} \, da + \frac{\partial}{\partial t} \int_V \left(\frac{\mathbf{H} \cdot \mathbf{B}}{2} + \frac{\mathbf{E} \cdot \mathbf{D}}{2} \right) dv = \int_V -\mathbf{E} \cdot \mathbf{J} \, dv \qquad (4)$$

The second term is the increase in energy stored in the field inside the volume; the last term is the rate of production of energy inside the volume since $E \cdot J$ is the energy lost to heat or other nonelectrical sinks, and $-E \cdot J$ is the production of electromagnetic energy by nonelectrical sources. The first term is thus the flow of power across the boundary of the volume. At any point we may call S the vector which represents the amount of energy per unit time crossing unit area at any point. We have not proved this—we have merely shown that the integral of this vector represents the loss of energy through the surface. However, we never get results that disagree with experiments if we assume that S is the flow of energy at a point. S is called Poynting's vector.

Applying the idea of Poynting's vector to the plane polarized wave we have for the power flow

$$S = |E \times H| = E_x H_y \tag{5}$$

Since both E_x and H_y are in time phase with each other we can average this

$$\bar{S} = E_x H_y \overline{\sin^2 \omega t} = \frac{E_x H_y}{2} = \frac{H_y^2 Z_0}{2} = \frac{E_x^2}{2 Z_0} \tag{6}$$

This is the average power flow. Since S is always in the z direction, $\bar{S}$ is also in this direction. At any instant the energy stored in the electric field is equal to the energy stored in the magnetic field because

$$\frac{\mu H^2}{2} = \frac{\mu E^2}{2 Z_0^2} = \frac{\epsilon E^2}{2} \tag{7}$$

If we compute the stored energy in a volume of unit-area cross section and c meters long, we get

$$W = 2 \frac{\epsilon \overline{E_x^2}}{2} c = \frac{E_x^2}{2} \frac{\epsilon}{\sqrt{\epsilon \mu}} = \frac{E_x^2}{2 Z_0} \tag{8}$$

Comparison with (6) shows that the energy crossing unit area in unit time is just the energy stored in a volume of unit area and c meters long, which is what we would expect.

If we were to look carefully at the average flow of energy and average stored energy in more complicated cases such as in elliptically polarized plane waves we would find that we must be more sophisticated about the computation. We would obtain

$$\bar{S} = \frac{1}{2} Re\ (E \times H^*) \tag{9}$$

where H^* is the complex conjugate of H, obtained by replacing j by $-j$ in H. This is the same type of calculation done in circuit theory when computing the power delivered to a load where the current and voltage are not in phase.   A similar remark applies to computation of stored energy.

PROBLEMS

1. A uniformly magnetized sphere of radius a has a magnetization M along the axis of spherical coordinates.   The sphere also carries a charge C. Compute Poynting's vector at $\theta = 45°$, $r = 2a$.   What is the integral of $\bar{S}$ over a sphere of radius $2a$?

2. Sunlight brings in 1,540 watts per square meter.   Considering this to be a plane polarized wave, find the peak value of E and H in such a wave.

3. Given a cylindrical wire carrying a current, find the values of E and H on the surface of the wire, compute Poynting's vector, and show that it represents a flow of energy into the wire.   Show that the amount flowing into a given length of wire is just enough to supply the energy that appears as heat. Note that the surface of a wire carrying current is not an equipotential so that there can be a component of electric field parallel to it.

4. A coaxial line of length l, inner and outer radii a and b, carries a steady current I.   The resistance of the inner conductor is R_i, that of the outer conductor R_0, and the load resistance is R.   Find expressions for the components of E and H at any point between the conductors.   Show that the component of E parallel to the axis reverses direction as one moves from the inner to the outer conductor, and that it is zero at a radius r_0 given by

$$\log \frac{r_0}{a} = \frac{R_i}{R_0 + R_i} \log \left(\frac{b}{a}\right)$$

Compute the Poynting vector and discuss the power flow in this field.   Integrate the radial component of the Poynting vector over the surface of both inner and outer conductor, and show that these integrals yield the I^2R losses in each.

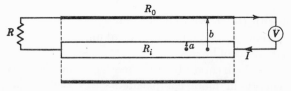

5. A battery is connected across a circular loop of resistive wire.   Consider this battery to have a voltage V_0 and the wire to have a resistance R and to be 1 meter long.   Let the battery have the shape of a thin cylinder 10 centimeters long with the two terminals at opposite ends.   Sketch as well as you can the distribution of Poynting's vector in the neighborhood of this complete circuit, giving separate sketches of Poynting's vector near the outside of the battery and also near the wire.

8

Rectangular Waveguides

In the previous chapter we discussed the propagation of plane waves in lossy dielectric media. This is only one of many possible solutions of the wave equation. We shall now discuss the propagation of electromagnetic waves inside hollow pipes. In order to develop this subject in a sensible manner we shall first give an outline of our method of deriving this type of solution. The basic boundary condition that we shall use is that tangential E must be zero at the wall of the pipe. This is because we shall restrict ourselves to the case in which the pipe has infinite conductivity; a finite tangential E would require an infinite ohmic current to flow, causing infinite magnetic fields nearby. This cannot be, since it implies an infinite stored energy.

If we proceed to the solution of the wave equation with this boundary condition, we find that there are two types of waves that can be propagated through the pipe, a transverse electric wave or a transverse magnetic wave. A TE wave has the electric vector only in the transverse direction and no E along the pipe (i.e., no longitudinal component of E). A longitudinal H will in general exist. A corresponding statement applies to a TM wave; only transverse components of H are present. Further investigation will show that we can derive all the components of E and H in a waveguide if we know the longitudinal component E_z in a TM wave or H_z in a TE wave. This suggests that we might express the basic boundary condition in terms of this longitudinal component. The longitudinal component of a wave thus turns out to be like a scalar potential from which we can derive all the other components of the wave if we apply the correct boundary condition to this longitudinal component. Actually the longitudinal component itself is not a scalar potential, but a simple function of the longitudinal component can be used as a scalar potential to derive the transverse components of the same vector. The other vector ($\mathbf{H}$ in a TM mode for instance) is found with the aid of Maxwell's equations.

Knowing the above we can proceed in an orderly fashion. We shall first show how the transverse components of the same vector can be obtained from the longitudinal component and we shall discuss boundary conditions on the longitudinal component of a wave. Then we shall proceed to solve the wave equation and discuss the solutions. In later chapters we shall discuss how exactly the same procedure can be carried out for the propagation of spherical waves; also we shall discuss the small perturbing effects of finite wall conductivity and lossy dielectrics, other types of TEM waves, etc.

The above discussion holds for simple media in which ϵ or μ is a simple scalar rather than a tensor. This treatment will not hold for optically active materials such as those crystals which exhibit double refraction or for ferrites which have unusual magnetic characteristics.

8.1   A Scalar Potential for the Transverse Components

We shall first start to solve the wave equation and learn how to compute the transverse components. From the above discussion we are only interested in the z component, presuming that propagation occurs in the z direction. For the present we shall discuss only a TM wave. The wave equation for $\mathbf{E}$ without time is

$$\nabla^2\mathbf{E} + \frac{\omega^2}{c^2}\,\mathbf{E} = 0 \tag{1}$$

In rectangular components the z component of (1) is

$$\nabla^2 E_z + \frac{\omega^2}{c^2}\,E_z = 0 \tag{2}$$

When we solve this wave equation later we shall use exactly the same procedure that we used in solving Laplace's equation—separation of variables. We shall let $E_z = X(x)Y(y)Z(z)$ as before, and this will lead to separation if we rewrite (2) as

$$\frac{1}{E_z}\,\nabla_{xy}{}^2\,E_z + \underbrace{\frac{1}{E_z}\,\frac{\partial^2 E_z}{\partial z^2} + \frac{\omega^2}{c^2}}_{\longrightarrow\ =\ k_z{}^2} = 0 \tag{3}$$

By $\nabla_{xy}{}^2(E_z)$ we mean those components of the Laplacian that depend only on x and y, namely $(\partial^2 E_z/\partial x^2) + (\partial^2 E_z/\partial y^2)$. For propagation in the z direction we let the last two terms equal a constant $k_z{}^2$ as indicated above.   This will separate out the z dependence of the above equation. Thus we have

$$\nabla_{xy}^2(E_z) = -k_z^2 E_z \tag{4}$$

We presume now that the transverse component of $\mathbf{E}$, $\mathbf{E}_t$, can be derived from a scalar potential

$$\mathbf{E}_t = \text{grad } V \tag{5}$$

We shall later show this to be possible for a TE or a TM wave.   One of Maxwell's equations is

$$\nabla \cdot \mathbf{E} = 0 \qquad \text{since } \rho = 0 \text{ here} \tag{6}$$

Inserting (5) into (6) we have

$$\nabla_{xy}^2(V) = -\frac{\partial E_z}{\partial z} \tag{7}$$

Comparing (4) and (7) we see that

$$\frac{1}{k_z^2} \frac{\partial}{\partial z}(\nabla_{xy}^2 E_z) = \nabla_{xy}^2 V \tag{8}$$

However, ∇_{xy}^2 does not involve z, so we can reverse the order of differentiation in (8), obtaining

$$\nabla_{xy}^2 \left[\frac{1}{k_z^2} \frac{\partial E_z}{\partial z} \right] = \nabla_{xy}^2(V) \tag{9}$$

Thus the potential V that we seek in (5) becomes

$$V = \frac{1}{k_z^2} \frac{\partial E_z}{\partial z} \tag{10}$$

except for an added function ϕ which satisfies $\nabla_{xy}^2 \phi = 0$.

Such a function ϕ satisfies Laplace's equation for electrostatics in two dimensions and cannot exist inside our waveguide as there is no other conductor to support a static difference of potential.   If there were another conductor inside the guide, as in a coaxial line, such a function could exist and would give rise to a TEM wave.   We shall discuss this subject later when we consider TEM guided waves.   For the present, however, we shall take ϕ to be zero.   The transverse components of $\mathbf{E}$ thus become

$$\begin{aligned} E_x &= \frac{\partial}{\partial x}\left(\frac{1}{k_z^2} \frac{\partial E_z}{\partial z} \right) \\ E_y &= \frac{\partial}{\partial y}\left(\frac{1}{k_z^2} \frac{\partial E_z}{\partial z} \right) \end{aligned} \tag{11}$$

An exactly similar relation holds between $\mathbf{H}_t$ and H_z in a TE wave.

It remains to show as mentioned above that in a TE (or TM) wave the transverse components of H (or E) can be derived by taking the gradient of a scalar potential. Consider first a TM wave. Faraday's law is

$$\nabla \times E = -j\omega\mu H$$

However, H is only in the transverse direction since we are discussing TM waves here. Thus $\nabla \times E$ is in the transverse plane and

$$\int_{S'} (\nabla \times E) \cdot n \, da = \oint E \cdot dl = 0$$

where the area S' is normal to z, and where n is a unit vector in the longitudinal direction (the direction of propagation). But E_z cannot contribute to $E \cdot dl$ in the above equation since the path of integration lies in the transverse plane. Thus $\oint E_t \cdot dl = 0$ which implies that $E_t = \text{grad } V$. This argument holds for any orthogonal system of coordinates.

A similar calculation can be made for H_t in the case of a TE wave. If we do the above calculation for cylindrical coordinates exactly the same potential is obtained, for the z components of both ∇^2 (vector) and $\nabla \cdot$ (vector) are the same in both cylindrical and rectangular coordinates. In fact the potential given in (10) applies to any TE or TM wave propagating in the z direction in any type of cylindrical coordinates, such as elliptical cylinder coordinates.

We shall later obtain a similar relation between the longitudinal and transverse components in TE or TM waves in spherical coordinates for propagation in the r direction. Note that the above derivation rests on the separation of variables as done in (3). This means that we must choose the direction of propagation and also presumes that the "propagating" component of the wave equation will yield to a separation-of-variables treatment. It is easy to obtain the transverse field vector from Maxwell's equations. For instance in a TM wave E is obtained as above. H can then be obtained from

$$\nabla \times E = -j\omega\mu H \tag{12}$$

A similar arrangement holds for a TE wave.

8.2   Impedance in a Waveguide

There is a very useful and simple relation between the transverse components of E and H, which enables us to compute one of these transverse components from the other. We shall obtain this relation for a TM wave which is propagating in the positive z direction and hence has a z dependence $e^{-\gamma z}$. Ampere's law states

$$\nabla \times \mathbf{H} = j\omega\epsilon\mathbf{E} \tag{1}$$

However, there is only transverse $\mathbf{H}$ here and $H_z = 0$. The two components of (1) are then

$$j\omega\epsilon E_x = \frac{\partial H_z}{\partial y} - \frac{\partial H_y}{\partial z} = -\frac{\partial H_y}{\partial z} = \gamma H_y \tag{2}$$

and

$$j\omega\epsilon E_y = \frac{\partial H_x}{\partial z} - \frac{\partial H_z}{\partial x} = \frac{\partial H_x}{\partial z} = -\gamma H_x \tag{3}$$

which leads to

$$\frac{E_x}{H_y} = -\frac{E_y}{H_x} = \frac{\gamma}{j\omega\epsilon} \equiv Z_{\text{TM}} \tag{4}$$

In a similar fashion we can show that for a TE wave

$$\frac{E_x}{H_y} = -\frac{E_y}{H_x} = \frac{j\omega\mu}{\gamma} \equiv Z_{\text{TE}} \tag{5}$$

It should be clear that if we consider a wave traveling in the negative z direction the sign of γ will be reversed, which will change the sign of Z_{TE} or Z_{TM}. Thus for a negatively traveling wave we have

$$\frac{E_x}{H_y} = -\frac{E_y}{H_x} = -Z_{\text{TM}} \quad \text{or} \quad -Z_{\text{TE}} \tag{6}$$

where Z_{TM} and Z_{TE} are defined in (4) and (5).

When we study TEM waves we shall find that $\gamma = j\omega/c$. Substituting this in either (4) or (5) we obtain

$$-\frac{E_y}{H_x} = \frac{E_x}{H_y} = \sqrt{\frac{\mu}{\epsilon}} = Z_0 \quad \text{for TEM waves} \tag{7}$$

For a negatively traveling wave we would of course have $-Z_0$.

In any case it is clear that

$$E_x H_x + E_y H_y = \mathbf{E}_t \cdot \mathbf{H}_t = 0 \tag{8}$$

Thus the transverse components of $\mathbf{E}$ and $\mathbf{H}$ in a propagating wave are perpendicular to each other in TE, TM, and TEM waves.

Our use of the word "impedance" in a waveguide may seem curious, for there is no lumped circuit present. However, the ratio E/H does have the dimensions of impedance and the usage here is quite similar to that used in transmission lines.

8.3 Boundary Conditions in Waveguides

The boundary conditions for a TM wave include $E_z = 0$ at the walls of the guide. This is a sufficient condition to ensure that tangential **E** will also be zero at the walls as we shall now show for a rectangular guide.

Assume that E_z will be found in the form $E_z = X(x)Y(y)Z(z)$ by a separation of variables technique. If the wave is propagating in a rectangular waveguide bounded by the planes $x = 0$ or a and $y = 0$ or b, and if $E_z = 0$ on these four planes, then at $y = 0$ or b, $Y(y) = 0$ on these surfaces since in general $X(x)$ and $Z(z)$ will not be zero on these surfaces. However, as shown above,

$$E_x = \frac{\partial}{\partial x}\left(\frac{1}{k_z{}^2}\frac{\partial E_z}{\partial z}\right) = \frac{1}{k_z{}^2}\,Y(y)\,\frac{\partial X}{\partial x}\frac{\partial Z}{\partial z} = 0$$

at $y = 0$ or b since $Y(y) = 0$ at these planes. We see that $E_z = 0$ at these planes ensures that all tangential components of **E** vanish at these surfaces of the waveguide. A similar discussion holds for the planes $x = 0$ or a. Therefore, the requirement that $E_z = 0$ at the walls of a rectangular waveguide is sufficient to meet the boundary condition that tangential **E** vanish at these walls.

For a TE wave the situation is somewhat more complicated, as we wish to express the requirement that tangential **E** $= 0$ at the walls in terms of H_z. This is done as follows. For a TE wave we can apply one of Maxwell's equations

$$\nabla \times \mathbf{E} = -j\omega\mu\mathbf{H} \tag{1}$$

The y component of (1) is

$$\frac{\partial E_x}{\partial z} - \frac{\partial E_z}{\partial x} = \frac{\partial E_x}{\partial z} = -j\omega\mu\,\frac{\partial}{\partial y}\left(\frac{1}{k_z{}^2}\frac{\partial H_z}{\partial z}\right) \tag{2}$$

Rearranging the order of differentiation in the last term of (2) and integrating with respect to z we get

$$E_x = -\frac{j\omega\mu}{k_z{}^2}\frac{\partial H_z}{\partial y} \tag{3}$$

In (3) there is no constant of integration as uniform fields will not result in any of our problems. In a similar manner we obtain

$$E_y = \frac{j\omega\mu}{k_z{}^2}\frac{\partial H_z}{\partial x} \tag{4}$$

We now consider a contour of constant H_z in the transverse xy plane. Such a contour or locus is defined by

$$dH_z = \frac{\partial H_z}{\partial x}\,dx + \frac{\partial H_z}{\partial y}\,dy = 0 \tag{5}$$

and this contour has a slope in the xy plane given by

$$\frac{dy}{dx} = -\frac{\partial H_z/\partial x}{\partial H_z/dy} \tag{6}$$

However, the direction of **E** (only transverse components are present here) is given by

$$\frac{dy}{dx} = \frac{E_y}{E_x} = -\frac{\partial H_z/\partial x}{\partial H_z/\partial y} \tag{7}$$

from (3) and (4) above.   Therefore a line of constant H_z in the xy plane is in the same direction as E at the same point. $\partial H_z/\partial n = 0$ implies that H_z is not changing as we move in toward the boundary along the normal direction n.   Thus if $\partial H_z/\partial n$ is zero at the boundary, where n is the normal direction, then the line of constant H_z is perpendicular to the boundary and **E** is likewise perpendicular to the boundary.   This implies that tangential **E** is zero.   The boundary conditions that we shall use are thus

$$E_z = 0 \quad \text{for a TM wave} \qquad \frac{\partial H_z}{\partial n} = 0 \quad \text{for a TE wave} \tag{8}$$

8.4   Solution of the Wave Equation in Rectangular Coordinates

We are now in a position to discuss the solutions of the wave equation that apply to waves propagating in the z direction in a rectangular

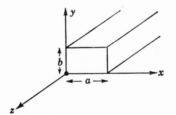

Fig. 8.4a. Rectangular waveguide.

waveguide parallel to the z direction, having a cross section $a \times b$ meters.   We shall choose the origin of coordinates at one edge of the waveguide so that the cross section of the waveguide lies in the first quadrant.

We shall first consider a TM wave.   The wave equation for E_z is

$$\nabla^2 E_z + \frac{\omega^2}{c^2} E_z = 0 \tag{1}$$

Let $\qquad\qquad E_z = X(x)Y(y)Z(z) \tag{2}$

where $X(x)$ is a function of x only, etc. Substituting (2) into (1) and dividing through by (2) we get

$$\underbrace{\frac{1}{X}\frac{\partial^2 X}{\partial x^2}}_{=\,-k_x{}^2} + \underbrace{\frac{1}{Y}\frac{\partial^2 Y}{\partial y^2}}_{=\,-k_y{}^2} + \underbrace{\frac{1}{Z}\frac{\partial^2 Z}{\partial z^2} + \frac{\omega^2}{c^2}}_{=\,k_z{}^2} = 0 \qquad (3)$$

In (3) the first term is a function of x alone, the second term is a function of y alone and the third term a function of z alone. We associate the fourth term with the third term and call these two a constant $k_z{}^2$. We do this because it will turn out that this fixes the direction of propagation to be the z direction. The first and second terms must also be taken as constants, which we call $-k_x{}^2$ and $-k_y{}^2$. To simplify matters we write

$$\gamma^2 = k_z{}^2 - \frac{\omega^2}{c^2} \qquad (4)$$

The equation corresponding to the auxiliary condition [see Equation (8), Section 2.2] is

$$k_z{}^2 = k_x{}^2 + k_y{}^2 \qquad (5)$$

The reason we have to choose these terms as constants is discussed in Chapter 2. The equations to be solved for X, Y, and Z are thus

$$\frac{d^2 X}{dx^2} = -k_x{}^2 X \qquad \frac{d^2 Y}{dy^2} = -k_y{}^2 Y \qquad \frac{d^2 Z}{dz^2} = \gamma^2 Z \qquad (6)$$

The general solution for E_z is thus

$$E_z = A e^{\pm \gamma z} \begin{Bmatrix} \sin \\ \cos \end{Bmatrix} k_x x \begin{Bmatrix} \sin \\ \cos \end{Bmatrix} k_y y \qquad (7)$$

We shall choose the minus sign for γ in (7), since this will result in propagation in the positive z direction for cases where γ is imaginary. An exactly similar equation holds for H_z in a TE wave.

If we consider first a TM wave, E_z must be zero at the walls of the guide—i.e., at $x = 0$ or a and $y = 0$ or b. Of the many solutions represented by (7) we must choose $k_x = \pi l/a$, $k_y = \pi m/b$ where l and m are integers and use the sine rather than the cosine solutions. We thus get

$$E_z = A e^{-\gamma z} \sin \frac{\pi l x}{a} \sin \frac{\pi m y}{b} \qquad (8)$$

The other components of **E** can be obtained from Equation (11), Section 8.1, and the components of **H** from Equation (1), Section 8.3, or Equation (4), Section 8.2. The results are, for TM waves

$$E_x = -\frac{A\gamma}{k_z^2}\frac{\pi l}{a}e^{-\gamma z}\cos\frac{\pi l x}{a}\sin\frac{\pi m y}{b} \tag{9}$$

$$E_y = -\frac{A\gamma}{k_z^2}\frac{\pi m}{b}e^{-\gamma z}\sin\frac{\pi l x}{a}\cos\frac{\pi m y}{b} \tag{10}$$

$$H_x = \frac{j\epsilon\omega}{k_z^2}Ae^{-\gamma z}\frac{\pi m}{b}\sin\frac{\pi l x}{a}\cos\frac{\pi m y}{b} = -\frac{E_y}{Z_{\text{TM}}} \tag{11}$$

$$H_y = -\frac{j\epsilon\omega}{k_z^2}Ae^{-\gamma z}\frac{\pi l}{a}\cos\frac{\pi l x}{a}\sin\frac{\pi m y}{b} = \frac{E_x}{Z_{\text{TM}}} \tag{12}$$

where $Z_{\text{TM}} = \dfrac{\gamma}{j\omega\epsilon}$

We now consider TE waves. The boundary condition that we must use here is that $\partial H_z/\partial n = 0$ at the walls of the guide. This means

$$\frac{\partial H_z}{\partial x} = 0 \qquad \text{at } x = 0 \text{ or } a$$

and

$$\frac{\partial H_z}{\partial y} = 0 \qquad \text{at } y = 0 \text{ or } b \tag{13}$$

Applying (13) to an equation for H_z that is the same as that for E_z given in (7), we find that we must choose for TE waves

$$H_z = Be^{-\gamma z}\cos\frac{\pi l x}{a}\cos\frac{\pi m y}{b} \tag{14}$$

Using Section 8.1 and $\nabla \times \mathbf{H} = j\omega\epsilon\mathbf{E}$ we get

$$H_x = \frac{B\gamma}{k_z^2}\frac{\pi l}{a}e^{-\gamma z}\sin\frac{\pi l x}{a}\cos\frac{\pi m y}{b} \tag{15}$$

$$H_y = \frac{B\gamma}{k_z^2}\frac{\pi m}{b}e^{-\gamma z}\cos\frac{\pi l x}{a}\sin\frac{\pi m y}{b} \tag{16}$$

$$E_x = \frac{j\omega\mu}{k_z^2}Be^{-\gamma z}\frac{\pi m}{b}\cos\frac{\pi l x}{a}\sin\frac{\pi m y}{b} = Z_{\text{TE}}H_y \tag{17}$$

$$E_y = -\frac{j\omega\mu}{k_z^2}Be^{-\gamma z}\frac{\pi l}{a}\sin\frac{\pi l x}{a}\cos\frac{\pi m y}{b} = -Z_{\text{TE}}H_x \tag{18}$$

where $Z_{\text{TE}} = \dfrac{j\omega\mu}{\gamma}$

In the above equations we must choose l and m to be integers. The choice that we make for l and m is usually denoted by subscripts as for example, a TM_{23} wave is a TM wave with $l = 2$ and $m = 3$. Inspection of (8) and (14) shows that we cannot choose both l and m to be zero. In (8) neither l nor m can be zero, or E_z vanishes. In (14) we can choose l or m to be zero, but not both. Thus there may be a TE_{10} or TE_{01} wave but there cannot be a TM_{10} or TM_{01} wave. Our choice of k_x and k_y changes (5) to

$$k_z{}^2 = \left(\frac{\pi l}{a}\right)^2 + \left(\frac{\pi m}{b}\right)^2 \tag{19}$$

The propagation constant γ is given by (4). If $\omega^2/c^2 > k_z{}^2$ γ will be imaginary. We see that above some critical frequency propagation can take place. This frequency is called the cutoff frequency and the corresponding free-space wavelength ($\lambda f = c$) is called the cutoff wavelength. Equation (4) can be put into more convenient form if we write

$$\frac{\omega}{c} = \frac{2\pi}{\lambda_0} \qquad k_z = \frac{2\pi}{\lambda_c} \qquad \gamma = \frac{2\pi j}{\lambda_g} \tag{20}$$

Equation (4) then becomes

$$\frac{1}{\lambda_g{}^2} = \frac{1}{\lambda_0{}^2} - \frac{1}{\lambda_c{}^2} \tag{21}$$

For propagation λ_g must be real. Equation (19) becomes

$$\lambda_c = \frac{2}{\sqrt{(l/a)^2 + (m/b)^2}} \tag{22}$$

It is clear from the above that λ_0 is the free-space wavelength corre-

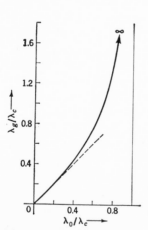

Fig. 8.4b. Normalized guide wavelength versus normalized free-space wavelength.

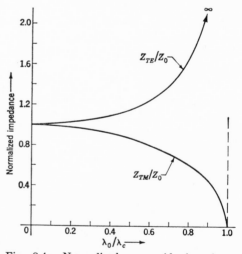

Fig. 8.4c. Normalized waveguide impedance versus normalized free-space wavelength. The same curves also describe the normalized phase velocity v_p/c (upper curve) and the normalized group velocity v_g/c (lower curve).

sponding to the frequency being propagated. Equations (20) and (21) then state that if λ_0 is less than a certain cutoff wavelength, λ_c, then propagation can take place. The wavelength in the guide is λ_g. This guide wavelength is always longer than λ_0, which implies a phase velocity greater than that of light. This does not violate the theory of relativity, for signals are propagated at group velocity, not phase velocity.

From the above it is easily shown that

$$Z_{TE} = \frac{j\omega\mu}{\gamma} = Z_0 \left[1 - \left(\frac{\lambda_0}{\lambda_c}\right)^2 \right]^{-\frac{1}{2}} = Z_0 \frac{\lambda_g}{\lambda_0} \tag{23}$$

and

$$Z_{TM} = \frac{\gamma}{j\omega\epsilon} = Z_0 \left[1 - \left(\frac{\lambda_0}{\lambda_c}\right)^2 \right]^{\frac{1}{2}} = Z_0 \frac{\lambda_0}{\lambda_g} \tag{24}$$

where

$$Z_0 = \sqrt{\frac{\mu}{\epsilon}} = 377\Omega \quad \text{for vacuum}$$

8.5   Phase and Group Velocity

We have seen in Section 7.2 that the phase velocity of a wave v_p is

$$v_p = \frac{\omega}{\beta} \tag{1}$$

This is the speed with which a position of constant phase moves in a traveling wave. Signals cannot be sent with this velocity, for a signal can be sent only by making some change in the wave and the velocity with which the signal is sent is the velocity with which this modulation is propagated.

A simple type of modulated signal is a carrier of unit amplitude and frequency ω modulated (by amplitude modulation) with a fractional modulation index m at a frequency $\Delta\omega$ where $\Delta\omega \ll \omega$. Such a signal is written as

$$\begin{aligned} E(t) &= (1 + m \cos \Delta\omega t) \cos \omega t \\ &= \cos \omega t + m \cos \Delta\omega t \cos \omega t \\ &= \cos \omega t + \frac{m}{2} \left[\cos (\omega + \Delta\omega)t + \cos (\omega - \Delta\omega)t \right] \end{aligned} \tag{2}$$

The last equation of (2) is recognized as the standard carrier and two sidebands for an amplitude modulated signal. If this signal is propagating in a waveguide or some other dispersive medium such that the phase velocity $v_p = \omega/\beta$ varies with frequency so slowly that we can say that there is, as an approximation, a linear relation between β and ω, these sidebands will propagate with slightly different phase velocities and the propagation of this signal in the z direction will be written as

$$E(z,t) = \cos(\omega t - \beta z) + \frac{m}{2} \{\cos[(\omega + \Delta\omega)t - (\beta + \Delta\beta)z]$$
$$+ \cos[(\omega - \Delta\omega)t - (\beta - \Delta\beta)z]\}$$
$$= [1 + m\cos(\Delta\omega t - \Delta\beta z)]\cos(\omega t - \beta z) \tag{3}$$

From (3) it is seen that the modulation travels with a velocity called the group velocity

$$v_g = \frac{\Delta\omega}{\Delta\beta} \to \frac{d\omega}{d\beta} \tag{4}$$

Amplitude-modulated radio waves will propagate the envelope modulation at this group velocity; a pulse of energy caused by turning on an oscillator for a short time and then turning it off again will also travel with this group velocity. This presumes that β is a smooth, slowly varying function of ω and that the bandwidth needed is small compared to the frequency of the signal.

From (1) and (4) we have

$$v_g = \frac{d\omega}{d\beta} = v_p + \beta\frac{dv_p}{d\beta} = v_p + \frac{\omega}{v_p}\frac{dv_p}{d\omega}v_g \tag{5}$$

which gives

$$v_g = \frac{v_p}{1 - (\omega/v_p)(dv_p/d\omega)} \tag{6}$$

If the phase velocity varies with frequency, dispersion is said to occur. If there is no dispersion it is clear from (6) that $v_p = v_g$.

8.6 Waveguide Modes

The many different modes of wave propagation in a pipe present a difficulty that can be overcome by proper choice of waveguide dimensions for a given frequency range. From an engineering standpoint we wish to have only one mode propagating in a waveguide so that coupling in and out of a guide can be done for just one mode. We also wish a given guide to operate well over a reasonable range of frequencies.

Inspection of Equation (22), Section 8.4, shows that if we choose l and m to be as small as possible for the desired frequency, then modes with higher values of l and m will not propagate at this frequency. The lowest values of l and m are 1,0 or 0,1. These permit TE_{10} or TE_{01} waves to exist. The lowest possible TM mode is a TM_{11} wave.

By properly choosing a and b we can arrange matters so that only TE_{10} waves will exist over quite a large range of frequencies. The cutoff wavelength for the modes of interest are

$$\text{TE}_{10}: \lambda_c = 2a$$
$$\text{TE}_{01}: \lambda_c = 2b$$
$$\text{TE}_{20}: \lambda_c = a$$

$$\text{TE}_{lm} \text{ or } \text{TM}_{lm}: \lambda_c = \frac{2a}{l[1 + (am/bl)^2]^{\frac{1}{2}}} = \frac{2b}{m[1 + (bl/am)^2]^{\frac{1}{2}}}$$

λ_c for $l \geq 1$ and $m \geq 1$ are all smaller than λ_c for TE_{10} or TE_{01}. If we make $a = 2b$, $\lambda_c(\text{TE}_{10})$ will be twice $\lambda_c(\text{TE}_{01})$. Under these conditions only TE_{10} waves will propagate over a 2 to 1 range of frequency. We can choose dimensions so that TE_{10} propagation will take place over a frequency range of more than 1.5 to 1 without operating too near cutoff or too near double-mode operation. Typical sizes of standard waveguide are:

Outside dimensions, in.	*Useful range of wavelength, cm*	
1½ × 3 (0.080 wall)	7.6–11.8	*S* band
1 × 2	5 – 7.6	
½ × 1	2.4– 3.7	*X* band
⅜ × ¾	1.7– 2.6	
¼ × ½	Near 1.25	*K* band

The major advantage of waveguides for transmission of microwave power will appear in Chapter 9; this is the very small attenuation compared with coaxial or two-wire transmission lines. In addition they are cheap and quite rugged mechanically. Transmission lines have a further disadvantage in that waveguide modes are possible unless the lateral dimensions are quite small. These points will be discussed in Chapter 10.

8.7 TE$_{10}$ Mode

We shall give the values of the field components for TE_{10} waves since this is the most important mode used in rectangular waveguides. It will be convenient to use the peak value of E_y rather than the peak value of H_z for this case. Making this change, we have for TE_{10} waves

$$E_y = E_0 \sin \frac{\pi x}{a} e^{-\gamma z} \tag{1}$$

$$H_x = -\frac{E_0}{Z_{\text{TE}}} \sin \frac{\pi x}{a} e^{-\gamma z} \tag{2}$$

$$H_z = jE_0 \left(\frac{\lambda_0}{2a}\right) \frac{1}{Z_0} \cos \frac{\pi x}{a} e^{-\gamma z} \tag{3}$$

where $\quad Z_{\text{TE}} = \dfrac{Z_0}{\sqrt{1 - (\lambda_0/2a)^2}} \qquad Z_0 = \sqrt{\dfrac{\mu}{\epsilon}} = 377\Omega \qquad$ for vacuum

$$\tag{4}$$

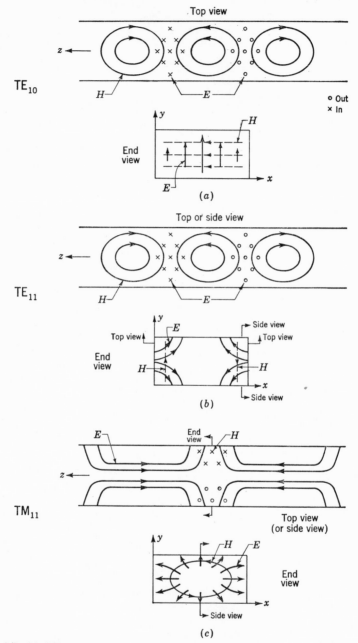

Fig. 8.7. (a) TE_{10} rectangular waveguide; (b) TE_{11} rectangular waveguide; (c) TM_{11} rectangular waveguide.

In the above γ will have to be imaginary for propagation to take place. The j in (3) will add a phase angle $\pi/2$ to $-\gamma z$. The z and t dependence of (1), for instance, is cos $(\omega t - 2\pi z/\lambda_g)$. Clearly this implies a wave motion down the guide in the $+z$ direction. A sketch of the fields is given in Figure 8.7a. It is seen that none of the components depends on y, that E_y arises from real charges on the top and bottom of the guide, and that to supply these charges currents must flow in the top and side walls.

From Maxwell's equations, **E** must always arise from either real charges (div **D** $= \rho$) or from a changing magnetic field ($\nabla \times \mathbf{E} = -\dot{\mathbf{B}}$). In this case the sources of **E** are real charges, so that **E** need not circle around a changing **H**. There is, of course, a changing **H** here, near the side walls of the guide. A current does indeed circle around this changing **H**, being a real current in the walls and a displacement current in the center of the guide. The lines of **H**, on the other hand, must always circulate around some current ($\nabla \times \mathbf{H} = \mathbf{J} + \dot{\mathbf{D}}$). Here they circulate around the displacement current in the center of the guide. If we had been discussing a coaxial line, the **H** could circulate around the real current carried in the central conductor. Since a waveguide is by definition a hollow pipe and cannot have a central conductor, **H** will always surround a displacement current in any waveguide. **E** can either surround changing **H** or can arise from real charges on the walls.

8.8 Transmission of Radiation between Two Planes

Clearly, a pair of infinite parallel conducting planes can support a TEM wave, since two such planes can act as terminating boundaries

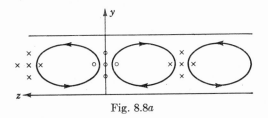

Fig. 8.8a

for a plane polarized wave such as that discussed in Section 7.2. In such a wave, propagation is in a direction parallel to the planes, and **E** is normal to them. We attack here the question of the possibility of the existence of TE waves propagating in such a structure, leaving TM waves to a problem at the end of this chapter.

Let the planes be normal to the y axis, separated by a distance b.

Propagation takes place in the z direction. We first look for waves which have no variation with x. H_z will be given by

$$H_z = A \cos \frac{\pi m y}{b} e^{-\gamma z} \qquad (1)$$

since $\partial H_z/\partial y$ must be zero at $y = 0$ and b. Here we have chosen the origin in the lower plate. From Section 8.1 we have

$$H_y = \frac{A\gamma}{k_z{}^2} \frac{\pi m}{b} \sin \frac{\pi m y}{b} e^{-\gamma z} \qquad (2)$$

and from Equation (5), Section 8.2,

$$E_x = Z_{\mathrm{TE}} H_y \qquad (3)$$

where $$Z_{\mathrm{TE}} = Z_0 \left[1 - \left(\frac{\lambda_0}{\lambda_c}\right)^2 \right]^{-\frac{1}{2}} = Z_0 \frac{\lambda_g}{\lambda_0} \qquad (4)$$

Here $k_x = 0$, $k_y = k_z = \pi m/b$, and we have $\lambda_c = 2\pi/k_z = 2b/m$. Propagation takes place at any $\lambda_0 < \lambda_c$. A sketch of the TE_1 mode is given in Figure 8.8a. We can see that the field components are the same as those for a TE_{01} wave in a rectangular waveguide. It is clear that if we place an infinite number of TE_{lm} rectangular waveguides between the plates, removing the rectangular waveguides will leave a field distribution that will also satisfy the boundary conditions.

We can show that the above TE modes (and also the TM modes) can be obtained by considering plane polarized waves propagating in a direction at an angle to the z axis. The multiple reflections at the plates will give a standing-wave pattern that results in the same field patterns as obtained above. Some authors approach the whole subject of rectangular waveguides from this viewpoint. While this approach works quite well for rectangular waveguides, it is not applicable to cylindrical waveguides, whereas the more general methods of this chapter apply directly to other types of waveguides.

8.9 Current Flow in Walls

An understanding of the currents that flow in the walls of a waveguide can be had from Ampere's law. We shall show in the next chapter that the current flow in metals at high frequencies will be restricted to a very thin surface layer, and that both the current and the magnetic field will drop off exponentially with depth very rapidly. We shall also show that in a good conductor the real conduction current will be much larger than the displacement current, so that the latter can be ignored in a metal. Ampere's law then states that

$$\oint \mathbf{H} \cdot d\mathbf{l} = I \tag{1}$$

We apply (1) to Figure 8.9a where only H_y is present. Current will flow in the $-z$ direction into the paper, as denoted by the x's. The right side of the contour of integration is taken to be so far into the metal that $H_y = 0$ along this side. Equation (1) then gives

$$|H_y| = \int_0^\infty J_z \, dx = J_s \tag{2}$$

where J_s is a surface current flowing in the $-z$ direction. This can be put into general terms

$$\mathbf{J_s} = \mathbf{n} \times \mathbf{H_t} \tag{3}$$

This equation states that at high frequencies in a good conductor there will always be a surface current in the metal whose absolute value is

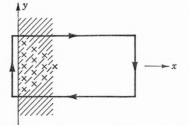

Fig. 8.9a. Current flow in a conductor.

equal to the tangential magnetic field just outside the conductor. (Our boundary conditions for perfect conductors prohibit any normal $\mathbf{H}$ in this case.) The units for each, of course, are the same—namely, amperes per meter.

We shall now compute the flow of power down a waveguide operating in the TE_{10} mode, using Poynting's vector. We only need the component of Poynting's vector in the z direction, which is $S_z = -E_y H_x$. The instantaneous power is thus

$$P = \int_0^b \int_0^a \frac{E_0^2}{Z_{\mathrm{TE}}} \sin^2 \frac{\pi x}{a} \, dx \, dy \cos^2 \omega t \tag{4}$$

and the average power

$$\bar{P} = \frac{E_0^2}{2Z_{\mathrm{TE}}} \int_0^b \int_0^a \sin^2 \frac{\pi x}{a} \, dx \, dy = \frac{ab E_0^2}{4 Z_{\mathrm{TE}}} \tag{5}$$

If we choose $a = 3'' = 2b$ for 10-centimeter waves and pick E_0 so that sparking is just about to occur (E_0 about 10 or 20 kv/cm) we can easily show that the guide can handle several megawatts without flashing over.

8.10   Waves beyond Cutoff

If we consider propagation in those cases where $\omega^2/c^2 < k_z^2$ then γ is real and instead of propagation of a wave in which the phase of the wave varies with z we have very rapid attenuation with no phase change with z. Instead of the propagation exponential, $\exp j(\omega t - \beta z)$, we have $\exp (j\omega t - \gamma z)$ where γ is now a real number and

$$\gamma^2 = k_z^2 - \frac{\omega^2}{c^2} = (2\pi)^2 \left(\frac{1}{\lambda_c^2} - \frac{1}{\lambda_0^2}\right) \tag{1}$$

For sufficiently long waves we can neglect the λ_0 term in (1) and obtain

$$\gamma = k_z = \frac{2\pi}{\lambda_c} = \sqrt{\left(\frac{\pi l}{a}\right)^2 + \left(\frac{\pi m}{b}\right)^2} \tag{2}$$

Since $\lambda_0 \gg \lambda_c$, $Z_{\text{TE}} \to 0$, $Z_{\text{TM}} \to \infty$.

It is clear then from a glance at the equations giving the components of TE and TM waves in Section 8.4, that for a TM wave only the electric fields remain at low frequencies, while for a TE wave only the magnetic fields remain. We now notice that for a TM solution the one we have obtained is of just the same type we had in solving an electrostatic problem in Chapter 2 using Laplace's equation. The only difference is that here we have a time variation, $e^{j\omega t}$, for all vectors.

We repeat here the general solution of Laplace's equation in rectangular coordinates in which we choose an exponential solution for z and add a time variation:

$$V = \begin{Bmatrix} \sin \\ \cos \end{Bmatrix} \frac{\pi l x}{a} \begin{Bmatrix} \sin \\ \cos \end{Bmatrix} \frac{\pi m y}{b} \, e^{\pm k_{lm}z} e^{j\omega t} \tag{3}$$

where $k_{lm}^2 = \left(\frac{\pi l}{a}\right)^2 + \left(\frac{\pi m}{b}\right)^2$. The various components of **E** are of this same general form, where the choice of function depends on the boundary conditions. The situation represented by (3) is another example of the quasi-stationary case where the d-c solution also holds when the system is excited by an alternating source rather than a static source as long as the frequency is not too high.

Equation (2) is the basis of the design of a signal generator at frequencies of a few megacycles or so. An important problem at these frequencies is the construction of a signal attenuator that will operate over an extremely large range of attenuation with a maximum signal of about 1 volt. The absolute level should be accurately set. This can be accomplished by exciting H_x in a square waveguide by a coil transverse to the guide and providing a similar pickup coil a distance z down the guide. The attenuation of the TE modes is then

TE mode	Attenuation, nepers
TE_{10} or TE_{01}	$\dfrac{\pi z}{a}$
TE_{11}	$\dfrac{\pi z}{a} \sqrt{2}$
TE_{lm}	$\dfrac{\pi z}{a} \sqrt{l^2 + m^2}$

Since an attenuation of 1 neper is e^{-1} or 8.68 db, the attenuation is quite rapid. Choosing a minimum distance between the two coils, so that the TE_{11} and higher modes provide a much smaller signal than the TE_{10} mode, we can excite the driver to provide an easily measured output at the pickup coil of, for example, 1 volt. Calling this position $z = 0$, further attenuation is given by $\exp(-\pi z/a)$. With good shielding we can easily work down to output levels of a microvolt or so, the accuracy of the attenuation being subject only to knowing the waveguide dimensions and the change in position of the pickup coil. The useful frequency of such an attenuator is considerably below the cutoff frequency, although it would be quite easy to make a correction using (1) if operation up to about one-half the cutoff frequency were desired. In an actual signal generator we would use a cylindrical waveguide, as accurate knowledge of the waveguide dimensions can be determined more easily in this case.

PROBLEMS

1. Show for TE and TM waves in a waveguide that $v_p v_g = c^2$ where $c^2 = 1/\epsilon\mu$.

2. Develop completely the theory of TM waves propagating between two parallel conducting infinite plates. Consider propagation to take place in the z direction, and no variation in the wave with x. The plates are normal to the y axis.

3. Sketch the field components in both a TE_{11} and TM_{11} guide. Discuss the sources of E and H in each case, and sketch the current flow in the walls.

4. Consider a TE_{11} and a TM_{11} wave to be both present in a rectangular waveguide of cross section $a \times b$ meters. Find the ratio of E_z to H_z such that $E_x = 0$.

5. Consider a waveguide 10 centimeters wide and 5 centimeters high. What is the lowest possible frequency for propagation of a TE_{10} wave? What is the lowest possible frequency for a TM_{23} wave?

6. A square rectangular waveguide is operated at a frequency and in such a manner that both TE_{10} and TE_{01} waves are present. By suitably placing resistance wires across the guide and by cutting thin slots in the guide, the TE_{01} mode can be suppressed with very little effect on the TE_{10} mode. What is this arrangement of wires and slots and how does it work?

7. In the design of an "Eagle" type radar antenna it is necessary to change the guide wavelength by a factor of 1.3 (ratio of max λ_g to min λ_g). This variation is accomplished by varying the "a" dimension of a rectangular waveguide operating in the TE_{10} mode. The radar set operates at 3,000 megacycles (10 cm). Design such a waveguide so that the minimum cutoff wavelength of the TE_{10} mode is 12 centimeters, and the maximum wavelength that can be propagated in any other mode is 8 centimeters. Find the maximum and minimum a and choose the maximum possible b (so that the losses will be kept to a minimum).

8. A TE_{10} wave having peak $H_z = 1$ amp/m is traveling down a waveguide 7.5×3.5 cm in cross section. The frequency is 3,000 mc. A small loop of wire is inserted in the middle of the top of the guide with its plane parallel to the z direction. If the area of the loop is 0.1 sq cm, what is the voltage induced in this loop?

9. A TM_{11} wave of frequency ω is traveling down a waveguide $a \times b$ meters in cross section $(a > b)$. Sketch the electric field lines and find out where the surface charge density is a maximum. What is the value of this maximum charge density?

10. Show that in a waveguide operating beyond cutoff, as in Section 8.9, there is no net average power flow down the waveguide.

9

Skin Effects and Losses in Waveguides

In this chapter we shall discuss the currents that flow in good but not perfectly conducting materials under the influence of high-frequency fields. We shall find that current will flow in a thin layer ("skin") on the surface of the metal. When we discuss the losses that occur in a waveguide, we shall first compute the currents that flow in a perfect conductor, assume that these same currents will flow in a good conductor, and then compute the losses in the good conductor. We should check this method by showing that the electric fields that result from Ohm's law are small compared with the electric fields present in the case of the perfect conductor. This will be the case for normal metals such as copper, brass, etc.

9.1 Eddy-current Equation

We shall first show that in all engineering applications using at least fairly good conductors we can neglect the displacement current in the metal. Equation (5), Section 7.2, when written without time, is

$$\nabla^2 \mathbf{E} - j\omega\mu\sigma\mathbf{E} + \frac{\omega^2}{c^2}\,\mathbf{E} = 0 \qquad (1)$$

The last term arises from the displacement current and the second term from the conduction current. The ratio of the second term to the third term is

$$|R| = \frac{\omega\mu\sigma}{\omega^2/c^2} = \frac{\mu\sigma}{\omega\epsilon\mu} = \frac{\sigma}{\omega\epsilon} \qquad (2)$$

It is difficult to determine ϵ in a metal exactly, but it is about equal to ϵ_0. If we consider a free-space wavelength of 1 millimeter ($\omega = 6\pi \times 10^{11}$)

135

and take $\epsilon = \epsilon_0 = 8.85 \times 10^{-12}$ we obtain

$$|R| = \frac{\sigma}{16.7} \tag{3}$$

Thus if $\sigma \gg 20$, the second term in (1) is much larger than the third and this last term can be neglected. The usual material for waveguides is copper, for which $\sigma = 5.7 \times 10^7$, and almost all metals have $\sigma > 10^6$, so $|R|$ will always be very large. Equation (1) thus becomes, for the interior of a metal,

$$\nabla^2 \mathbf{E} - j\omega\mu\sigma\mathbf{E} = 0 \tag{4}$$

This is called the eddy-current equation and is quite similar to the equations that govern the diffusion of heat or gases. An exactly similar equation holds for $\mathbf{H}$, and also for the current density, since $\mathbf{J} = \sigma\mathbf{E}$.

9.2 Skin Effect

We shall now consider current flowing in a semi-infinite slab in the $-z$ direction under the influence of a tangential H in the y direction, as in Figure 9.2a. Since there is only J_z, and J_z is a function of x only, we have

$$\nabla^2 J_z - j\omega\mu\sigma J_z = 0 \tag{1}$$

We rewrite (1) as

$$\frac{d^2 J_z}{dx^2} - \tau^2 J_z = 0 \tag{2}$$

the solution of which is

$$J_z = A e^{\tau x} + B e^{-\tau x} \tag{3}$$

Here we have chosen $\tau^2 = j\omega\mu\sigma$

or

$$\tau = \frac{1 + j}{\delta} \tag{4}$$

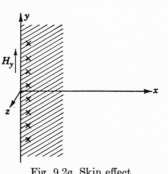

Fig. 9.2a. Skin effect.

where

$$\delta = \sqrt{\frac{2}{\omega\mu\sigma}} \tag{5}$$

and δ is known as the skin depth. Since J_z must $\to 0$ as $x \to \infty$ we must choose $A = 0$ in (3) and the solution becomes

$$J_z = J_0 e^{-(1+j)x/\delta} \tag{6}$$

This means that the current density falls off exponentially with x and also changes phase with depth. The surface current is

$$J_s = \int_0^\infty J_0 e^{-(1+j)x/\delta}\, dx = \frac{J_0 \delta}{1 + j} = \frac{J_0 \delta}{\sqrt{2}} e^{-j\pi/4} \tag{7}$$

It is this surface current that is equal to tangential H.

We now compute the power lost in a square meter of surface of a conductor, as in Figure 9.2a. This is

$$\bar{P} = \tfrac{1}{2} \int_0^\infty \frac{(J_z\, dx)^2}{\sigma\, dx} = \frac{J_0^2}{2\sigma} \int_0^\infty e^{-2x/\delta}\, dx = \frac{J_0^2 \delta}{4\sigma} \qquad (8)$$

Comparing this with the absolute value of J_s as given in (7) we obtain

$$\bar{P} = \frac{J_s^2}{2\sigma\delta} = \frac{|H_T|^2}{2\sigma\delta} \qquad (9)$$

The power lost per unit area is just the same as if a current J_s flowed uniformly in a layer of metal having conductivity σ and thickness δ. At distances into the metal much greater than δ all the field components drop to zero.   We shall sometimes use the surface resistivity R_s where

$$R_s = \frac{1}{\delta\sigma} = \sqrt{\frac{\omega\mu}{2\sigma}} \qquad \text{ohms/sq} \qquad (10)$$

For convenience we give the value of δ and R_s for copper, for which $\sigma = 5.7 \times 10^7$ mhos/m.

$$\delta = \frac{6.65}{\sqrt{f_{\mathrm{mc}}}} \times 10^{-5}\ \mathrm{m} = \frac{2.62}{\sqrt{f_{\mathrm{mc}}}} \times 10^{-3}\ \mathrm{in.}$$
$$R_s = 2.64\ \sqrt{f_{\mathrm{mc}}} \times 10^{-4} \qquad \text{ohm/sq}$$

where f_{mc} is the frequency in megacycles.

The skin effect in a round wire can be treated in much the same way.   We consider a round wire of radius a coaxial with the z axis. We consider only currents flowing in the z direction.   Equation (1) becomes

$$\frac{1}{r}\frac{\partial}{\partial r}\left(r\frac{\partial J_z}{\partial r}\right) - j\omega\mu\sigma J_z = 0 \qquad (11)$$

This can be rewritten as

$$\frac{d^2 J_z}{dr^2} + \frac{1}{r}\frac{dJ_z}{dr} + \tau^2 J_z = 0 \qquad (12)$$

which is Bessel's equation of zero order, where we write $\tau = j^{-\frac{1}{2}}\sqrt{\omega\mu\sigma}$. The solution of (12) is

$$J_z = A J_0(\tau r) + B N_0(\tau r) \qquad (13)$$

N_0 goes to infinity when r goes to 0, and so $B = 0$.   Equation (13) becomes

$$J_z = A_0 \frac{J_0(\tau r)}{J_0(\tau a)} \qquad (14)$$

Here we use A_0 for the peak value of the current density at the surface. The functions $J_0(j^{-\frac{1}{2}}v)$ are complex and are tabulated in Dwight's Tables (see Reference 14) using

$$J_0(j^{-\frac{1}{2}}v) = ber\ v + j\ bei\ v \tag{15}$$

Through the use of these tables, problems involving eddy currents in cylindrical geometry can be easily handled. This is covered extensively by Ramo and Whinnery (see Reference 5).

9.3 Copper Losses in Waveguides

If at $z = 0$ a power W_T is flowing down a waveguide, the power z meters further down the guide will be

$$W_T(z) = W_T(0)e^{-2\alpha z} \tag{1}$$

Here we use $2\alpha z$ instead of αz because we wish α to refer to the attenuation of a field component, and W_T varies as the square of any one of the components. We can also write

$$dW_T = -W_L\ dz \tag{2}$$

where W_L is the watts lost per meter in the waveguide. Comparison of (1) and (2) shows that

$$\alpha = \frac{W_L}{2W_T} \tag{3}$$

and that any field component will be attenuated with z as $e^{-\alpha z}$. It is obvious that the effect of losses in the walls of the waveguide will be to multiply the expressions for all the field components in any given mode by $e^{-\alpha z}$. We thus replace $-\gamma$ by $-\alpha - j\beta$ where $\beta = 2\pi/\lambda_g$ for a wave traveling in the $+z$ direction.

On the basis of the above ideas we can compute the loss per unit length in the walls of a waveguide carrying a given power. As an

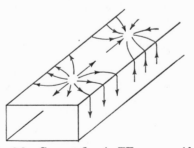

Fig. 9.3a. Current flow in TE_{10} waveguide.

example we shall use a TE_{10} wave flowing down a rectangular guide having walls of conductivity σ. Here we will presume the power to be lost only from ohmic losses in the walls of the waveguide. In Section 8.7 it is shown that the absolute values of the components of $\mathbf{H}$ are, suppressing $e^{j\omega t-\gamma z}$,

$$|H_x| = A \sin \frac{\pi x}{a}$$

$$|H_z| = B \cos \frac{\pi x}{a}$$

(4)

where

$$A = -\frac{E_0}{Z_{TE}} = -\frac{E_0}{Z_0}\left[1 - \left(\frac{\lambda}{2a}\right)^2\right]^{1/2}$$

$$B = \frac{E_0}{Z_0}\frac{\lambda}{2a}$$

The absolute value of the square of the surface current is given by

$$|J_s|^2 = |H|^2 = |H_x|^2 + |H_z|^2$$

(5)

To compute the watts lost per meter of waveguide we have

$$W_L = \oint \frac{J_s^2 R_s}{2}\,dl = \oint (H_x^2 + H_z^2)\frac{R_s}{2}\,dl$$

(6)

where the line integral is taken around the periphery of the waveguide. Thus

$$W_L = 2\int_0^a \left(A^2\sin^2\frac{\pi x}{a} + B^2\cos^2\frac{\pi x}{a}\right)\frac{R_s}{2}\,dx + 2\int_0^b \frac{B^2 R_s}{2}\,dy$$

(7)

$$= R_s\left[\frac{a}{2}\left(A^2 + B^2\right) + bB^2\right]$$

$$= \frac{E_0^2 R_s}{Z_0^2}\left[\frac{a}{2} + b\left(\frac{\lambda}{2a}\right)^2\right] = \frac{E_0^2 R_s}{Z_0^2}\frac{a}{2}\left[1 + \frac{2b}{a}\left(\frac{\lambda}{2a}\right)^2\right]$$

The power transmitted is, by Equation (5), Section 8.8,

$$W_T = \frac{E_0^2 ab}{4Z_{TE}} = \frac{E_0^2 ab}{4Z_0}\left[1 - \left(\frac{\lambda}{2a}\right)^2\right]^{1/2}$$

(8)

The attenuation coefficient for copper losses then is

$$\alpha_c = \frac{W_L}{2W_T} = \frac{R_s}{Z_0}\frac{1}{[1 - (\lambda/2a)^2]^{1/2}}\frac{1}{b}\left[1 + \frac{2b}{a}\left(\frac{\lambda}{2a}\right)^2\right]$$

(9)

This is for a TE_{10} wave. More complicated expressions can be obtained for TE_{lm} or TM_{lm} waves in general.

As an example we compute the loss in decibels per foot for a TE_{10} wave traveling down a copper waveguide 7 cm $\times$ 3.5 cm at a wavelength of 10 cm. Here $a = 7$ cm, $\lambda = 10$ cm. For copper R_s is 14.5 $\times$ 10^{-3} ohms per sq at this frequency.

Substitution into (9) gives $\alpha_c = 2.36 \times 10^{-3}$ neper per m. A neper is a measure of attenuation; if a field component is attenuated by an amount $e^{-\alpha z}$, αz is the attenuation in nepers. One neper is e^{-1}, and substitution in the formula defining decibel gives

$$1 \text{ neper} = 20 \log_{10} \frac{F_1}{F_2} = 20 \log_{10} e^{-1} = -8.69 \text{ db} \qquad (10)$$

Thus the attenuation is 0.0204 db per m or 0.62 db per 100 ft. We see that waveguides are in fact excellent conductors of microwave power. A typical coax line RG-58U has an attenuation of 32 db per 100 ft at 10 cm. In such a solid dielectric coax line the dielectric losses are considerably larger than the conductor losses.

9.4   A Typical Problem

We shall now solve a problem in two dimensions where the skin depth is not neglected. Consider the region between $x = 0$ and $x = a$

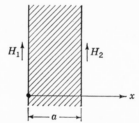

Fig. 9.4a. Eddy currents in a slab of magnetic material.

to be filled with a conducting material having given μ, σ. Let there be a tangential H at each face in the z direction only, i.e.,

$$H_z = H_1 e^{j\omega t} \qquad \text{at } x = 0 \qquad H_z = H_2 e^{j\omega t} \qquad \text{at } x = a \qquad (1)$$

The problem is to determine $\mathbf{H}$ and $\mathbf{J}$ in the conducting material. The equation governing $\mathbf{H}$ is

$$\nabla^2 \mathbf{H} - j\omega\mu\sigma\mathbf{H} = 0 \qquad (2)$$

Since only H_z is present and it is only a function of x, we have

$$\frac{d^2 H_z}{dx^2} - \tau^2 H_z = 0 \qquad (3)$$

where $\tau^2 = j\omega\mu\sigma$. Instead of using a solution similar to Equation (3), Section 9.2, it will be easier to match the boundary condition if we write the solution of (3) as

$$H_z = A \sinh \tau(a - x) + B \sinh \tau x \qquad (4)$$

The boundary conditions are $H_z = H_1$ at $x = 0$, and $H_z = H_2$ at $x = a$. Substitution into (4) gives

$$H_z = \frac{H_1 \sinh \tau(a - x)}{\sinh \tau a} + \frac{H_2 \sinh \tau x}{\sinh \tau a} \qquad (5)$$

To find the current density $\mathbf{J}$, we remember that in a conductor the displacement current is neglected so that $\nabla \times \mathbf{H} = \mathbf{J}$; since we only have H_z, a function of x, there will exist only J_y, where

$$J_y = -\frac{\partial H_z}{\partial x} \qquad (6)$$

This permits calculation of J_y in the conductor. An obvious extension of this problem permits calculation of the magnetic field and current density in a transformer lamination with sinusoidal excitation.

9.5   Transient Eddy Currents in Pulse Transformer Laminations

We shall now consider a rather complicated problem involving eddy currents—namely the variation of $\mathbf{H}$ with time and the spatial

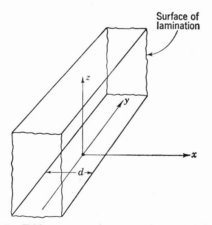

Fig. 9.5a. Eddy currents in a transformer lamination.

distribution of $\mathbf{H}$ in a transformer lamination which is driven by a step function in voltage across the primary. We shall make many simplifying assumptions—that the permeability of the iron μ is a constant, that the coil is wound tightly around the iron core so that leakage inductance can be neglected, and that the laminations are so closely packed that *all* the flux is carried by the iron laminations. Under these conditions the basic boundary condition is that the rate of rise of flux in the iron is equal to the volts per turn on the primary V. We shall choose axes such that there is only H_z and the neutral plane of a lamination is the yz plane. The flux will vary essentially only with x if the lamination thickness d is small compared with its other dimensions.

For reasons discussed in the beginning of this chapter, the differential equation that governs this phenomenon is the wave equation without the term due to the displacement current. Here, of course, there is no fixed frequency so we must use [see Equation (6), Section 7.1]

$$\nabla^2 \mathbf{H} - \mu\sigma \frac{\partial \mathbf{H}}{\partial t} = 0 \tag{1}$$

or, since there is only $H_z(x,t)$,

$$\frac{\partial^2 H_z}{\partial x^2} = \mu\sigma \frac{\partial H_z}{\partial t} \tag{2}$$

The general solution of (2) that will fit a step-function voltage drive is a steady-state term plus a transient term:

$$H_z = A_0 \left[\left(t + \frac{\mu\sigma}{2} x^2 + C \right) + \sum_{n=1}^{\infty} A_n e^{-p_n t} \cos k_n x \right] \tag{3}$$

In the transient term we use only a cosine term since H will be an even function of x. There is no $n = 0$ term as this is taken care of by C in the first term. Since we wish to expand the transient term in a Fourier series of period d, the width of the lamination, the proper value of k_n is

$$k_n = \frac{2\pi n}{d} \tag{4}$$

Substitution into (2) gives

$$p_n = \frac{4\pi^2 n^2}{\sigma\mu d^2} \tag{5}$$

At large t the transient terms will die out, leaving

$$H_\infty = A_0 \left(t + \frac{\mu\sigma}{2} x^2 + C \right) \tag{6}$$

The total flux represented by (6) must rise at a constant rate so that

$$\Phi = Vt = \mu A_i \frac{2}{d} \int_0^{d/2} H_\infty \, dx = \mu A_i A_0 \left[t + \frac{\mu\sigma}{6} \left(\frac{d}{2} \right)^2 + C \right] \tag{7}$$

or
$$A_0 = \frac{V}{\mu A_i} \qquad C = -\frac{\mu \sigma d^2}{24} \tag{8}$$

where A_i is the area of the iron core. The value of H_z is then

$$H_z = \frac{V}{\mu A_i} t + \frac{\mu \sigma V}{2\mu A_i}\left(x^2 - \frac{d^2}{12} + \sum_{n=1}^{\infty} B_n e^{-p_n t} \cos \frac{2\pi n x}{d}\right) \tag{9}$$

At $t = 0$, H_z must be zero. Thus the parenthesis in (9) must vanish for $t = 0$. This gives the condition

$$\frac{d^2}{12} - x^2 = \sum_{n=1}^{\infty} B_n \cos \frac{2\pi n x}{d} \tag{10}$$

Applying the usual methods of Fourier analysis we obtain

$$B_n = (-1)^{n+1}\left(\frac{d}{\pi n}\right)^2 \tag{11}$$

The final answer is given by

$$H_z(x,t) = \frac{Vt}{\mu A_i} + \frac{\sigma V}{2A_i}\left[x^2 - \frac{d^2}{12} - \sum_{n=1}^{\infty}(-1)^n\left(\frac{d}{\pi n}\right)^2 e^{-4\pi^2 n^2 t/\mu d^2 \sigma} \cos \frac{2\pi n x}{d}\right] \tag{12}$$

It is convenient to present (12) in dimensionless form. This is done by defining

$$A = \frac{V\sigma d^2}{12 A_i} \qquad T = \frac{\mu \sigma d^2}{12} \qquad \tau = \frac{t}{T} \qquad u = \frac{2x}{d}$$

Using the new dimensionless variables τ for time and u for distance we have for (12)

$$H_z(u,\tau) = A\left[\tau + \frac{3}{2}u^2 - \frac{1}{2} - \frac{6}{\pi^2}\sum_{n=1}^{\infty}(-1)^n \frac{1}{n^2} e^{-\pi^2 n^2 \tau/3} \cos \pi n u\right] \tag{13}$$

If we are interested in the current flowing in the coil required to drive these eddy currents we must consider the value of H_z at the surface of the lamination. For a tightly wound coil H_z at the surface of the outside lamination must equal the ampere-turns per meter in the coil. Thus $H_z(1,\tau) = ni$ and we have

$$ni = A\left[\tau + \left(1 - \frac{6}{\pi^2}\sum_{n=1}^{\infty}\frac{1}{n^2} e^{-\pi^2 n^2 \tau/3}\right)\right] \tag{14}$$

Noting that

$$\frac{\pi^2}{6} = \frac{1}{1^2} + \frac{1}{2^2} + \frac{1}{3^2} \cdots \tag{15}$$

it is clear that ni is always positive, starts at zero with infinite slope, and at large τ approaches $A(\tau + 1)$.

The distribution of current in the lamination is also of interest. This is given by $\nabla \times \mathbf{H} = \mathbf{J}$. The current distribution in the lamination is then

$$J_y = -\frac{\partial H_z}{\partial x} = -\frac{2}{d}\frac{\partial H_z}{\partial u} = -\frac{6A}{d}\left[u - \sum_{n=1}^{\infty} \frac{2}{\pi n}(-1)^{n+1}e^{-\pi^2 n^2 \tau/3}\sin \pi n u \right] \tag{16}$$

Noting Equation (4), Appendix H, it is seen that at $\tau = 0$ the last term in (16) just cancels the first term at $\tau = 0$. However, the very rapid decay of the higher terms of the summation at even small τ will "dull the saw" of the saw tooth, because the rapid diminution of the higher terms in the summation will affect only those parts of the Fourier expansion that are needed for rapid changes and this is only near $u = 1$. As τ increases, the saw tooth becomes even duller and eventually only the first term of (16) survives. The transient eddy-current effects thus die out for $\tau > 1$ leaving this steady-state eddy current. We see that both the current and magnetic field diffuse into the lamination from the surface with a time constant of about T.

This problem is very similar to the heat-flow problem of a slab of cool metal suddenly inserted into a hot fluid. In this problem the effects of remanence in the iron, small gaps in the laminations due to stacking, etc., have been ignored and these may have an important effect. We can easily calculate tangential E from the above (from ohmic currents in the surface of the lamination) and hence compute Poynting's vector and the energy delivered to the lamination. The problem of the decay of the magnetic field after the voltage pulse is turned off can also be solved and the energy-flow bookkeeping is of interest to those designing pulse transformers.*

In problems in which the frequency is fixed (as in Section 9.4 or Problem 2 at the end of this chapter) it is sometimes useful to consider the resulting phenomena to be caused by damped propagating waves, propagating in the conducting media. It should be noticed that in the metal we have just such a wave which is a plane polarized wave propa-

* This subject is treated in great detail in G. N. Glasoe and Jean V. Lebacqz (eds.), "Pulse Generators," M.I.T. Radiation Laboratory Series, vol. 5, chap. 15, McGraw-Hill Book Company, Inc., New York, 1948.

gating in a medium having a complex impedance, where this impedance is the ratio of E to H. For layered materials it may be necessary to consider waves propagating in both directions in order to match the boundary conditions. These boundary conditions are the continuity of tangential E and H at the boundaries. This type of treatment is discussed more fully in the case of nonabsorbing media in Chapters 10 and 13. It can also be applied formally to absorbing media. This is sometimes useful in solving the problems of this chapter which correspond to plane polarized waves incident normally on a metal surface.

PROBLEMS

1. Compute δ for copper and for iron at 60 $\sim$. How would this affect the design of large a-c buses operating at 60 cycles per second?

2. Solve the problem of a tangential H at the surface of a semi-infinite conductor $(\mu_1\sigma_1)$ coated with another material $(\mu_2\sigma_2)$ of thickness d. Find H, J as a function of depth. The time variation is $e^{j\omega t}$.

3. Consider a slab of magnetic material of given σ, μ. Find the power loss per unit volume if the magnetic field in the material is parallel to one face and is increasing at a uniform rate $B = B_0(t/T)$. Consider a steady state to have been reached.

4. A long solenoid of n turns per unit length carries an alternating current of angular frequency ω and peak value I. If a nonmagnetic rod of conductivity σ just filling the solenoid is placed inside it, find the current distribution and the magnetic field. Discuss the behavior of your solution for the limiting cases of large and small conductivities.

5. Consider a sphere of soft magnetic material having permeability K_m and conductivity σ immersed in an alternating uniform external magnetic field $H_0 e^{j\omega t}$, where ω is small. Find the distribution of eddy currents in this sphere. ω is so small that the magnetic fields arising from the eddy currents can be neglected compared with the magnetic field in the sphere from the driving field. Does this answer satisfy the equation $\nabla \times \mathbf{H} = \mathbf{J} + \partial \mathbf{D}/\partial t$?

6. Develop the theory of steady-state eddy currents in a transformer lamination with sinusoidal excitation. After obtaining an exact expression for the eddy currents, make suitable approximations for δ much less than or much more than the lamination thickness and compute the watts lost per unit volume.

10

TEM Waves

Transverse electromagnetic waves, abbreviated TEM waves, are those waves in which both the electric and magnetic vectors are in the transverse plane. Practical applications are the plane waves already discussed and the usual coax and twin lead modes. There is no inherent frequency limitation to propagation in TEM waves as there is in TE and TM modes—in other words, $\lambda_c = \infty$ for TEM waves; transmission is good to direct current.

10.1 The TEM Mode

We shall approach these modes by considering the choice of the separation constant k_z^2 to be zero. The wave equation for $\mathbf{E}$ is

$$\nabla^2 \mathbf{E} + \frac{\omega^2}{c^2} \mathbf{E} = 0 \tag{1}$$

or

$$\frac{1}{\mathbf{E}} \nabla_{12}^2 \mathbf{E} + \frac{1}{\mathbf{E}} \frac{d^2\mathbf{E}}{dz^2} + \frac{\omega^2}{c^2} = 0 \tag{2}$$

$$\underbrace{\phantom{\frac{1}{\mathbf{E}} \frac{d^2\mathbf{E}}{dz^2}}}_{} \; \longrightarrow = 0 = k_z^2$$

The z dependence of $\mathbf{E}$ is thus $e^{\pm j(\omega/c)z}$ and we choose the minus sign so as to restrict the discussion to waves traveling in the $+z$ direction. This leaves

$$\nabla_{12}^2 \mathbf{E} = 0 \tag{3}$$

to describe the transverse variation. Our usual solution, when k_z^2 is not zero, gives the transverse components in terms of $1/k_z^2(\partial E_z/\partial z)$. As $k_z^2 \to 0$ this becomes ∞ unless $E_z \to 0$.

A similar argument holds for H_z. Equation (3) implies that the

146

transverse fields obey the d-c solutions, for in the case of $\mathbf{E}$ these are given by $\nabla \times \mathbf{E} = 0$ and taking the curl again we have

$$\nabla \times \nabla \times \mathbf{E} = \nabla(\nabla \cdot \mathbf{E}) - \nabla^2\mathbf{E} = 0$$

or $\nabla^2\mathbf{E} = 0$. Thus $\mathbf{E}$ is perpendicular to the conductors and $\mathbf{H}$ tangential to the conductors. The relationships between transverse $\mathbf{H}$ and $\mathbf{E}$ components still hold, namely $H_y = E_x/Z_0$ and $H_x = -E_y/Z_0$, and $\mathbf{E}$ is normal to $\mathbf{H}$ everywhere. Since $\mathbf{H}$ lines must surround either $\mathbf{J}$ or $\dot{\mathbf{D}}$, and since there is no longitudinal $\dot{\mathbf{D}}$, $\mathbf{H}$ lines must surround a real current $\mathbf{J}$ implying the existence of a current-carrying conductor about which $\mathbf{H}$ lines can curl. Likewise, $\mathbf{E}$ lines cannot surround $-\dot{\mathbf{B}}$, but must terminate on real charges.

These last two requirements are exactly the requirements that the d-c solution must satisfy for a cylindrical wave guiding system (i.e., the guide must have no variation in the z direction). The z variation of a TEM wave will of course be $e^{-j\omega z/c}$ whereas the d-c solution does not vary with z.

10.2 Coaxial Lines

With the above as a background we shall now discuss a coaxial line, i.e., that mode which has only an E_r and an H_θ. We presume that the wave is traveling only in the $+z$ direction. The connection between E_r and H_θ is given by

$$(\nabla \times \mathbf{E})_\theta = -j\omega\mu H_\theta = \frac{\partial E_r}{\partial z} = -j\frac{\omega}{c}E_r \tag{1}$$

or $$\frac{E_r}{H_\theta} = \frac{\mu}{(\epsilon\mu)^{1/2}} = \sqrt{\frac{\mu}{\epsilon}} = Z_0 = 120\pi \qquad \text{for air} \tag{2}$$

However, E and H must obey the d-c solutions, and these can easily be shown to be

$$E_r = \frac{\Delta V}{r \log (r_2/r_1)} \tag{3}$$

and $$H_\theta = \frac{I}{2\pi r} \tag{4}$$

Hence we have

$$\frac{E_r}{H_\theta} = Z_0 = \sqrt{\frac{\mu}{\epsilon}} = \frac{\Delta V}{I}\frac{2\pi}{\log (r_2/r_1)} \tag{5}$$

We now define Z_k to be the characteristic impedance of the transmission line, which is the ratio of the voltage to the current; this is

$$Z_k = \frac{\Delta V}{I} = \frac{Z_0}{2\pi} \log \frac{r_2}{r_1} = 60 \log \frac{r_2}{r_1} \qquad \text{ohms} \tag{6}$$

for air dielectric.   From the discussion in Chapter 8 of copper losses in waveguides, here also

$$\alpha_c = \frac{W_L}{2W_T} = \frac{I^2 R}{2I^2 Z_k} = \frac{R}{2Z_k} \qquad \text{nepers/m} \qquad (7)$$

Here R is the resistance of the coax line per unit length

$$R = \frac{R_s}{2\pi}\left(\frac{1}{r_1} + \frac{1}{r_2}\right)$$

At this point we shall discuss the dielectric losses in a coax cable as these are usually the major losses at high frequencies and this type of loss is usually absent in a waveguide.   Dielectrics are characterized by a power factor—when used as a dielectric in a condenser the power factor is that portion of the volt-amperes that appears as watts lost in the dielectric.   If the power factor is small this is the same as the loss tangent.   If we consider a condenser in the form of a 1-meter cube of dielectric arranged to operate with a uniform electric field the volt-amperes is

$$\overline{VA} = \tfrac{1}{2}|V|\,|I| = \frac{V^2|j\omega C|}{2} = \omega\tfrac{1}{2}CV^2 \qquad (8)$$

This means ω times the peak stored energy is the VA.

In a more general case we shall calculate the peak stored energy as $\mathbf{E}\cdot\mathbf{D}/2$ per unit volume.   The watts lost due to imperfect dielectric in a coax line is, per unit length,

$$W_L = \omega(pf)\int_{r_1}^{r_2}\frac{\epsilon}{2}\left[\frac{V}{r\log\,(r_2/r_1)}\right]^2 2\pi r\,dr$$

or
$$W_L = \frac{\omega\epsilon(pf)\pi V^2}{\log\,(r_2/r_1)} \qquad (9)$$

The watts transmitted is

$$W_T = \frac{V^2}{2Z_k} = \frac{V^2\pi}{Z_0\log\,(r_2/r_1)} \qquad (10)$$

The attenuation due to dielectric losses is then

$$\alpha_D = \frac{W_L}{2W_T} = \frac{\omega\epsilon Z_0(pf)}{2} = \frac{\pi}{\lambda_0}\,(pf) \qquad (11)$$

where λ_0 is the wavelength in the dielectric medium.

An entirely different method of obtaining this result is similar to that used in Equation (17), Section 7.2, where attenuation due to plane waves in a conducting medium is discussed.   It is usual to refer to lossy dielectrics by the form

$$\epsilon = \epsilon_0(k' - jk'') \tag{12}$$

where k''/k' is the power factor. We shall consider cases where this quantity is small ($pf \leq 0.1$).

Comparison with Equation (17), Section 7.2, then shows that

$$\gamma = \pm j \frac{\omega}{c} \sqrt{1 - j(pf)} \approx \pm \left(\frac{j\omega}{c}\right)\left(1 - j\frac{pf}{2}\right) \tag{13}$$

For slightly conducting media we can then define the power factor as $\sigma/\epsilon\omega$. In addition to the usual imaginary part of γ there is thus added a real part $\pi(pf)/\lambda_0$, as above. A similar arrangement holds in the case of a TE waveguide, where we obtain

$$\alpha_D = \frac{\pi}{\lambda_0} (pf) \frac{1}{[1 - (\lambda_0/\lambda_c)^2]^{\frac{1}{2}}} \tag{14}$$

We can easily see that the major advantage of the waveguide, as far as loss is concerned, is merely in the absence of dielectrics under usual conditions of operation. The presence of the central conductor in the coax line, however, implies an insulating support, and since the attenuation varies inversely as the wavelength, losses in these supports become very large at high frequencies. The copper losses (α_c) vary as R_s and hence inversely as the square root of the wavelength. The waveguide has a fair advantage over the coax line since the current is not crowded in a central conductor, but the main advantage is in the absence of dielectric supports.

10.3 Standing and Traveling Waves on Transmission Lines

If we consider a TEM wave we can easily show from Maxwell's equations that

$$\frac{E_x}{H_y} = -\frac{E_y}{H_x} = \pm \frac{j\omega\mu}{\gamma} = \pm Z_0 \tag{1}$$

where the $+$ sign is used for a wave traveling in the $+z$ direction and vice versa. From this it is evident that the relation between current and voltage in a negatively traveling wave is opposite to that of a positively traveling wave.

Thus if both types of waves are present, we can write

$$V = V_1 e^{-\gamma z} + V_2 e^{+\gamma z} \tag{2}$$

$$I = \frac{1}{Z_k} (V_1 e^{-\gamma z} - V_2 e^{+\gamma z})$$

Here V_1 and V_2 are the amplitudes of the positively and negatively traveling waves; Z_k is the characteristic impedance of the transmission line. γ is the propagation constant, which for a lossless line is $j\beta$, where $\beta = \omega/c$ for a TEM wave, and in general we have $\gamma = \alpha + j\beta$. If there is a load Z_L at $z = 0$, we have

$$Z_L = \frac{V_1 + V_2}{V_1 - V_2} Z_k \tag{3}$$

or, after some algebra,

$$V_2 = \frac{Z_L - Z_k}{Z_L + Z_k} V_1 \tag{4}$$

Equation (2) then becomes

$$V = V_1 \left(e^{-\gamma z} + \frac{Z_L - Z_k}{Z_L + Z_k} e^{+\gamma z} \right)$$

$$I = \frac{V_1}{Z_k} \left(e^{-\gamma z} - \frac{Z_L - Z_k}{Z_L + Z_k} e^{+\gamma z} \right) \tag{5}$$

We now call the voltage at the load V_L and obtain

$$V = V_L \left(\cosh \gamma z - \frac{Z_k}{Z_L} \sinh \gamma z \right)$$

$$I = \frac{V_L}{Z_L} \left(\cosh \gamma z - \frac{Z_L}{Z_k} \sinh \gamma z \right) \tag{6}$$

Equation (6) refers to a load at $z = 0$, and might be used in the region of negative z, where a wave traveling toward the load corresponds to $\gamma z = -j\beta z$. It is conventional to refer to z as the distance between the point of observation and the load and to consider this distance between observation point and load to be positive. This corresponds to changing the sign of z in (6), giving

$$V = V_L \left(\cosh \gamma z + \frac{Z_k}{Z_L} \sinh \gamma z \right)$$

$$I = \frac{V_L}{Z_L} \left(\cosh \gamma z + \frac{Z_L}{Z_k} \sinh \gamma z \right) \tag{7}$$

We shall continue this nomenclature throughout the rest of this chapter.

If now the line is lossless, $\gamma = j\beta$, and we can apply the formulas

$$\cosh j\beta z = \cos \beta z \qquad \sinh j\beta z = j \sin \beta z \tag{8}$$

Equation (7) becomes

$$V = V_L \left(\cos \beta z + j \frac{Z_k}{Z_L} \sin \beta z \right)$$

$$I = \frac{V_L}{Z_L} \left(\cos \beta z + j \frac{Z_L}{Z_k} \sin \beta z \right) \tag{9}$$

The impedance looking into the line at any point z is

$$Z_{in} = \frac{V}{I} = Z_L \frac{\cos \beta z + j(Z_k/Z_L) \sin \beta z}{\cos \beta z + j(Z_L/Z_k) \sin \beta z} \tag{10}$$

This can be rewritten as

$$Z_{in} = Z_k \frac{Z_L \cos \beta z + jZ_k \sin \beta z}{Z_k \cos \beta z + jZ_L \sin \beta z} \tag{11}$$

In this way we can find the impedance looking into a line of length z, having characteristic impedance Z_k terminated in a load Z_L.

Several simple examples will be given here. If $Z_L = 0$, we have a shorted line, or as it is often called, a stub. In this case

$$Z_{in} = jZ_k \tan \beta z \tag{12}$$

This impedance goes to infinity at $\beta z = \pi/2$ if there are no losses. Such a shorted quarter-wave line is often used as a plate tank circuit at UHF in place of the familiar LC tank circuit. If $\beta z = \pi/2$ we have a quarter-wave transformer:

$$Z_{in} = \frac{Z_k^2}{Z_L} \tag{13}$$

This is often used to match a load to a generator. Clearly, a half-wave line ($\beta z = \pi$) reflects the load impedance directly to the end of the line.

We shall not pursue this important subject further, except to note that the use of the "Smith Chart" permits us to bypass a great deal of dreary mathematics when matching loads to lines. Other subjects of importance are the broadbanding of such matching, the use of fixed or movable stubs on lines, etc. The above techniques are all directly transferable to waveguides if we interpret V and I to be the electric field and magnetic field as sampled by a probe and let $\beta = 2\pi/\lambda_g$.

10.4 Shorted Quarter-wave Line as a Resonator

We shall now treat in detail the use of a shorted quarter-wave transmission line, including losses, as a tank circuit. From Equation (7), Section 10.3, if $Z_L = 0$, we have

$$Z_{in} = Z_k \tanh (\gamma z) \tag{1}$$

Now we let $\gamma = \alpha + j\beta$ and obtain, after some algebra,

$$Z_i = R_i + jX_i \tag{2}$$

where

$$R_i = \frac{\sinh \alpha z \cosh \alpha z}{\cosh^2 \alpha z \cos^2 \beta z + \sinh^2 \alpha z \sin^2 \beta z} Z_k$$

$$X_i = \frac{\sin \beta z \cos \beta z}{\cosh^2 \alpha z \cos^2 \beta z + \sinh^2 \alpha z \sin^2 \beta z} Z_k \tag{3}$$

Here we are interested in the behavior of R_i and X_i near $\beta z = \pi/2$. We therefore let

$$\beta z = \frac{\pi}{2} + \delta \tag{4}$$

and substitute into (3), presuming δ to be small enough so that $\sin \beta z \approx 1$, $\cos \beta z \approx -\delta$. In addition we assume that the losses of the line are very small so that $\sinh \alpha z = \alpha z$ and $\cosh \alpha z = 1$. Performing the indicated operations we obtain

$$R_i = Z_k \frac{\alpha z}{\delta^2 + (\alpha z)^2}$$
$$jX_i = -jZ_k \frac{\delta}{\delta^2 + (\alpha z)^2} \tag{5}$$

It follows that

$$|Z_{in}|^2 = Z_k{}^2 \frac{1}{(\alpha z)^2 + \delta^2} \tag{6}$$

These last equations are similar to those of a resonant circuit.

To correlate this with the usual Q used in circuit theory, remember that the response of a circuit (essentially proportional to $|Z|$) is related to Q by

$$\frac{1}{Q} = \frac{2 \, \Delta f}{f} \tag{7}$$

where Δf is the frequency deviation to reduce $|Z|$ to 0.707 of peak response, and f is the resonant frequency. $|Z_{in}|^2$ is reduced to half its peak response when $\alpha z = \pm \delta$. Now $\beta z \approx \pi/2$ or $z = \pi/2\beta$. Thus $\delta = \alpha z = \alpha \pi/2\beta$ for Δf, and

$$\frac{\delta}{\pi/2} = \frac{\Delta f}{f} = \frac{\alpha}{\beta} \tag{8}$$

Hence it is seen that $Q = \beta/2\alpha$.

At resonance one has

$$R_i = Z_k \frac{2\beta}{\alpha\pi} = Z_k \frac{4Q}{\pi} \tag{9}$$

We see that if no dielectric materials are present, very high impedances can result from (9), since Q may easily be several thousand rather than several hundred as is usual with lumped circuit elements. Of course the use of a $\lambda/4$ shorted line is very inconvenient at frequencies below several hundred megacycles ($\lambda/4 = 30$ in. at 100 mc). Actually in any real device there is usually a lumped capacity (usually small, of the order of a few $\mu\mu f$) inside the vacuum tube which is connected to the

shorted $\lambda/4$ resonator. Resonance of this circuit can be computed
from (1):

$$Z_k \tan \beta z = \frac{1}{\omega C} \tag{10}$$

or, if βz is near $\pi/2$,

$$\tan^{-1}\left(\frac{1}{\omega C Z_k}\right) = \beta z = \frac{\pi}{2} - \omega C Z_k + \cdots \tag{11}$$

If the capacity is small, the correction term is small and the shorted
transmission line is used as an inductance to resonate with the inter-
electrode capacity. The length of this line will be approximately $\lambda/4$
and the Q connected with this inductance will be about that computed
above.

10.5 Optimum Coaxial Lines

The ratio of outside to inside diameters of a coaxial transmission
line can be varied to obtain different characteristics. Among these are
the ability to handle maximum voltage or power, minimum α_c, etc.
Clearly all these properties will be improved by using a larger coax line
so we shall fix the outer radius and determine the ratio of the radii for
the optimum property desired. The line is presumed to be terminated
in its characteristic impedance.

As an example we shall determine the best Z_k for handling maximum power. There will be a maximum E, E_m, above which sparking
will occur. This will of course occur at minimum radius, the radius of
the inner conductor. Let the outer radius be a, the inner radius be b,
and the ratio $a/b = x$. From Equation (3), Section 10.2, we have, at
maximum voltage V_m,

$$E_m = \frac{V_m}{b \log (a/b)} = \frac{V_m x}{a \log x}$$

or

$$V_m = \frac{E_m a(\log x)}{x} \tag{1}$$

The power transmitted by the line at this maximum voltage is

$$P = \frac{V_m{}^2}{2Z_k} = \frac{(E_m a)^2 (\log x/x)^2}{120 \log x} = C \frac{\log x}{x^2} \tag{2}$$

This will be a maximum when $dP/dx = 0$:

$$\frac{dP}{dx} = C\left(\frac{1}{x^3} - \frac{2 \log x}{x^3}\right) = 0 \qquad \text{or} \qquad \log x = \tfrac{1}{2} \tag{3}$$

giving a characteristic impedance of 30 ohms ($a/b = 1.65$).

By similar computations it can be shown that maximum voltage can be handled by a 60-ohm line, minimum α_c by a 77-ohm line and that a 133-ohm line will give the maximum input impedance for a shorted $\lambda/4$ transmission line. Maximum Q for a shorted $\lambda/4$ line occurs for a 77-ohm line. All these are for fixed outer radius.

10.6　Transmission-line Theory Using Distributed Parameters

So far we have been discussing the transmission-line problem from the standpoint of field theory. We shall now present another treatment, using circuit theory. Consider a transmission line to consist of distributed impedances such that it has Z ohms series impedance per unit length and a shunt admittance between the two conductors of Y mhos per unit length. It is clear then that the drop in voltage per unit length is ZI, where I is the current in the line, and that the drop in current per unit length is YV where V is the voltage between the two conductors. This gives

$$\frac{\partial V}{\partial z} = -ZI \tag{1}$$

and

$$\frac{\partial I}{\partial z} = -YV \tag{2}$$

We can differentiate (1) with respect to z and use (2) to obtain

$$\frac{\partial^2 V}{\partial z^2} = ZYV = \gamma^2 V \tag{3}$$

where

$$\gamma^2 = YZ \tag{4}$$

Likewise we can obtain

$$\frac{\partial^2 I}{\partial z^2} = \gamma^2 I \tag{5}$$

The solution of (3) and (5) is

$$V = V_1 e^{-\gamma z} + V_2 e^{\gamma z} \tag{6}$$

and

$$I = I_1 e^{-\gamma z} + I_2 e^{\gamma z} \tag{7}$$

Substituting these two solutions into (1) and (2) we obtain

$$I = \frac{1}{Z_k} (V_1 e^{-\gamma z} - V_2 e^{\gamma z}) \tag{8}$$

where $Z_k = \sqrt{Z/Y}$, which is the same as Equation (2), Section 10.3. From here on the derivation of the characteristics of the transmission lines is the same as in Section 10.3.

Some interesting conclusions can be drawn from our identification of γ and Z_k. Consider first a dissipationless line where $Z = j\omega L$ and $Y = j\omega C$, L being the inductance per unit length and C the capacity per unit length. Suppose further, that the line is uniform (i.e., none of the parameters varies with z, as in a coax line or two-wire line). Then from Section 10.1 we know that $\gamma = j\omega/c$, where c is the velocity of light in the material in the line $(\epsilon\mu)^{-\frac{1}{2}}$. However, from (4) we have

$$\gamma = \sqrt{j\omega L \cdot j\omega C} = j\omega \sqrt{LC} \tag{9}$$

We can now draw the interesting conclusion that

$$LC = c^{-2} = \epsilon\mu \tag{10}$$

which will permit us to compute the inductance per unit length if we know the capacity per unit length of a uniform line. Likewise,

$$Z_k = \sqrt{\frac{L}{C}} = \frac{\sqrt{\epsilon\mu}}{C} = \frac{L}{\sqrt{\epsilon\mu}} \tag{11}$$

which will give the characteristic impedance if we know either L or C. As an example we consider a parallel-wire transmission line made of wires of radius a, the distance between centers being D. From Equation (9), Section 1.7, we have

$$C = \frac{\pi\epsilon}{\cosh^{-1}(D/2a)} \qquad \text{farads/m} \tag{12}$$

Using this in (11) we obtain

$$Z_k = \frac{Z_0}{\pi} \cosh^{-1}\left(\frac{D}{2a}\right) \approx \frac{Z_0}{\pi} \log\left(\frac{D}{a}\right) \tag{13}$$

where $Z_0 = \sqrt{\mu/\epsilon}$.

PROBLEMS

1. A two-wire transmission line consists of two strips of metal of width w and separation $d(w \gg d)$. Assuming the conductivity of the metal to be infinite, compute Poynting's vector if the difference of the potential is V volts and a current of I amperes flows down one wire and back the other. Neglect edge effects. What is the total power transmitted down the wire?

2. Find the input impedance and Q of a shorted quarter-wave transmission line constructed of two parallel strips of metal w meters wide and separated by d meters $(d \ll w)$. The metal has conductivity σ and permeability μ. δ is much less than the thickness of the strips.

3. A coaxial line of characteristic impedance 100 ohms is 30 centimeters long, is shorted at one end, and has a capacity at the other end.   What is the capacity needed for resonance to occur at 125 megacycles?

4. A quarter-wave resonant transmission line of characteristic impedance 100 ohms is shorted at one end and open at the other.   It is excited by an oscillator which delivers 1 watt to this tank circuit.   If this circuit has a Q of 1,000, what is the peak current at the shorted end of the line?

5. Derive the results quoted at the end of Section 10.5 concerning best line impedance for maximum voltage, minimum α_c, and maximum resonant cavity impedance.

6. Calculate the attenuation due to dielectric losses in a rectangular waveguide filled with a dielectric of dielectric constant K and power factor (*pf*) operating in either a TM or a TE mode.

7. Solve the general problem of the input impedance and Q of a transmission line operating in the TEM mode which is n quarter wavelengths long and is either short-circuited or open-circuited at the far end.

Answer. $R_i = 8Z_k^2/n\lambda R$ for a high impedance case or $R_i = n\lambda R/8$ for a low impedance case, where R is the resistance per unit length of the line.

11

Solution of the Wave Equation
in Spherical Coordinates
and Elementary Antennas

We have discussed the propagation of electromagnetic waves by guiding systems such as waveguides, coax lines, etc. We now take up the solution of the wave equation in spherical coordinates which will lead to an understanding of radiation in space from a singularity (elementary antenna driven by a generator) at the origin. We shall find that the field near the elementary antenna (inductive field) and the field very far from the antenna (radiation field) will be of quite different form.

11.1 Solution of Wave Equation in Spherical Coordinates

First we discuss TM waves, considering the case where propagation is in the r direction. We shall show how the transverse components of **E** can be obtained from E_r by finding a potential V, as we did in Chapter 7. The r component of the wave equation is, as can be found from Appendix D,

$$\frac{1}{r}\nabla^2(rE_r) + \frac{\omega^2}{c^2}E_r = 0 \tag{1}$$

or

$$\nabla^2 u + \frac{\omega^2}{c^2}u = 0 \tag{2}$$

where $u = rE_r$. Separating the variables in (2) we have

$$\frac{r^2}{u}\nabla_{\theta\phi}{}^2(u) + \frac{r^2}{u}\nabla_r{}^2(u) + \frac{\omega^2}{c^2}r^2 = 0 \tag{3}$$

Here ∇_r^2 is the first term in ∇^2, and $\nabla_{\theta\phi}^2$ the next two terms. The first term in (3) is not a function of r. The second two terms are a function of r only and thus must be placed equal to a constant. Later it will turn out that this constant should be chosen for convenience to be $l(l + 1)$. Thus (3) becomes, after multiplying through by ru and taking r inside $r^2\nabla_{\theta\phi}^2$ since this operation does not involve r,

$$r^2\nabla_{\theta\phi}^2(ru) = -l(l + 1)(ru) \tag{4}$$

Since $\mathbf{E}_t = \text{grad } V$, as is proved for any wave in any orthogonal system of coordinates in Section 8.1, and $\nabla \cdot \mathbf{E} = 0$, we have

$$r^2\nabla_{\theta\phi}^2(V) = -\frac{\partial}{\partial r}(ru) \tag{5}$$

Comparison of (4) and (5) shows that

$$\frac{1}{l(l+1)}\frac{\partial}{\partial r}[r^2\nabla_{\theta\phi}^2(ru)] = r^2\nabla_{\theta\phi}^2(V) \tag{6}$$

Since $r^2\nabla_{\theta\phi}^2$ is not a function of r we can take $[1/l(l+1)](\partial/\partial r)$ inside the brackets in this equation giving

$$r^2\nabla_{\theta\phi}^2\left[\frac{1}{l(l+1)}\frac{\partial}{\partial r}(ru)\right] = r^2\nabla_{\theta\phi}^2(V) \tag{7}$$

Thus
$$V = \frac{1}{l(l+1)}\frac{\partial}{\partial r}(ru) \tag{8}$$

except for an added term W which satisfies

$$\nabla_{\theta\phi}^2(W) = 0 \tag{9}$$

Such potentials W satisfy Laplace's equation where there is no r dependence or which arise from an alternating monopole (single charge) at the origin and will not be considered here.

The solution of the wave equation in spherical coordinates is now in principle complete. If u can be found from (2), $\mathbf{E}_t$ can be found by taking the gradient of (8) in the transverse directions. $\mathbf{H}$ can then be found from $\nabla \times \mathbf{E} = -j\omega\mu\mathbf{H}$. An exactly similar solution holds for a TE wave. There is unfortunately no simple relation between the transverse components of $\mathbf{E}$ and $\mathbf{H}$ as in waveguides.

The solution of (2) is obtained by the usual method of separation of variables. If we let $u = R(r)\Theta(\theta)\Phi(\phi)$, substitute in (2), and multiply through by r^2/u, we obtain

$$\frac{1}{R}\frac{\partial}{\partial r}\left(r^2\frac{\partial R}{\partial r}\right) + \frac{1}{\Theta\sin\theta}\frac{\partial}{\partial\theta}\left(\sin\theta\frac{\partial\Theta}{\partial\theta}\right) + \frac{1}{\Phi\sin^2\theta}\frac{\partial^2\Phi}{\partial\phi^2} + \frac{\omega^2}{c^2}r^2 = 0 \tag{10}$$

Clearly the solution for Φ is

$$\Phi = \begin{Bmatrix} \sin \\ \cos \end{Bmatrix} m\phi \qquad \text{where } m \text{ is an integer} \qquad (11)$$

We shall associate the first and last terms together. The first and last terms together then must be a constant, $l(l + 1)$. This gives

$$\frac{1}{r^2} \frac{d}{dr} \left(r^2 \frac{dR}{dr} \right) + \left(\frac{\omega^2}{c^2} - \frac{l(l+1)}{r^2} \right) R = 0 \qquad (12)$$

The equation for Θ is then

$$\frac{1}{\sin \theta} \frac{d}{d\theta} \left(\sin \theta \frac{d\Theta}{d\theta} \right) + \left[l(l + 1) - \frac{m^2}{\sin^2 \theta} \right] \Theta = 0 \qquad (13)$$

The solution of this equation is, for the purposes at hand, $P_l^m (\cos \theta)$. Equation (12) is solved by substituting $R = F/\sqrt{r}$ where F is a function of r. F is then seen to be a Bessel function of order $l + \frac{1}{2}$ (see Appendix G). The solution of (12) is thus

$$R(r) = r^{-\frac{1}{2}} J_{l+\frac{1}{2}} \left(\frac{\omega r}{c} \right) \qquad \text{or} \qquad r^{-\frac{1}{2}} N_{l+\frac{1}{2}} \left(\frac{\omega r}{c} \right) \qquad (14)$$

It is usual to define spherical Bessel functions as follows

$$j_l(x) = \sqrt{\frac{\pi}{2x}} J_{l+\frac{1}{2}}(x) \qquad n_l(x) = \sqrt{\frac{\pi}{2x}} N_{l+\frac{1}{2}}(x) \qquad (15)$$

The properties of these functions for integer l are as follows

$$j_0(x) = \frac{\sin x}{x} \qquad n_0(x) = - \frac{\cos x}{x}$$

$$j_1(x) = \frac{\sin x}{x^2} - \frac{\cos x}{x} \qquad n_1(x) = - \frac{\sin x}{x} - \frac{\cos x}{x^2} \qquad (16)$$

$$j_2(x) = \left(\frac{3}{x^2} - 1 \right) \frac{\sin x}{x} - \frac{3}{x^2} \cos x \qquad n_2(x) = \left(\frac{3}{x^2} - 1 \right) \frac{\cos x}{x} + \frac{3}{x^2} \sin x$$

At large values of x $(x \gg l)$, we get

$$j_l(x) \rightarrow \frac{1}{x} \cos \left(x - \frac{l + 1}{2} \pi \right)$$

$$n_l(x) \rightarrow \frac{1}{x} \sin \left(x - \frac{l + 1}{2} \pi \right) \qquad (17)$$

At very small x we have

$$j_l(x) \rightarrow \frac{x^l}{1 \times 3 \times 5 \cdots (2l + 1)}$$

$$n_l(x) \rightarrow \frac{1 \times 3 \times 5 \cdots (2l - 1)}{x^{l+1}} \qquad (18)$$

The solution of the wave equation is thus

$$u = \left\{ \begin{matrix} j_l \\ n_l \end{matrix} \left(\frac{\omega r}{c} \right) \right\} P_l{}^m(\mu) \left\{ \begin{matrix} \sin \\ \cos \end{matrix} m\phi \right\} \tag{19}$$

The same solution applies for **H** in a TE wave.

The solutions given in (19) are useful for regions which do not extend to infinity. The usual radiation problem, on the other hand, is concerned with traveling waves in the r direction whereas (19) gives solutions which represent standing waves. It is easy, however, to combine the j_l and n_l functions so that at large r we get traveling waves. Using (17) we have at large x

$$h_l{}^{(1)}(x) = j_l(x) + jn_l(x) \to \frac{1}{x} \exp\left[+j\left(x - \frac{l+1}{2}\pi \right) \right]$$

$$h_l{}^{(2)}(x) = j_l(x) - jn_l(x) \to \frac{1}{x} \exp\left[-j\left(x - \frac{l+1}{2}\pi \right) \right] \tag{20}$$

The new functions $h_l{}^1(x)$ and $h_l{}^2(x)$ are called spherical Hankel functions. $h_l{}^{(1)}(x)$ represents the r dependence of a wave traveling inward along r, and $h_l{}^{(2)}(x)$ represents an outgoing wave, where we replace (x) by $(\omega r/c)$.

11.2 Spherical Radiation

We shall now consider the simplest solutions of the wave equation that have the characteristics of outgoing waves at large distances. These solutions will turn out to have fields like those of simple dipoles or multipoles close to the origin, but at large r will have a completely different character. If any fields exist they must be a function of the angle variables, since we must take derivatives of V [see Equation (8), Section 11.1] with respect to the angles in order to have any transverse components at all. The simplest choice is to take $l = 1$ and $m = 0$.

We shall first consider outgoing TM waves. The solutions in this case are obtained from

$$u = A \cos \theta [j_1(kr) - jn_1(kr)] \tag{1}$$

or, using Equation (16), Section 11.1, after some algebra,

$$u = A \cos \theta \left[-\frac{1}{kr} + \frac{j}{(kr)^2} \right] e^{-jkr} \tag{2}$$

Here we use $\omega r/c = 2\pi r/\lambda = kr$. Performing the gradient operation in the θ and ϕ directions on the potential given in Equation (8), Section

11.1, we have, inserting the time variation $e^{j\omega t}$,

$$E_r = \frac{u}{r} = Ak \cos \theta \left[-\frac{1}{(kr)^2} + \frac{j}{(kr)^3} \right] e^{j(\omega t - kr)} \tag{3}$$

$$E_\theta = \frac{1}{r} \frac{\partial}{\partial \theta} \left[\frac{1}{2} \frac{\partial}{\partial r} (ru) \right] \tag{4}$$

or

$$E_\theta = A \frac{k}{2} \sin \theta \left[-\frac{j}{kr} - \frac{1}{(kr)^2} + \frac{j}{(kr)^3} \right] e^{j(\omega t - kr)} \tag{5}$$

and from $\nabla \times \mathbf{E} = -j\omega\mu\mathbf{H}$,

$$H_\phi = A \frac{k}{2} \sqrt{\frac{\epsilon}{\mu}} \sin \theta \left[-\frac{j}{kr} - \frac{1}{(kr)^2} \right] e^{j(\omega t - kr)} \tag{6}$$

The other field components are zero.   Each component is seen to have the term $e^{j(\omega t - kr)}$ indicating propagation in the $+r$ direction.

The solutions just obtained have quite different forms at small and at large kr.   At very small kr, $(kr \ll 1)$, the important terms in (3) and (5) are

$$E_r = \frac{Aj \cos \theta}{k^2 r^3} e^{j\omega t}$$
$$E_\theta = \frac{Aj \sin \theta}{2k^2 r^3} e^{j\omega t} \tag{7}$$

These should be compared with the field of an electric dipole of strength m.

$$E_r = \frac{2m}{4\pi\epsilon_0} \frac{\cos \theta}{r^3}$$
$$E_\theta = \frac{m}{4\pi\epsilon_0} \frac{\sin \theta}{r^3} \tag{8}$$

Comparison of (7) and (8) shows that the electric field near the origin is like that of an oscillating electric dipole, and would be just that of an electric dipole of strength m if A were chosen to be $-jk^2m/2\pi\epsilon_0$.   Thus the electric field near the origin is just like that of an electric dipole that is changing with time as $e^{j\omega t}$.   The current element associated with a dipole of strength m which is changing with time as $e^{j\omega t}$ is $j\omega m e^{j\omega t}$, which would have a magnetic field given by

$$H_\phi = \frac{j\omega m e^{j\omega t}}{4\pi} \frac{\sin \theta}{r^2} \tag{9}$$

as is shown in Chapter 4.   This is likewise the same field as that given by (6) at $kr \ll 1$.   We see that in each case the fields near the origin

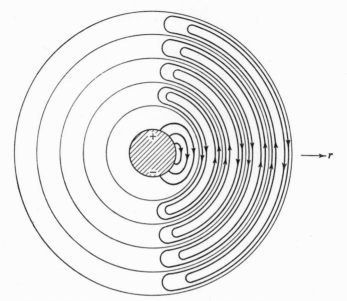

Fig. 11.2a. Electric field lines from a small oscillating dipole.

are just those given by an electric dipole varying slowly with time so that $m \rightarrow me^{j\omega t}$.

At large distances the fields are very different. In this case we observe that E_r becomes very small and only E_θ and H_ϕ are of importance. The important terms (except near $\theta = 0°$) are

$$E_\theta = - \frac{k^3 m}{4\pi\epsilon_0} \frac{\sin \theta}{kr} e^{j(\omega t - kr)}$$

$$H_\phi = - \frac{\omega m k^2}{4\pi} \frac{\sin \theta}{kr} e^{j(\omega t - kr)} \tag{10}$$

This region is called the radiation field. The components fall off inversely as r, $\mathbf{E}$ is perpendicular to $\mathbf{H}$, and the ratio E/H becomes $\sqrt{\mu/\epsilon}$. These are the properties of a free wave, such as the plane wave discussed earlier. Of course, at very large distances from an oscillator we would expect just such fields. Poynting's vector becomes, after some algebra,

$$\overline{S_r} = \frac{E_\theta H_\phi}{2} = \frac{\mu \sqrt{\epsilon\mu} \; \omega^4 m^2}{32\pi^2} \frac{\sin^2 \theta}{r^2} \tag{11}$$

To find the total power radiated we integrate over a sphere of large radius

$$P = \int_0^\pi \bar{S} 2\pi r^2 \sin \theta \; d\theta = \frac{\mu \sqrt{\epsilon\mu} \; \omega^4 m^2}{12\pi} \tag{12}$$

This gives the power radiated from a dipole. If the current in the dipole is $\omega m/l$, where l is the length of the dipole (this gives $m = ql$ and the current element $= dm/dt$), (12) becomes

$$P = \frac{\mu \sqrt{\epsilon\mu}}{12\pi} \left(\frac{2\pi c}{\lambda}\right)^2 l^2 i^2 = 40\pi^2 \left(\frac{l}{\lambda}\right)^2 i^2 \tag{13}$$

if we have free space where $\sqrt{\mu/\epsilon} = 120\pi$. This is the same power that would be absorbed in a resistor R_0 where $P = i^2 R_0/2$. R_0 is called the radiation resistance of an elementary dipole of length l (where $l \ll \lambda$). The value of R_0 is clearly

$$R_0 = 80\pi^2 \left(\frac{l}{\lambda}\right)^2 \qquad l \ll \lambda \tag{14}$$

11.3   Simple Antennas

The general antenna problem is to compute the fields and impedance of a length of wire which is not short compared to a wavelength. This is a very complicated subject and only a very rudimentary treatment will be given here. The complications arise not only from the messy mathematics but also from the lack of easily handled boundary conditions for the problem. The approach that we shall use here is to *assume* a current distribution in the antenna that is somewhat reasonable (and actually corresponds quite well to experiment). Once we have this as a boundary condition we can add up the effects of the elementary dipoles at large distances.

We shall now consider a length of wire of length $2l$ and compute the fields at large distances. The geometry of the situation is shown in Figure 11.3*a*. The assumption here is that the current in the antenna is symmetric about its center and sinusoidal in z with the current becoming zero at the ends. This assumption sounds reasonable, corresponds quite well to actual measurements, and can be obtained from some rather complicated considerations which will not be treated here.

The current is then given by

$$I = I_m \sin k(l \pm z) \tag{1}$$

where $\pm$ refers to the regions of negative or positive z. Each elementary dipole will make a contribution at large r

$$dE_\theta = Z_0 \, dH_\phi = \frac{jZ_0 kI \, dz}{4\pi r'} e^{-jkr'} \sin \theta' \tag{2}$$

as can be seen from Equation (10), Section 11.2. Here we use

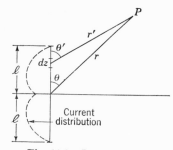

Fig. 11.3a. Long antenna.

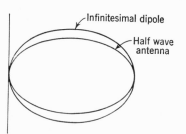

Fig. 11.3b. Radiation from an elementary dipole and from a half-wave dipole. (*By permission from J. C. Slater, "Microwave Transmission," McGraw-Hill Book Company, Inc., New York, 1942.*)

$j\omega m = I_m \, dz$.   If we choose r to be very large, the difference between r and r' will be apparent only in the phase of the radiation at P and not on its magnitude.   For the phase difference (the exponential term) we shall use

$$r' = \sqrt{r^2 + z^2 - 2rz \cos \theta} \approx r - z \cos \theta \qquad (3)$$

In other places in (2), however, we shall use $r = r'$, $\theta = \theta'$ and obtain

$$E_\theta = \frac{jZ_0 k I_m}{4\pi r} e^{-jkr} \left[\int_{-l}^{0} e^{jkz \cos \theta} \sin k(l + z) \, dz \right.$$
$$\left. + \int_{0}^{l} e^{jkz \cos \theta} \sin k(l - z) \, dz \right] \qquad (4)$$

The integrals can be evaluated using no. 937 of B. O. Peirce's "Table of Integrals."   The result is

$$E_\theta = \frac{jZ_0 I_m}{2\pi r} e^{-jkr} \left[\frac{\cos (kl \cos \theta) - \cos kl}{\sin \theta} \right] \qquad (5)$$

The time average of Poynting's vector is

$$\bar{S} = \frac{1}{2}(E_\theta)(H_\phi) = \frac{Z_0 I_m^2}{8\pi^2 r^2} \left[\frac{\cos (kl \cos \theta) - \cos kl}{\sin \theta} \right]^2 \qquad (6)$$

The total power radiated is

$$P = \int_{0}^{\pi} \bar{S} \, 2\pi r^2 \sin \theta \, d\theta = \frac{Z_0 I_m^2}{4\pi} \int_{0}^{\pi} \frac{[\cos (kl \cos \theta) - \cos kl]^2}{\sin \theta} \, d\theta \qquad (7)$$

If $kl = \pi/2$ we have what is known as a half-wave dipole.   A plot of (5) in this case results in the familiar radiation pattern shown in Figure 11.3*b*. This is not very different from the field of an elementary dipole. In this case the radiation resistance measured at the center of the antenna can be found to be 73 ohms. The integration of (7) to obtain this result is quite complicated.

We have not really solved the antenna problem. For instance we have not considered any reactance at the driving point, and there will in general be some. In the case of the half-wave dipole, however, this reactance is not very large. If the antenna is thick, the reactance and resistance do not vary rapidly with frequency. This is important for applications using a wide frequency band. Once the solution of a single dipole has been obtained, many such dipoles can be arranged in a regular pattern to give very high directivity. The properties of such arrays can be computed quite easily by known optical principles. For instance we can obtain a pattern very much like that of an optical grating.

PROBLEM

1. Find the fields from a small loop of wire carrying a current I at frequency ω. What is the radiation resistance of a small loop?

Answer. $R = 5 \times 2^6 \times \pi^4 \times A^2/\lambda^4$.

12

Cavities and Cylindrical Waveguide Modes

Up to this point we have sought solutions to Maxwell's equations in which propagation was an important feature. We now wish to consider cases in which the entire region where the fields will exist is bounded by conducting walls. The results of our investigations will be that such regions, called cavities, act very much like resonant circuits. In particular, if a small loop of wire is coupled into this cavity and excited by an oscillator, very large fields will exist in the cavity at certain frequencies only.

12.1 Rectangular Cavities

There are several approaches that we can use in discussing cavities. One simple technique is to set up a standing-wave pattern in a waveguide such that the basic boundary condition (tangential $E = 0$ at a metallic surface) is still satisfied when the waveguide is shorted by two metal sheets placed across the guide at two places, forming a rectangular cavity. We shall use this method for TE_{10} waves traveling in both the $+z$ and $-z$ directions in a rectangular waveguide. Let the amplitude of H_z for the positively traveling wave be B_1. Then from Section 8.4 we have

$$H_z^+ = B_1 e^{-\gamma z} \cos \frac{\pi x}{a}$$

$$H_x^+ = B_1 \frac{a\gamma}{\pi} e^{-\gamma z} \sin \frac{\pi x}{a} \tag{1}$$

$$E_y^+ = -Z_{TE} H_x^+$$

The negatively traveling wave will have the amplitude of H_z equal to B_2. The components are obtained from (1) by changing the sign of γ

and of Z_{TE}, giving

$$H_z^- = B_2 e^{\gamma z} \cos \frac{\pi x}{a}$$

$$H_x^- = -B_2 \frac{a\gamma}{\pi} e^{\gamma z} \sin \frac{\pi x}{a} \tag{2}$$

$$E_y^- = Z_{\text{TE}} H_x^-$$

where

$$\gamma = j\beta = \frac{2\pi j}{\lambda_0} \left[1 - \left(\frac{\lambda_0}{\lambda_c} \right)^2 \right]^{\frac{1}{2}}$$

and

$$Z_{\text{TE}} = Z_0 \left[1 - \left(\frac{\lambda_0}{\lambda_c} \right)^2 \right]^{-\frac{1}{2}} \tag{3}$$

If we wish to combine these two waves so that $E_y = 0$ at $z = 0$ and at $z = c$, we must choose $B_1 = -B_2$ and $\beta = \pi p/c$ so as to make the z dependence of E_y be $\sin \pi p z/c$. Making these substitutions we obtain for the fields, when the two waves are present,

$$H_z = 2jB_2 \cos \frac{\pi x}{a} \sin \frac{\pi p z}{c}$$

$$H_x = -2jB_2 \frac{ap}{c} \sin \frac{\pi x}{a} \cos \frac{\pi p z}{c} \tag{4}$$

$$E_y = 2B_2 \frac{ap}{c} Z_{\text{TE}} \sin \frac{\pi x}{a} \sin \frac{\pi p z}{c}$$

We shall find it convenient to use the value of peak E_y as the amplitude. To this end we choose B_2 so that

$$2B_2 \frac{ap}{c} Z_{\text{TE}} = E_0 \tag{5}$$

Equation (4) then becomes

$$H_z = \frac{jE_0\lambda_0}{2aZ_0} \cos \frac{\pi x}{a} \sin \frac{\pi p z}{c}$$

$$H_x = \frac{-jE_0\lambda_0 p}{2cZ_0} \sin \frac{\pi x}{a} \cos \frac{\pi p z}{c} \tag{6}$$

$$E_y = E_0 \sin \frac{\pi x}{a} \sin \frac{\pi p z}{c}$$

It is seen that E_y is not only zero at $z = 0$ but also when $z = c$ if p is an integer. It should be obvious that we can place conducting walls at $z = 0$ and at $z = c$ so that the boundary condition that tangential $E \to 0$ at the walls will be met. Clearly what we have done is to combine traveling waves to form standing waves. These standing waves can match boundary conditions at a given frequency in a rectangular box if the length of the box is chosen correctly. Conversely, if the length of the box is given, there will exist a frequency such that this pure "mode" can be excited.   Since $\beta = 2\pi/\lambda_g$, the requirement on the length of the box c in the z direction is that

$$c = p \frac{\lambda_g}{2} \tag{7}$$

where p is an integer.

A more general approach is to find solutions to the wave equation that will match the boundary conditions imposed by the cavity.   Just as in the case of waves in a waveguide, it is convenient to divide the possible solutions into two types, TE and TM, depending on whether E_z or H_z is absent in the solution.   We can use the same method of separation of variables and the relation derived in Section 8.1 between H_z and $\mathbf{H}_t$ in a TE mode and between E_z and $\mathbf{E}_t$ in a TM mode still holds.   Thus $\mathbf{H}_t = \text{grad } V$ where $V = 1/k_z{}^2(\partial H_z/\partial z)$.   If we work only with imaginary $\gamma(= j\beta)$ the z dependence of the fields will be, since we seek standing waves,

$$Z(z) = \begin{Bmatrix} \sin \\ \cos \end{Bmatrix} \beta z \tag{8}$$

If shorting plates are to be placed p half-guide wavelengths apart, it is clear that we must choose $\beta = \pi p/c$.   In a TE mode the solution for H_z must be chosen so that $\partial H_z/\partial n \to 0$ at the side walls of the cavity:

$$H_z = B \cos \frac{\pi l x}{a} \cos \frac{\pi m y}{b} \begin{Bmatrix} \sin \\ \cos \end{Bmatrix} \frac{\pi p}{c} z \tag{9}$$

We must choose $\sin \pi p z/c$ rather than $\cos \pi p z/c$ since this will insure that there is no normal H at the end plates at $z = 0$ and $z = c$. This is equivalent to the boundary condition that tangential E vanish, for if there were a normal H, Faraday's law would require that $\oint \mathbf{E} \cdot d\mathbf{l} = -j\omega\mu \int_S H_n \, da \neq 0$, where the contour of integration for the line integral is at the surface of the metal wall.   This implies a tangential E; hence there must be no normal H.   The other two components of H can be obtained by taking the gradient of V where

$$V = \frac{1}{k_z{}^2} \frac{\partial H_z}{\partial z} \tag{10}$$

We obtain

$$H_z = B \cos \frac{\pi l x}{a} \cos \frac{\pi m y}{b} \sin \frac{\pi p z}{c}$$

$$H_x = \frac{-B}{k_z{}^2} \frac{\pi l}{a} \frac{\pi p}{c} \sin \frac{\pi l x}{a} \cos \frac{\pi m y}{b} \cos \frac{\pi p z}{c} \tag{11}$$

$$H_y = \frac{-B}{k_z{}^2} \frac{\pi m}{b} \frac{\pi p}{c} \cos \frac{\pi l x}{a} \sin \frac{\pi m y}{b} \cos \frac{\pi p z}{c}$$

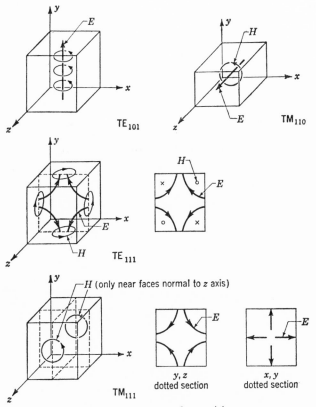

Fig. 12.1a. Rectangular cavities.

The components of $\mathbf{E}$ can be obtained from $\nabla \times \mathbf{H} = j\omega\epsilon\mathbf{E}$ giving

$$E_x = \frac{j\omega\mu B}{k_z^2} \frac{\pi m}{b} \cos \frac{\pi l x}{a} \sin \frac{\pi m y}{b} \sin \frac{\pi p z}{c}$$

$$E_y = \frac{-j\omega\mu B}{k_z^2} \frac{\pi l}{a} \sin \frac{\pi l x}{a} \cos \frac{\pi m y}{b} \sin \frac{\pi p z}{c} \qquad (12)$$

where

$$k_z^2 = \left(\frac{\pi l}{a}\right)^2 + \left(\frac{\pi m}{b}\right)^2$$

A similar calculation for TM modes gives

$$E_z = A \sin \frac{\pi l x}{a} \sin \frac{\pi m y}{b} \cos \frac{\pi p z}{c}$$

$$E_x = -\frac{A}{k_z^2} \frac{\pi p}{c} \frac{\pi l}{a} \cos \frac{\pi l x}{a} \sin \frac{\pi m y}{b} \sin \frac{\pi p z}{c} \qquad (13)$$

$$E_y = -\frac{A}{k_z^2} \frac{\pi p}{c} \frac{\pi m}{b} \sin \frac{\pi l x}{a} \cos \frac{\pi m y}{b} \sin \frac{\pi p z}{c}$$

$$H_x = \frac{j\omega\epsilon A}{k_z{}^2} \frac{\pi m}{b} \sin\frac{\pi lx}{a} \cos\frac{\pi my}{b} \cos\frac{\pi pz}{c}$$

$$H_y = \frac{-j\omega\epsilon A}{k_z{}^2} \frac{\pi l}{a} \cos\frac{\pi lx}{a} \sin\frac{\pi my}{b} \cos\frac{\pi pz}{c}$$

(14)

Here we see that the choice of $\cos\frac{\pi pz}{c}$ for the z dependence of E_z leads to a solution in which tangential E is 0 at $x = 0$ and a; $y = 0$ and b; and $z = 0$ and c. The phase of the H field is 90 degrees out of phase with the electric field, as shown by the presence of the j in the H components. Except for this factor of j, the absolute value of the ratio of E_t to H_t is Z_{TM} or Z_{TE}. If we inspect the E field, it is evident that the H field must be shifted 90 degrees from its position with respect to the E field in a traveling wave. The cavity can be constructed by placing conducting walls across the waveguide carrying this standing wave by inspection and applying the boundary condition that tangential E must be zero at the walls, or $dH_z/dn = 0$ at the walls. Some problems at the end of this chapter will give practice in this technique. After a little practice we can write the field components directly from the traveling-wave solutions.

Since the relation between γ and k_z still holds

$$\gamma^2 = k_z{}^2 - \left(\frac{2\pi}{\lambda_0}\right)^2 = -\beta^2 = -\left(\frac{\pi p}{c}\right)^2 \tag{15}$$

we have

$$\left(\frac{\pi l}{a}\right)^2 + \left(\frac{\pi m}{b}\right)^2 - \left(\frac{2\pi}{\lambda_0}\right)^2 = -\left(\frac{\pi p}{c}\right)^2 \tag{16}$$

The free space wavelength λ_0 corresponding to the resonant frequency is then

$$\lambda_0 = \frac{2}{\sqrt{(l/a)^2 + (m/b)^2 + (p/c)^2}} \tag{17}$$

This corresponds to the resonant frequency of a cavity operating in either a TM or TE mode. It is clear from the method of derivation of the transverse components from the longitudinal that E_z and H_z cannot both vanish. Thus for a TE wave we may choose l or $m = 0$, but not $p = 0$. Since k_z must not vanish we cannot let both l and $m = 0$ in either TE or TM modes. For a TM wave neither l nor m may be zero, but p may be zero.

The nomenclature for a given mode in a cavity is TE_{lmp} or TM_{lmp} where l, m, and p are the number of half-wave variations of the components in the x, y, and z directions. If $p = 0$, this corresponds to operating the cavity by setting up a standing-wave pattern using waveguide modes operating just at cutoff so that $\lambda_g \to \infty$.

Some modes with different designations may have the same resonant frequency and field configuration if the cavity is rotated 90 degrees about one of the coordinate axes.   Thus the TM_{110} mode is essentially the same as the TE_{101} mode if we rotate the cavity 90 degrees about the x axis and interchange the values of a and c.   Some modes are degenerate, i.e., have the same frequency but different field configurations—for instance λ_0 for both TE_{111} and TM_{111} are the same but the fields are different.

12.2 Q of a Cavity

The Q of an inductance or capacitance is a measure of its ability to act as a pure reactance.   In this section we shall only consider cases where $Q = 10$ or more.   In any real case there will be dielectric or ohmic losses that will cause a small energy loss every time energy is stored in the reactance.   The standard lumped-circuit definition of Q is

$$Q = \frac{R_{sh}}{Z_0} = \frac{Z_0}{R_s} \qquad (1)$$

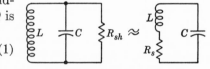

Fig. 12.2a. Resonant circuits.

where R_{sh} is the equivalent shunt resistance and R_s the equivalent series resistance. Z_0 is the reactance at the operating frequency, ωL for an inductance or $1/\omega C$ for a capacitor.

Frequently we speak of the Q of a resonant circuit, in which case $\omega(= \omega_0)$ is the resonance frequency, Z_0 is the reactance of one of the branches at resonance which is $\sqrt{L/C}$ ohms, and the losses are those of both the inductor and the capacitor.   For a coil in series with a small resistance R_s we have

$$Q = \frac{\omega_0 L}{R_s} \qquad (2)$$

Multiplying top and bottom by $\frac{1}{2}I_0^2$, where I_0 is the peak current through the coil and resistance, we have

$$Q = \omega \frac{\frac{1}{2}LI_0^2}{\frac{1}{2}I_0^2 R} = \omega_0 \frac{\text{(peak stored energy)}}{\text{(watts lost)}} \qquad (3)$$

This more general definition is useful for cavities.   Here we shall abbreviate "peak stored energy" as U and watts as W. U can be calculated either when the energy is all stored in the electric fields (and the magnetic field is zero) or 90 degrees later in time when all the energy is in the magnetic field:

$$U = \int_V \frac{\epsilon E_m^2}{2}\,dv \quad \text{or} \quad \int_V \frac{\mu H_m^2}{2}\,dv \qquad (4)$$

E_m and H_m are the maximum values of E or H.   If there are no dielectric losses, the losses will all be due to ohmic losses in the conducting walls of the cavity:

$$W = \int_S \frac{|H_t|^2 R_s}{2}\, da \tag{5}$$

where H_t, the absolute value of tangential H, is numerically equal to the surface current and $R_s = 1/\sigma\delta$, the surface resistivity.   The integral in (5) is over the whole inside surface of the cavity.

It can easily be shown that the general definition of Q is consistent with the following law of reduction of the stored energy U of a freely oscillating cavity:

$$U = U_0 e^{-\omega t/Q} \tag{6}$$

and the corresponding reduction of one of the field components

$$F = F_0 e^{-\omega t/2Q} \tag{7}$$

The Q of a cavity is a dimensionless number but will, in general, vary with the square root of the resonant wavelength as the cavity size is scaled up or down.   Using (4) and (5) and remembering that $R_s = 1/\sigma\delta$ and $\delta = \sqrt{2/\omega\mu\sigma}$ we have

$$Q = \omega\mu\sigma\delta \frac{\int_V H^2\, dv}{\int_S H^2\, da} = \frac{\lambda}{\delta} \frac{2}{\lambda} \frac{\int_V H^2\, dv}{\int_S H^2\, da} \tag{8}$$

$$Q \frac{\delta}{\lambda} = \frac{2}{\lambda} \frac{\int_V H^2\, dv}{\int_S H^2\, da} \tag{9}$$

This expression is independent of the size of the cavity and is called the form factor.   Since the magnetic field will be in general a maximum at the walls and the spatial distribution of H can be approximated by a cosine wave, the form factor can be approximated as

$$Q \frac{\delta}{\lambda} \approx \frac{2}{\lambda} \frac{(\text{mean of } H^2 \text{ over the volume} \times \text{volume})}{(\text{mean of } H^2 \text{ over the surface} \times \text{surface})} \tag{10}$$

or

$$F = Q \frac{\delta}{\lambda} \approx \frac{V}{\lambda S} \tag{11}$$

This is quite approximate and may give a low value of F.   We see that highly reentrant cavities will have a poor V/S ratio and will be expected to have low F.   Spheres, cylinders having a length about equal to their diameter, cubes, etc., will have high F.   In such cases F will be about 0.2 or so.

As an example we shall compute the Q of a rectangular cavity operating in the TE_{101} mode. The field components were calculated in Section 12.1 and are

$$H_z = \frac{jE_0\lambda}{2aZ_0} \sin\frac{\pi z}{c} \cos\frac{\pi x}{a}$$

$$H_x = -\frac{jE_0\lambda}{2cZ_0} \cos\frac{\pi z}{c} \sin\frac{\pi x}{a} \tag{12}$$

$$E_y = E_0 \sin\frac{\pi z}{c} \sin\frac{\pi x}{a}$$

We note that the magnetic field is 90 degrees out of time phase with the electric field, as shown by the j in the expression for H. The peak stored energy can be obtained from

$$U = \int_0^c \int_0^b \int_0^a \frac{\epsilon_0 E_0^2}{2} \sin^2\frac{\pi z}{c} \sin^2\frac{\pi x}{a}\, dx\, dy\, dz = \frac{\epsilon_0 E_0^2 abc}{8} \tag{13}$$

The watts lost on the side walls are

$$W_{\text{sides}} = \frac{E_0^2\lambda^2 R_s}{8Z_0^2}\left(\frac{bc}{a^2} + \frac{ab}{c^2}\right) \tag{14}$$

The power lost on the top and bottom is

$$W_{\text{top and bottom}} = \frac{E_0^2\lambda^2 R_s}{8Z_0^2}\left(\frac{c}{2a} + \frac{a}{2c}\right) \tag{15}$$

Since $\lambda = 2/\sqrt{(1/a^2) + (1/c^2)}$, Q becomes

$$Q = \frac{\pi Z_0}{4R_s}\left[\frac{(a^2 + c^2)^{3/2}}{a^3 + c^3 + (ac/2b)(a^2 + c^2)}\right] \tag{16}$$

If $a = b = c$, as in a cube,

$$Q = \frac{Z_0}{R_s}\frac{\pi}{4}\frac{2^{3/2}}{3} = 0.74\frac{Z_0}{R_s} \tag{17}$$

To compute the form factor we let

$$Q = \frac{Z_0}{R_s}G$$

After some algebra it can be shown that $Z_0/R_s = \lambda/(\delta\pi)$ so that $G = \pi F$ where F is the form factor in (11) above. In this case $F = 0.236$, twice what the approximate formula (11) for F would give. If we let $b \to \infty$ and $a = c$, it can easily be shown that $F = 0.354$. Later we shall compare this with a corresponding cylindrical cavity.

For a cubical cavity constructed of copper operating at 1,000 mc, we have $R_s = 8.3 \times 10^{-3}$ at 1,000 mc and $Q = 33,600$. Here $\lambda = \sqrt{2}a$, $\lambda = 30$ cm, so $a = 21.2$ cm $= 8.4$ in. In practice, a poorly constructed box would have a Q about half that computed, and a carefully constructed box with polished walls and compression fits made with the use of liquid air might have 85 per cent or more of the computed Q.

12.3 Other Types of Cavities

We can determine the resonant frequencies of spherical cavities from the information given in Chapter 11. The solutions given in Equation (19), Section 11.1, are already standing waves in r. Only $j_l(\omega r/c)$ can occur since n_l goes to ∞ at $r = 0$. The resonant frequencies are obtained by requiring that tangential E or normal H be zero at $r = a$.

The above discussion of cavities is suitable for simple geometric shapes whose boundaries can be easily described in the various coordi-

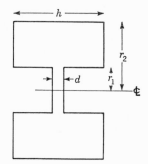

Fig. 12.3a. Microwave cavity.

nate systems (cylindrical cavities will be discussed later in this chapter). Other shapes have sharp resonances but are usually difficult to handle mathematically. One other type used in microwave and particle accelerator work can be approximately handled by lumped-circuit analysis.

An example is shown in Figure 12.3a. If d is small compared to the other dimensions, the center section acts very much as a condenser and the outside part as an inductance. Neglecting fringing fields

$$C = \frac{\epsilon_0 A}{d} = \frac{\epsilon_0 \pi r_1^2}{d} \tag{1}$$

$$L = \frac{1}{\frac{1}{2}I^2} \int_{r_1}^{r_2} \frac{\mu_0 H^2}{2}\, dv = \frac{1}{\frac{1}{2}I^2} \int_{r_1}^{r_2} \frac{\mu_0 I^2}{2(2\pi r)^2}\, 2\pi r h\, dr = \frac{\mu_0 h}{2\pi} \log \frac{r_2}{r_1} \tag{2}$$

The resonant frequency of this "classical" mode is obtained from $\omega^2 = 1/LC$. The surface current J_s at the various surfaces outside the condenser section can be obtained by noting that

$$J_s 2\pi r = I \tag{3}$$

where I is the total current flowing. The peak stored energy is $\frac{1}{2}LI^2$ and the Q of this cavity is

$$Q = \omega \frac{\frac{1}{2}LI^2}{\int_{r_1}^{r_2} J_s^2 R_s 2\pi r \, dr + (hI^2 R_s/4\pi)(1/r_1 + 1/r_2)} \tag{4}$$

This expression can be easily evaluated, giving

$$Q \frac{\delta}{\lambda} = F = \frac{h}{\lambda} \frac{\log (r_2/r_1)}{\log (r_2/r_1) + (h/2)(1/r_1 + 1/r_2)} \tag{5}$$

Here we have neglected any magnetic fields stored in the condenser section and there will be some because of the displacement current in the condenser. Likewise the ohmic losses of the surface currents charging up the condenser in the condenser section itself are omitted. These give small correction terms. In addition the fringing field of the condenser has been neglected—this will be a good approximation if d is small.

The above analysis is quite accurate as long as d is small and none of the other dimensions of the cavity is much larger than $\lambda/8$. If $r_2 - r_1$ approaches a quarter of a wavelength, the inductive section becomes similar to a shorted quarter-wave transmission line and more advanced techniques must be used to treat this problem. These "parallel plate radial transmission lines" are treated extensively in Ramo and Whinnery (Reference 5).

12.4 Propagation in Cylindrical Waveguides

We shall treat this subject in a manner very similar to that used for rectangular waveguides. We have already shown that in cylindrical coordinates the components of a wave traveling in the z direction can be derived from the longitudinal component; i.e., H_z in a TE wave and E_z in a TM wave. The boundary condition will be $E_z = 0$ at $r = a$ in a TM wave and $\partial H_z/\partial r = 0$ at $r = a$ for a TE wave where a is the radius of the waveguide. The transverse components of $\mathbf{E}$ in a TM wave are obtained by taking the r and θ components of the gradient of $V = 1/k^2(\partial E_z/\partial z)$ where k will be found later from the boundary condition. We shall now obtain E_z from the z component of the wave equation

$$\nabla^2(E_z) + \frac{\omega^2}{c^2} E_z = 0 \tag{1}$$

This can be rewritten as

$$\frac{1}{E_z} \nabla_{r\theta}^2(E_z) + \frac{1}{E_z} \frac{\partial^2 E_z}{\partial z^2} + \frac{\omega^2}{c^2} = 0 \tag{2}$$

where $\nabla_{r\theta}^2$ are those parts of the scalar Laplacian that have to do with differentiation with respect to r and θ. If we let $E_z = R(r)\Theta(\theta)Z(z)$, the first term of (2) is a function of r and θ but not of z and the second two terms are a function of z alone. For (2) to hold we must choose the last two terms to be equal to a constant, which we will here take to be k^2. The equation for $Z(z)$ is thus

$$\frac{d^2 Z}{dz^2} = \left(k^2 - \frac{\omega^2}{c^2} \right) Z = \gamma^2 Z \tag{3}$$

Equation (2) then becomes

$$\frac{r}{R} \frac{\partial}{\partial r} \left(r \frac{\partial R}{\partial r} \right) + \frac{1}{\Theta} \frac{d^2\Theta}{d\theta^2} + r^2 k^2 = 0 \tag{4}$$

The first and last terms together are a function of r alone and the second term is a function of θ alone. Placing the second term equal to $-n^2$ we obtain

$$\frac{d^2\Theta}{d\theta^2} = -n^2\Theta \tag{5}$$

and

$$r \frac{d}{dr} \left(r \frac{dR}{dr} \right) + (k^2 r^2 - n^2)R = 0 \tag{6}$$

The solutions of (3) and (5) are exponential and trigonometric functions. Equation (6) is Bessel's equation, the solutions of which are $J_n(kr)$ (Bessel's function) and $N_n(kr)$ (Neumann's function). These functions are both oscillatory with gradually changing phase and decreasing amplitude with increasing argument. $N_n(kr)$ goes to infinity at $r = 0$ and so cannot be used in problems where the origin is not excluded. The solution for E_z in a cylindrical waveguide is thus:

$$E_z = J_n(kr) \begin{Bmatrix} \sin \\ \cos \end{Bmatrix} n\theta \, e^{\pm\gamma z} \tag{7}$$

A similar solution holds for H_z in a TE wave. For propagation γ must be imaginary where

$$\gamma^2 = k^2 - \frac{\omega^2}{c^2} \tag{8}$$

Just as in Chapter 8, this can be rewritten as

$$\frac{1}{\lambda_g{}^2} = \frac{1}{\lambda_0{}^2} - \frac{1}{\lambda_c{}^2} \tag{9}$$

where λ_g is the guide wavelength, λ_0 the free-space wavelength, and $k = 2\pi/\lambda_c$, λ_c being the cutoff wavelength. The determination of k results from the boundary condition $E_z = 0$ at $r = a$ for a TM wave, implying $J_n(ka) = 0$ and $\partial H_z/\partial r = 0$ for a TE wave implying $J'_n(ka) = 0$. Here J'_n is the derivative of J_n with respect to its argument. If p_{nl} is the lth root of J_n, this means that for a TM wave k_{nl} is determined from

$$k_{nl} = \frac{p_{nl}}{a} \tag{10}$$

where we now add the subscripts n and l to k since each choice of n and l will in general give a different value of k. The subscript n must of course be an integer since increasing θ by 2π must return E_z to the same value. The subscript l is by definition an integer. For a TE wave we must choose

$$k_{nl} = \frac{p'_{nl}}{a} \tag{11}$$

where p'_{nl} is the lth root of $J'_n(x)$. Some values of p_{nl} and p'_{nl} are given in Tables 1 and 2.

Table 1.
For TM Modes, p_{nl}

l \ n	0	1	2	3
1	2.40	3.83	5.14	6.38
2	5.52	7.02	8.42	9.76
3	8.65	10.17	11.62	13.02

Table 2.
For TE Modes, p'_{nl}

l \ n	0	1	2	3
1	3.83	1.84	3.05	4.20
2	7.02	5.33	6.71	8.02
3	10.17	8.54	9.97	11.35

The modes of a cylindrical waveguide are referred to by two subscripts n, l, as TE_{nl} and TM_{nl}.   Here n is the number of circumferential variations and l is the number of radial variations.   The general solution for TM modes is

$$E_z = J_n(kr) \cos n\theta \, e^{-\gamma z}$$

$$E_r = -\frac{\gamma}{k} J'_n(kr) \cos n\theta \, e^{-\gamma z}$$

$$E_\theta = \frac{\gamma n}{rk^2} J_n(kr) \sin n\theta \, e^{-\gamma z} \tag{12}$$

$$H_r = -\frac{j\omega\epsilon n}{rk^2} J_n(kr) \sin n\theta \, e^{-\gamma z}$$

$$H_\theta = \frac{-j\omega\epsilon}{k} J'_n(kr) \cos n\theta \, e^{-\gamma z}$$

In (12) it should be noted that

$$\frac{E_r}{H_\theta} = \frac{-E_\theta}{H_r} = Z_0 \sqrt{1 - \left(\frac{\lambda_0}{\lambda_c}\right)^2} = \frac{\gamma}{j\omega\epsilon} = Z_{TM} \tag{13}$$

which is easily derived from Ampere's law.

For TM waves $k = 2\pi/\lambda_c = p/a$.   In the above, for simplicity, we have used k instead of k_{nl} and p instead of p_{nl}.

The solutions for TE modes are:

$$H_z = J_n(kr) \cos n\theta \, e^{-\gamma z}$$

$$H_r = -\frac{\gamma}{k} J'_n(kr) \cos n\theta \, e^{-\gamma z}$$

$$H_\theta = \frac{\gamma n}{rk^2} J_n(kr) \sin n\theta \, e^{-\gamma z} \tag{14}$$

$$E_r = \frac{j\omega\mu n}{rk^2} J_n(kr) \sin n\theta \, e^{-\gamma z}$$

$$E_\theta = \frac{j\omega\mu}{k} J'_n(kr) \cos n\theta \, e^{-\gamma z}$$

As before

$$\frac{E_r}{H_\theta} = \frac{-E_\theta}{H_r} = \frac{j\omega\mu}{\gamma} = Z_0 \frac{1}{\sqrt{1 - (\lambda_0/\lambda_c)^2}} = Z_{TE} \tag{15}$$

Here k is written for k_{nl} where $k_{nl} = p'_{nl}/a$ and p'_{nl} is the lth root of $J'_n(x) = 0$.

As in rectangular waveguides, one of the modes has a longest λ_c for a given a.   From Tables 1 and 2 we see that the smallest p_{nl} or p'_{nl} is $p'_{11} = 1.84$, giving $\lambda_c = 3.41a$ for TE_{11} waves.   As we might expect,

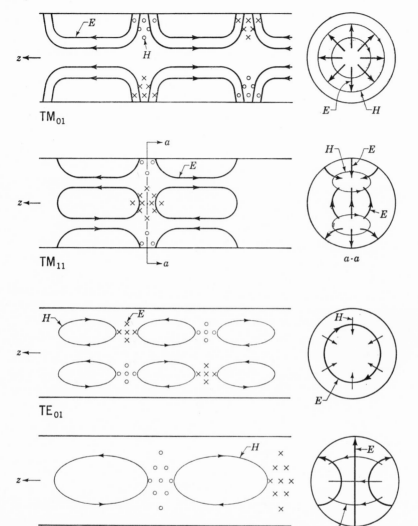

Fig. 12.4a. Cylindrical waveguide modes.

this mode is quite similar to the TE_{10} mode in rectangular waveguides.
Cutoff wavelengths for the various modes are

Mode	TM_{01}	TM_{02}	TM_{11}	TE_{01}	TE_{11}
λ_c	$2.61a$	$1.14a$	$1.64a$	$1.64a$	$3.41a$

Sketches of TM_{01}, TM_{11}, TE_{01}, and TE_{11} are given in Figure 12.4a.

12.5   Waveguide Modes in Coaxial Lines

It is of interest at this time to discuss higher order waves that can be propagated in coaxial structures.   If the inner conductor has a radius r_i and the outer conductor a radius r_0, the solution which we must use will include the Neumann functions $N_n(kr)$ since the axis is excluded and the infinity that occurs is no longer bothersome.   The general radial solution for E_z will be for TM waves

$$R(r) = A_n J_n(kr) + B_n N_n(kr) \tag{1}$$

Here E_z must go to zero at $r = r_i$ and $r = r_0$, and we have

$$A_n J_n(kr_i) + B_n N_n(kr_i) = 0 \tag{2}$$
$$A_n J_n(kr_0) + B_n N_n(kr_0) = 0 \tag{3}$$

or

$$\frac{N_n(kr_i)}{J_n(kr_i)} = \frac{N_n(kr_0)}{J_n(kr_0)} = -\frac{A_n}{B_n} \tag{4}$$

For TE waves we must have $\partial H_z/dr \to 0$ at $r = r_i$ and $r = r_0$ and we have

$$\frac{N_n'(kr_i)}{J_n'(kr_i)} = \frac{N_n'(kr_0)}{J_n'(kr_0)} \tag{5}$$

Solutions of (4) and (5), exhibited in Ramo and Whinnery (see Reference 5), can be obtained as a function of r_0/r_i by numerical methods. The longest λ_c occurs in a TE wave with one circumferential variation, corresponding to a TE_{10} mode in a rectangular waveguide.   For this mode, over quite a large range of r_0/r_i, we have

$$\lambda_c \approx \frac{2\pi(r_0 + r_i)}{2} \approx \text{the average circumference} \tag{6}$$

Thus we may expect waveguide modes to propagate in a coax line at wavelengths shorter than the average circumference.   This is a limitation on the size of coax lines that can be used at very high frequencies, since we usually use a coax line in the TEM mode and cannot tolerate the presence of any other mode.

12.6   Cylindrical Cavities

Cylindrical cavity modes are used more than rectangular cavity modes because of the ease of construction and better efficiency.   Cylindrical cavities are described by three subscripts, the first describing the number of θ variations, the second the number of r variations, and the third the number of z variations.   Thus a TM_{010} mode is a TM_{01} waveguide mode being propagated exactly at cutoff. E is only in the z direction and lines of E are strong in the center and zero at the side wall. There is only H_θ, lines of H_θ surrounding the displacement current in the middle. None of the field components varies with θ and current flow is in the z direction on the side wall and in the r direction on the top and bottom. Clearly we have

$$E_z = E_0 J_0(kr) \tag{1}$$

where $ka = p_{01} = 2.40$ fixes k. The resonant wavelength is then

$$\lambda_0 = \frac{2\pi}{k} = \frac{2\pi a}{p_{01}} = 2.61a \tag{2}$$

Here H_θ is easily found from $\nabla \times \mathbf{E} = -j\omega\mu\mathbf{H}$. In this case $\lambda_g = \infty$, $\lambda_0 = \lambda_c$ and $k = \omega/c$. Since $J_0'(x) = -J_1(x)$ we obtain

$$H_\theta = j\frac{E_0}{Z_0} J_1(kr) \tag{3}$$

By methods similar to those used in the cubical cavity we obtain

$$Q = \frac{Z_0}{R_s} \frac{p_{01}}{2[(a/L) + 1]} \tag{4}$$

Here maximum Q occurs for $L \rightarrow \infty$ and the form factor $F = Q(\delta/\lambda)$ approaches 0.383. This is to be compared with $F = 0.354$ for a very

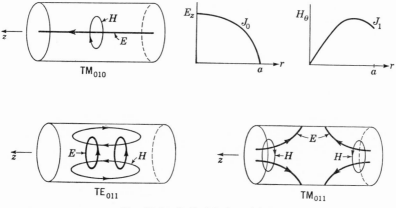

Fig. 12.6a. Cylindrical cavities.

similar TE_{101} rectangular cavity mode of long length. Distorting this cavity leads to the "classical mode" treated in Section 2.3.

Another interesting cylindrical mode is the TE_{011} mode. In this mode only E_θ occurs having a $J_1(kr)$ distribution, with H lines coming up through the center and returning down in the z direction by the side wall so as to surround the E lines.   Here current in the side walls and the ends flows *only* in the θ direction and there is no current flowing between the end plates and the side wall.   This mode is thus well adapted to use in a tunable cavity wavemeter, since good contact need not be made between a movable plunger at one end and the side wall. In this mode the resonant wavelength does, of course, depend on the length of the cylinder.

We shall now derive a general formula for the resonant frequency of a cylindrical cavity of length L and radius a.   Since $k = p/a = 2\pi/\lambda_c$ and $q\lambda_g/2 = L$ we have

$$\lambda_c = \frac{2\pi a}{p} \quad \text{and} \quad \lambda_g = \frac{2L}{q} \tag{5}$$

However, we still have

$$\frac{1}{\lambda_g{}^2} = \frac{1}{\lambda_0{}^2} - \frac{1}{\lambda_c{}^2} \tag{6}$$

Substituting (5) into (6) we obtain

$$\lambda_0 = \frac{2L}{\sqrt{q^2 + [(p/\pi)(L/a)]^2}} \tag{7}$$

Here q is the number of half-wave variations in the z direction and p is p_{nl} for TM modes and p'_{nl} for TE modes.   Since $J'_0(x) = -J_1(x)$ we should note that $p_{11} = p'_{01}$, so that TM_{11q} modes have the same resonant wavelength as TE_{01q} modes.   Choosing $q = 0$ corresponds to operating a waveguide exactly at cutoff since $L = q\lambda_g/2$, and $\lambda_g = \infty$ at cutoff.   We can see that boundary conditions for a cavity can be met with $n = 0, 1, 2, \ldots$; $l = 1, 2, 3, \ldots (l \neq 0)$, for either TM or TE modes; q can be $0, 1, 2, \ldots$ for TM modes, but $q = 1, 2, 3, \ldots (q \neq 0)$ for TE modes.

12.7   Coupling to Cavities

A practical problem of considerable importance is the proper design of coupling loops for coupling energy into a given cavity mode. The details of course depend on the actual problem.   We shall discuss here a problem which will demonstrate some of the methods that are useful.

At high frequencies cavities are often used to replace simple LC resonant circuits in Class A or Class C vacuum-tube amplifiers.   As an example of this we shall discuss the use of a shorted quarter-wave coaxial line for the plate load of an amplifier.   The output power is to be delivered to a matched coaxial transmission line (typically operating at an impedance level of 50 ohms). Here we shall assume that the Q of the cavity is large enough so that losses in the cavity walls and any dielectric materials present are small compared to the power delivered to the load. The characteristics of the vacuum tube will determine the proper impedance for the plate circuit. The cavity must present this impedance to the plate and we wish to know how to design the coupling loops to obtain this desired result. Since the plate load will

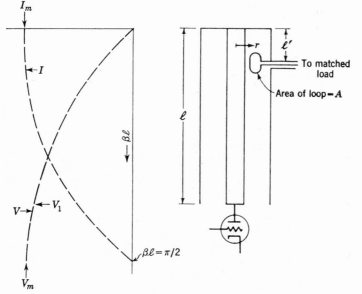

Fig. 12.7a. Coupling to a coaxial cavity.

in general be quite high, the plate is usually connected across the end of the resonator as shown in Figure 12.7a. The length of the cavity will be l, where l is determined by the resonance condition[f]

$$Z_k \tan \beta l = \frac{1}{\omega C} \tag{1}$$

Here C is the output capacity of the vacuum tube. In general, the output coupling loop would be placed at the shorted end of the cavity, but for generality we shall consider a small loop of area A to be at a distance l' from the shorted end of the cavity and at a distance r from the axis of the coaxial line.

In a coaxial line supporting a standing wave at a large standing-wave ratio we have the relation between maximum current I_m and maximum voltage V_m:

$$\frac{V_m}{I_m} = Z_k \qquad (2)$$

where Z_k is the characteristic impedance of the line. Here we do not have V_m at the plate of the vacuum tube, but V_1 where $V_1 = V_m \sin \beta l$ and βl is determined from (1). The voltage induced in the loop V_2 is

$$V_2 = A\dot{\Phi} = \frac{\omega\mu_0 A I_l}{2\pi r} \qquad (3)$$

Here I_l is the current in the line opposite the loop at a distance l' from the shorted end of the cavity. This is equal to $I_m \cos \beta l'$ and (3) becomes

$$V_2 = \frac{\omega\mu_0 A}{2\pi r} I_m \cos \beta l' \qquad (4)$$

The ratio of the loop voltage to the plate voltage is thus

$$\frac{V_2}{V_1} = \frac{\omega\mu_0 A}{2\pi r} I_m \cos \beta l' \frac{1}{I_m Z_k \sin \beta l}$$

or
$$\frac{V_2}{V_1} = \frac{\omega\mu_0 A \cos \beta l'}{2\pi r Z_k \sin \beta l} = \sqrt{\frac{Z_2}{Z_1}} \qquad (5)$$

We have constructed something very much like a transformer where the impedance ratio is given by (5). We can now easily choose A from (5) so as to give the required impedance transformation. If it is desired to include the cavity losses in the above, it is merely necessary to refer these losses to either terminal as a shunt resistance.

If we were to use the above cavity for a klystron or an electron accelerator where V_1 is the gap voltage, the contribution of the cavity losses to the impedance Z_1 would be merely the equivalent shunt resistance of the cavity which is given by Equation (9), Section 10.4, as $R_{sh} = 4QZ_k/\pi$. If the electrons crossing the gap can be analyzed by Fourier-series techniques to give a current component at the cavity frequency, the ratio of this current to the cavity voltage V_2 will give an admittance which represents the effects of the electron beam. If this admittance includes any susceptance it will result in a slight change in the resonant frequency of the cavity. This of course places a limitation on the use of the analogy of a transformer for this cavity system: Z_1 and Z_2 in (5) must be resistances. The operating Q of the cavity will of course be changed by adding a load.

The changes in the above calculation for the case of driving a cavity of a more general type should be clear. The important calculation is that which gives the flux through the coupling loop at a given cavity excitation.   This will give the voltage across the coupling loop and the current through the loop must supply all the power to cavity losses and other loops, accelerated particles, etc.   This will then set the impedance seen at the coupling loop terminals.

In the above we have not considered any effects due to coupling loop inductance.   This can either be tuned out or ignored if it is small. For a given coupling loop and a given mode of cavity excitation we can easily construct an equivalent circuit which consists of a loop inductively coupled with a mutual inductance M to a resonant circuit of known Q and $Z_0 = \sqrt{L/C}$.   Likewise, we can couple into a cavity with a capacitative probe; this is calculable if we can determine the number of E lines terminating on the capacitative probe at a given cavity excitation.

PROBLEMS

1. Consider a cylindrical cavity operating in the TE_{011} mode.   For a fixed resonant wavelength choose the ratio $L/a = \rho$ so that the resonant λ depends accurately only on the volume of the cavity and not on the precise value of either L or a alone.   Show how this can lead to a precise method of measuring the velocity of light c, using the fact that the volume of a cavity can be precisely measured by filling with water and weighing.   Discuss the effect on λ of a small hole halfway up the side of the cavity for coupling in energy. What is the resonant λ for TM_{111} for this cavity?
  Answer. $\rho = 1.16$.

2. Develop a method to measure accurately the velocity of light by constructing a cavity of only approximately known diameter but exactly known length.   Consider using TE_{012} and TE_{021} modes, measuring the resonant frequency of each mode and eliminating the diameter.   (The length can be found by an interferometer.)

3. A series of copper cavities are made of similar shape and are resonated in the same mode but are of various sizes.   By a simple discussion of the general definition of Q, find how the Q of these cavities should vary with their linear dimensions.

4. A cavity having dimensions $a \times b \times c$ resonates at a frequency f_0.   If the x, y, z axes are taken as parallel to the edges having dimensions a, b, c, respectively, this mode is the TE_{101} mode (TE_{10} waves with $c = \lambda_g/2$).   Sketch the fields.   Give another description of this mode by considering the z axis to be parallel to the edges having the dimensions b.   What is the waveguide mode corresponding to this other description?

5. A rectangular cavity $a \times b \times c$ operates in the TM_{211} mode.   Sketch the current flow on the walls.   Where should a small loop of wire be placed so as to couple energy magnetically into the cavity? Compute the field components.

6. A coil c_1 is mounted in a shield can and its Q at frequency ω_1 is measured to be Q_1. Another coil c_2, having a different number of turns but occupying the same space as c_1, replaces c_1 in this shield can and its Q is measured to be Q_2 at a different frequency ω_2. Assuming that *all* the losses in each case arise from eddy currents flowing in the shield can, find the ratio Q_2/Q_1. Assume the frequency to be so high in each case that the skin depth in the shield can is much less than the thickness of the can.

7. Develop the theory of spherical cavities in general. Determine the TE and TM modes that have the lowest resonant frequency and find these resonant frequencies.
Answer. $\lambda = 2.29a$ and $1.4a$.

8. The cavity discussed in Section 12.3 is driven by a small loop of area A at $r = r_2$. Determine the impedance reflected into this loop by the cavity. Find the ratio of the voltage across the capacity section to the voltage across the loop. Develop a method of measuring the Q of this cavity by measuring the impedance presented by this loop. Hint: Consider the equivalent resonant circuit composed of lumped circuit elements.

9. In a cylindrical TM_{010} cavity determine the effect on the resonant frequency of pushing out the wall of the cavity slightly over a small area in the top of the cavity and also on the side of the cavity.

13

Some Topics in Wave Propagation

In this chapter we shall first discuss the reflection and refraction of plane waves when incident on various media. Some insight into the theory of dispersion will be given. The propagation of radio waves as a surface wave over the surface of the earth will be treated, followed by a discussion of propagation in ionized media such as the ionosphere.

13.1 Reflection and Refraction of Plane Waves

We have shown already that in a plane wave only transverse components exist and that $\mathbf{E}$ is perpendicular to $\mathbf{H}$. We have also seen that the relation between $\mathbf{E}$ and $\mathbf{H}$ is $\mathbf{E} = \pm Z\mathbf{H}$, where $Z = \sqrt{\mu/\epsilon}$ (see Section 7.2). The plus sign is used for propagation in the $+z$ direction and the minus sign for propagation in the $-z$ direction. At the boundary between two dielectrics the boundary conditions are evidently

1. Tangential E and H must be continuous.

2. Normal D and B are continuous.

Fig. 13.1a. Boundary conditions between two dielectrics.

We shall now show that the continuity of normal D and B in passing through a boundary follows from the continuity of tangential E and H. If we consider Figure 13.1a and, using Faraday's law, inte-

187

grate around a small contour as shown, we have

$$\int_S \nabla \times \mathbf{E} \cdot \mathbf{n} \, da = \oint \mathbf{E} \cdot d\mathbf{l} = -j\omega \int_S \mathbf{B} \cdot \mathbf{n} \, da \qquad (1)$$

However, since tangential E is continuous the line integrals are the same in each medium; hence the surface integral of normal B is the same in each medium. If the contour is so small that B_n does not change appreciably inside the contour this means that normal B is continuous. A similar treatment of Ampere's law in the case where there is no real current $\mathbf{J}$ flowing in the surface between the two media will show that continuity of tangential H implies the continuity of normal D. Thus continuity of tangential E and H is sufficient to meet

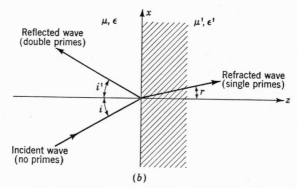

Fig. 13.1b. Plane wave incident on a dielectric.

all the boundary conditions for propagation of waves from one medium to another in those cases where there is no current flowing in the boundary surface.

From experience with optics it is expected that three types of waves must be considered—incident, reflected, and transmitted (or refracted). Assume that the surface of separation between the two media is the plane $z = 0$ and further that the wave normal is in the xz plane. In place of the former propagation exponential, $\exp j\omega(t - z/v)$, we must have a new propagation exponential in which we replace z by some other expression that measures distance along the direction of propagation, since the direction of propagation here is no longer the z direction but those directions indicated in Figure 13.1b. In general distance along any line having direction cosines l, m, n is given by $d = lx + my + nz + \text{constant}$. Since there is no propagation in the y direction, y will not appear. Clearly we must have these propagation exponentials:

Incident: $\exp j\omega \left[t - \dfrac{(x \sin i + z \cos i)}{v} \right]$

Reflected: $\exp j\omega \left[t - \dfrac{(x \sin i' - z \cos i')}{v} \right]$

Transmitted: $\exp j\omega \left[t - \dfrac{(x \sin r + z \cos r)}{v'} \right]$

where $v^2 = 1/\epsilon\mu$, $v'^2 = 1/\epsilon'\mu'$. At $z = 0$ all exponentials must be equal for all x's, for otherwise matching the boundary conditions at one point on the boundary would mean *not* matching them at some other point. This leads to

$$i = i' \qquad \text{the law of reflection}$$

and $\qquad \dfrac{\sin i}{\sin r} = \dfrac{v}{v'} = \dfrac{n'}{n} \qquad$ Snell's law of refraction $\qquad$ (2)

Here we define n, the index of refraction, to be c/v, where c is the velocity of light in vacuum ($c = 1/\sqrt{\epsilon_0\mu_0} = 3 \times 10^8$ m/sec) and $v = 1/\sqrt{\epsilon'\mu'} =$ the phase velocity of light in the medium.

We now consider normal incidence. Choosing a plane polarized incident wave with **E** along the x axis and **H** along the y axis, we have

$$\frac{E_x}{H_y} = Z = \sqrt{\frac{\mu}{\epsilon}} \qquad \text{incident wave}$$

$$\frac{E_x'}{H_y'} = Z' = \sqrt{\frac{\mu'}{\epsilon'}} \qquad \text{transmitted wave} \qquad (3)$$

$$\frac{E_x''}{H_y''} = -Z \qquad \text{reflected wave}$$

The boundary conditions can then be expressed in terms of E:

tangential E (continuous): $E_x + E_x'' = E_x'$

tangential H (continuous): $E_x - E_x'' = \dfrac{Z}{Z'} E_x'$ $\qquad$ (4)

Solving (4) for the ratio E_x''/E_x, we have

$$\frac{E_x''}{E_x} = \frac{Z' - Z}{Z' + Z} = -\frac{H_y''}{H_y} = R \qquad \text{the reflection coefficient} \qquad (5)$$

The ratio of the reflected power to the incident power is thus R^2. At high frequencies most materials have $\mu' = \mu = \mu_0$. Thus Z is inversely proportional to the index of refraction n and

$$R^2 = \frac{(n - n')^2}{(n + n')^2} \qquad (6)$$

For air, $n = 1$ and for glass $n = 1.5$. Thus $R^2 = 0.04$. Note that (6) is unchanged on reversing n and n' and so the same R^2 occurs for a glass to air transition as for an air to glass transition. The application of this to camera lenses which may have five or more components is obvious and has led to the development of coated lenses.

It should be noted that the above analysis is very similar to the analysis of waves traveling on a transmission line. Such an analogy should not be taken too seriously for the physics is in Maxwell's equations, not in some cooked-up analogy. Nevertheless the concept of "impedance of a material" is quite useful, and also has applications in acoustics.

We now consider the general case of arbitrary angles of incidence. Here we must specify the direction of polarization. This is usually taken to be the direction of **E** in electromagnetic phenomena, rather than **H** which is used in some of the older texts on optics. We shall consider two cases: Case 1 in which **E** is perpendicular to the xz plane (and hence parallel to the y axis), or Case 2 where **E** lies in the xz plane (and hence normal to y). In Figure 13.1c the y axis comes out of the paper for a right-handed system of coordinates. We must further choose assumed directions ($+$ or $-$) for **H** in either case—the choice here being that tangential H will be in the same direction at the interface for all waves. The direction of **E** is then chosen by noting that Poynting's vector $\mathbf{S} = \mathbf{E} \times \mathbf{H}$ must lie along the direction of travel of the wave.

Case 1. **E** lies along the y axis. For the assumed directions of **H** in Figure 13.1c, **E**, **E**′ are up and **E**″ down, where "up" is the $+y$ direction. This is normally referred to as "polarized normal to the plane of incidence," for **E** is normal to the plane of incidence—that plane containing the wave normal and the normal to the boundary.

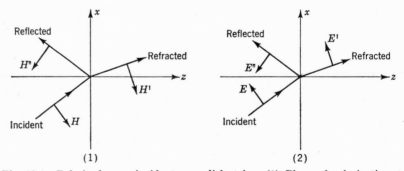

(1)   (2)

Fig. 13.1c. Polarized wave incident on a dielectric.   (1) Plane of polarization $\perp$ to plane of incidence: $E \parallel y$ axis; E, E' up $(+y)$; E'' down $(-y)$.   (2) Plane of polarization $\parallel$ to plane of incidence: $E \perp y$ axis; all H up $(+y)$.

The propagation exponentials are

$$\text{Incident: } \exp j\omega \left[t - \frac{(x \sin i + z \cos i)}{v} \right]$$

$$\text{Refracted: } \exp j\omega \left[t - \frac{(x \sin r + z \cos r)}{v'} \right]$$

$$\text{Reflected: } \exp j\omega \left[t - \frac{(x \sin i - z \cos i)}{v} \right]$$

The boundary conditions give

$$\text{tangential } E: \qquad E - E'' = E' \tag{7}$$
$$\text{tangential } H: (H + H'') \cos i = H' \cos r \tag{8}$$

However, $|H| = E/Z$, $|H''| = E''/Z$, and $|H'| = E'/Z'$, which permits (8) to be rewritten as

$$(E + E'') \frac{\cos i}{Z} = E' \frac{\cos r}{Z'} \tag{9}$$

From (2) we obtain

$$\frac{\sin i}{\sin r} = \sqrt{\frac{\mu' \epsilon'}{\mu \epsilon}} = \frac{\mu'}{\mu} \frac{Z}{Z'} = \frac{n'}{n} \tag{10}$$

Thus (9) becomes

$$E + E'' = E' \frac{\mu}{\mu'} \frac{\tan i}{\tan r} \tag{11}$$

Eliminating E' between (11) and (7) we obtain

$$\frac{E''}{E} = \frac{\mu \tan i - \mu' \tan r}{\mu \tan i + \mu' \tan r} \tag{12}$$

At high frequencies $\mu = \mu' = \mu_0$, so that (12) can be written as

$$\frac{E''}{E} = \frac{\tan i - \tan r}{\tan i + \tan r} = \frac{\sin i \cos r - \cos i \sin r}{\sin i \cos r + \cos i \sin r} \tag{13}$$

or
$$\frac{E''}{E} = \frac{\sin (i - r)}{\sin (i + r)} = R_\perp \tag{14}$$

We can easily show that the ratio of the transmitted amplitude to the incident amplitude is

$$\frac{E'}{E} = \frac{\sin (i + r) - \sin (i - r)}{\sin (i + r)} = T_\perp \tag{15}$$

Case 2. **E** is normal to the y axis. This case is referred to by saying that "**E** lies in the plane of incidence." Here we have presumed that all the **H**'s are in the $+y$ direction (see Figure 13.1c). The boundary conditions give

$$\text{tangential } E\colon (E - E'') \cos i = E' \cos r \qquad (16)$$

$$\text{tangential } H\colon (E + E'') \frac{1}{Z} = \frac{E'}{Z'} \qquad (17)$$

Using (10) to change Z/Z' to $\mu/\mu' \times \sin i/\sin r$ in (17), it is easy to eliminate E' from (16) and (17) to obtain

$$E \left(\frac{\mu}{\mu'} \frac{\sin i}{\sin r} - \frac{\cos r}{\cos i} \right) = E'' \left(\frac{\mu}{\mu'} \frac{\sin i}{\sin r} + \frac{\cos r}{\cos i} \right) \qquad (18)$$

which becomes, after some algebra,

$$\frac{E''}{E} = \frac{\mu \sin i \cos i - \mu' \sin r \cos r}{\mu \sin i \cos i + \mu' \sin r \cos r} \qquad (19)$$

If the frequency is high enough so that $\mu = \mu' = \mu_0$ this can be simplified by using the easily proved expansion

$$\sin (i \pm r) \cos (i \mp r) = \sin i \cos i \pm \sin r \cos r \qquad (20)$$

Using (20), (19) becomes

$$\frac{E''}{E} = \frac{\tan (i - r)}{\tan (i + r)} = R_{\parallel} \qquad (21)$$

Equation (21) contains the basis of Brewster's phenomena, for if $i + r = \pi/2$, which can easily happen, $R_{\parallel} = 0$. If we shine unpolarized light on a glass plate at this angle of incidence (Brewster's angle or the polarizing angle), only light with its electric vector normal to the plane of incidence will be reflected. Brewster's angle is found by requiring that $i + r = \pi/2$ together with Snell's law (10). When $i + r = \pi/2$, $\sin r = \cos i$. Thus, for $i =$ Brewster's angle,

$$\frac{\sin i}{\sin r} = \frac{\sin i}{\cos i} = \tan i = \frac{n'}{n} \qquad (22)$$

For a glass-air interface, with $n'/n = 1.5$, $i = 56°$. When using this method the reflection from the back face must be eliminated.

It can easily be shown that the ratio of the transmitted amplitude to the incident amplitude is

$$\frac{E'}{E} = \frac{\sin (i + r) - \sin (i - r)}{\sin (i + r) \cos (i - r)} = T_{\parallel} \qquad (23)$$

These formulas relating the reflected and transmitted rays to the incident ray in the two cases are called Fresnel's Formulae. The formulas given are for the **E** vector in each case and must be considered

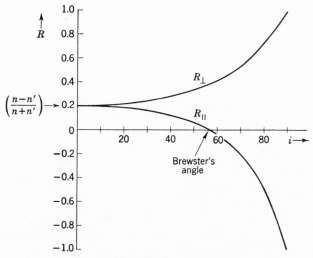

Fig. 13.1d. Reflection coefficients.

in connection with the assumed directions of **E** for the various cases. Some texts use a different convention for the direction of **E**, resulting in a change in sign for T or R.   A plot of $R_\perp$ and $R_\parallel$ is given in Figure 13.1d for the case of light incident from air onto a glass plate with index of refraction equal to 1.5.

13.2   Total Internal Reflection

From Snell's law, Equation (2), Section 13.1, we have the possibility of total internal reflection if n'/n is less than 1.   If we can let $n' = 1$ and $n > 1$, we are considering the case of an incident ray in a dense material such as glass incident on a glass-air interface.   Equation (2), Section 13.1, can be rewritten as

$$\sin r = n \sin i \tag{1}$$

and if $\sin i > 1/n$, $\sin r$ is greater than 1.   The way out of this difficulty is to consider the angle to be complex, writing

$$r = \frac{\pi}{2} + j\beta \tag{2}$$

Then we have

$$\sin r = \cos j\beta = \cosh \beta = n \sin i \tag{3}$$
$$\cos r = - \sin j\beta = -j \sinh \beta = -j \sqrt{n^2 \sin^2 i - 1}$$

The propagation exponent for the refracted wave becomes

$$\exp j\omega \left(t - \frac{x \sin r + z \cos r}{v'} \right) = \exp j\omega \left(\frac{t - x \cosh \beta}{v'} \right)$$

$$\times \exp \left(-\omega \sinh \beta \frac{z}{v'} \right) \quad (4)$$

Since $\cosh \beta > 1$, this wave travels along the interface in the x direction with a velocity less than v', while the amplitude diminishes rapidly with z. Clearly the amplitude will become very small in a distance equal to a wavelength or less in the second medium for values of $n \sin i$ much greater than 1.

It should be noted carefully that this wave is quite different from the type that has been considered up to now, because the surfaces of equal phase (normal to the x axis) are not parallel to the surfaces of equal amplitude (normal to z axis). It is difficult to check the existence of this curious wave by optical methods, but this experiment has been done at microwave frequencies using prisms made of pitch.

13.3   Properties of Dielectrics and Conductors at Various Frequencies

We shall now discuss some of the physical principles governing the behavior of dielectrics and conductors at different frequencies. If we compare the above theory of reflected and refracted waves using the d-c values of μ and ϵ, agreement with experiment is obtained at low frequencies, but operation at microwave and optical frequencies frequently shows strong disagreement. For instance, very pure water is essentially nonconducting and has $K \approx 80$ at low frequencies. At microwave frequencies, however, $K \approx 10$ or 20 for water and it is quite lossy. Likewise a salt solution is a good conductor at low frequencies but seemingly has $\sigma = 0$ at optical frequencies, since such a solution is quite transparent. Thin films of silver are good conductors up through optical frequencies, but become transparent in the ultraviolet region. The discussion of these phenomena follows.

We shall use a crude classical model of the refracting material; namely, that gases and solids are made up of molecules that can be considered as classical oscillators. We treat first the case of a gas where the separation of the oscillators is large enough so that they do not interact with each other. Our model is that of an electron of mass m and charge e bound to the molecule by a Hooke's law force of strength $-kx$. Thus the application of an electric field will cause an electron in a molecule to move a distance x from its equilibrium position, causing a small electric dipole moment to be formed. At very low frequencies the electron will vibrate in phase with the applied force and at very high frequencies will be out of phase with the force. In between we should expect a resonance phenomenon to occur, and a damping term—often due to reradiation of energy—will be added. Of course, quantum mechanics should be used to describe this system; it leads to a model very much like the classical model above. Actually several resonant frequencies will usually occur; the extension to this case shall not be treated here.

The equation of motion of the electron is

$$m\ddot{x} + mg\dot{x} + kx = eE_x \tag{1}$$

where the damping term is written as $mg\dot{x}$, a force proportional to the velocity. If $E_x = Ee^{j\omega t}$ the solution of (1) is

$$x = \frac{(e/m)E}{\omega_0{}^2 - \omega^2 + j\omega g}\, e^{j\omega t} \tag{2}$$

where we have placed $\omega_0{}^2 = k/m$. If we have N electrons of this type per unit volume, the dipole moment per unit volume P is

$$P = \frac{(e^2/m)EN}{\omega_0{}^2 - \omega^2 + jg\omega} \tag{3}$$

Referring to Section 3.2, $P = \epsilon_0 \chi E$ and $K = (1 + \chi)$. Thus

$$K = 1 + \frac{(e^2/m\epsilon_0)N}{\omega_0{}^2 - \omega^2 + jg\omega} \tag{4}$$

At low frequencies K is essentially real, but at higher frequencies a resonance takes place and K becomes complex. This implies that losses will take place even though no conduction current flows. The propagation constant γ will thus have both a real and an imaginary part. Using an absorption coefficient k as well as index of refraction n we can write

$$\gamma = \frac{j\omega}{c}\,(n - jk) \tag{5}$$

and the propagation exponent for a plane wave will be

$$\exp\,(j\omega t - \gamma z) = \exp\left(-\frac{\omega k z}{c}\right) \exp j\omega\left(t - \frac{nz}{c}\right) \tag{6}$$

The complex dielectric coefficient is then

$$K = (n - jk)^2 \tag{7}$$

Since we are discussing gases, K will be near 1; substituting (7) into (4) and expanding we have

$$n - jk = 1 + \frac{1}{2}\frac{(e^2/m\epsilon_0)N}{\omega_0{}^2 - \omega^2 + jg\omega} \tag{8}$$

The real and imaginary parts of (8) are

$$n = 1 + \frac{1}{2}\frac{(e^2/m\epsilon_0)N(\omega_0{}^2 - \omega^2)}{(\omega_0{}^2 - \omega^2)^2 + g^2\omega^2} \tag{9}$$

$$k = \frac{1}{2}\frac{(e^2/m\epsilon_0)Ng\omega}{(\omega_0{}^2 - \omega^2)^2 + g^2\omega^2} \tag{10}$$

If we plot $n - 1$ and k versus ω, we shall obtain the usual resonance curves, as shown in Figure 13.3a. We see that when the real part of the index of refraction changes rapidly there is also an absorption in the same region. It is just such a resonance that places a limit

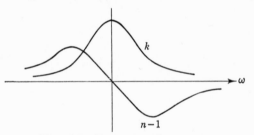

Fig. 13.3a. Resonance phenomena.

on the frequency of long-distance radar. A resonance in water vapor molecules at 1.25 centimeter provides a fairly serious absorption in this region. Another strong absorption at 0.5 centimeter from oxygen together with other higher frequency absorptions makes propagation above 0.5 centimeter difficult. Very strong absorption, due mostly to ozone and nitrogen at very high altitudes, keeps most of the ultraviolet light of the sun from penetration very far in the atmosphere. Another example of this phenomenon occurs in sodium vapor, which has a very strong resonance at 5,890 Angstrom units.

The above discussion is for gases. In solids a similar phenomenon takes place, but here we must include the effect of the neighboring dipoles, as the oscillators are packed much more closely together in a solid. What we want to know is the E from neighboring polarized material. Consider a small sphere to be cut in a dielectric, and compute the field at the center of this sphere (where an oscillating dipole is located) from the polarized material outside this sphere and from the sphere itself. Since the sphere is to be cut out (mathematically) without disturbing the state of polarization of the media, P remains constant, and the field from the uniformly polarized dielectric outside the sphere can be thought of as arising from a surface charge density $\sigma = P_n$, as is made clear in Chapter 3. The surface charge density is thus $-P \cos \theta$ where the polar axis is in the direction of P. The field at the center of the sphere due to this surface charge density was calculated in Chapter 1 to be $P/3\epsilon_0$. Thus we have for the total field at the center

$$E_{\text{total}} = E + \frac{P}{3\epsilon_0} \tag{11}$$

We must now show that the electric field at the center (where a dipole is located) that arises from the material inside the sphere is zero. The potential at the origin of a dipole r distant from the origin is

$$V = \frac{1}{4\pi\epsilon_0} \frac{\mathbf{p} \cdot \mathbf{r}}{r^3} = \frac{p_x x + p_y y + p_z z}{4\pi\epsilon_0 (x^2 + y^2 + z^2)^{3/2}} \tag{12}$$

and the resulting E_z is

$$E_z = -\nabla_z V = -\frac{1}{4\pi\epsilon_0} \left[\frac{p_z}{r^3} - \frac{3(p_x xz + p_y yz + p_z z^2)}{r^5} \right] \tag{13}$$

If there is only p_z, and $p_x = p_y = 0$, $E_z = 0$ if the average of (13) over the sphere is zero. This will in general be true for an isotropic substance whose properties do not vary with direction. In such a substance we have

$$E_z = -\frac{1}{4\pi\epsilon_0} \left(\frac{p_z}{r^3} - \frac{3p_z z^2}{r^5} \right) \tag{14}$$

and, over any spherical surface,

$$\overline{x^2} = \overline{y^2} = \overline{z^2} = \frac{r^2}{3} \tag{15}$$

If (14) and (15) are both true, $E_z = 0$.

Some explanation of (11) is required, for this E_{total} is not the average E inside the dielectric as calculated, for instance, in Chapter 3, but is the field at a typical dipole. We can show in general that the average of the macroscopic E is equal to the average of the microscopic E. If the dielectric material is homogeneous, amorphous, or a cubic crystal, the average field *at a dipole* will in general not be equal to the average field. Equation (11) expresses this difference, which shows up in the integration of the contributions from the dipoles inside the small sphere. As an example, we can show that in a cubic crystal the material inside the sphere contributes nothing to the E at a lattice point. Since the field from the other dipoles varies rapidly with position, moving this dipole a small distance from its normal position would give a real contribution.

A similar statement can be made *on the average* for materials which are isotropic. A fast electron passing through a polarized dielectric would experience the average microscopic or macroscopic field of Chapter 3. A dipole will, in general, experience a different field than the spatial average over the material.

Since $P = \epsilon_0(K - 1)E$, (11) can be rewritten as

$$E_{\text{total}} = E + \frac{P}{3\epsilon_0} = \frac{2 + K}{3} E \qquad (16)$$

We shall now take the effects of the neighboring dipoles into account if we use this new E_{total} instead of E in (3) and (4). This leads to

$$\frac{K - 1}{K + 2} = \frac{1}{3} \frac{N(e^2/m\epsilon_0)}{\omega_0{}^2 - \omega^2 + j\omega g} = \frac{(n - jk)^2 - 1}{(n - jk)^2 + 2} \qquad (17)$$

Here N is the number of oscillators per unit volume, and this will be proportional to the density of the material. This leads to some useful general relations between n or K and the density of a vapor or liquid. If we consider a nonabsorbing substance ($k = 0$) in the optical region, we have from (17) the Lorenz-Lorentz Law:

$$\frac{n^2 - 1}{n^2 + 2} \frac{1}{\rho} = \text{constant} \qquad (18)$$

At low frequencies where K is more proper to use than n, we have the Clausius-Mosotti Law:

$$\frac{K - 1}{K + 2} \frac{1}{\rho} = \text{constant} \qquad (19)$$

We consider now conducting materials. If a current density of J amperes per square meter is caused by N_e electrons per unit volume moving with a velocity v,

$$J = N_e e v \qquad (20)$$

If $E_x = E e^{j\omega t}$, we must use (1) with $k = 0$, or $\omega_0 = 0$. Equation (2) then gives

$$\dot{x} = \frac{(e/m)E j\omega}{j\omega g_e - \omega^2} e^{j\omega t} \qquad (21)$$

and thus $\qquad J = \sigma E = \dfrac{N_e \dfrac{e^2}{m} E j\omega}{j\omega g_e - \omega^2} = \dfrac{N_e e^2}{jm\omega + mg_e} E \qquad (22)$

or $\qquad \sigma = \dfrac{N_e e^2}{mg_e + jm\omega} \left(= \dfrac{N_e e^2}{mg_e} \text{ at } \omega \to 0 \right) \qquad (23)$

Thus the conductivity varies with frequency according to (23). g_e can be determined experimentally at low frequencies by (23).

Referring to Equation (17), Section 7.2, we have (presuming $\mu = \mu_0$ and $\epsilon = K\epsilon_0$)

$$\gamma = \sqrt{j\omega\mu\sigma - \frac{\omega^2}{c^2}K} = j\frac{\omega}{c}\sqrt{K - j\frac{\sigma}{\omega\epsilon_0}} = j\frac{\omega}{c}n \qquad (24)$$

Clearly we must replace K by $K - j\dfrac{\sigma}{\omega\epsilon_0}$ when considering transmission of plane waves in a conducting medium. The result is that when a conducting material containing free (or conduction) as well as bound electrons is considered, we have

$$K - j\frac{\sigma}{\omega\epsilon_0} = (n - jk)^2 = 1 + \frac{N_e(e^2/m\epsilon_0)}{-\omega^2 + j\omega g_e} + \frac{N(e^2/m\epsilon_0)}{\omega_0^2 - \omega^2 + jg\omega} \qquad (25)$$

Here the second term on the right is the result of the motion of the free electrons, which—since they are not bound—give a term like that in (4) with $\omega_0 = 0$. The third term is the contribution from the bound electrons. Equation (25) can be separated into real and imaginary parts, using the d-c value of σ in (23). The results are

$$n^2 - k^2 = 1 - \frac{\sigma_0}{g_e\epsilon_0}\frac{1}{1 + \omega^2/g_e^2} + \frac{N(e^2/m\epsilon_0)(\omega_0^2 - \omega^2)}{(\omega_0^2 - \omega^2)^2 + \omega^2 g^2} \qquad (26)$$

$$2nk = \frac{\sigma_0}{\omega\epsilon_0}\frac{1}{1 + \omega^2/g_e^2} + \frac{N(e^2/m\epsilon_0)\omega g}{(\omega_0^2 - \omega^2)^2 + \omega^2 g^2} \qquad (27)$$

For very low frequencies, $2nk$ becomes very large, but $n^2 - k^2$ does not become large. Thus $n \approx k \approx \sqrt{\sigma/2\epsilon_0\omega}$. At higher frequencies (near the visible light region) the contributions from the free and bound electrons become more complicated. In the far ultraviolet and X-ray regions the free electrons have little effect and metals and insulators react quite similarly to radiation.

If we consider normal incidence from air ($n = 1$) to an absorbing medium ($n' - jk'$), Equation (6), Section 13.1, must be replaced by

$$RR^* = |R|^2 = \frac{(1 - n')^2 + k'^2}{(1 + n')^2 + k'^2} \qquad (28)$$

Since at low frequencies $n' \approx k' \approx \sqrt{\sigma/2\epsilon_0\omega} \gg 1$, (28) becomes, at low frequencies,

$$R^2 = 1 - \frac{2}{n'} \qquad (29)$$

Since n' is large, almost all the energy is reflected and very little is absorbed. We may discover the reason for this by inspecting Poynting's vector in the conducting medium. In general we know that

$$\frac{E}{H} = \frac{j\omega\mu}{\gamma} \qquad (30)$$

Here, from Equation (17), Section 7.2, we have at low frequencies $\gamma = j\omega/c \sqrt{-j\sigma/\epsilon\omega}$. Substituting this into (30) we obtain, assuming $\mu = \mu_0$, $\epsilon = \epsilon_0$,

$$\frac{E}{H} = \sqrt{\frac{\mu_0}{\epsilon_0}} \sqrt{\frac{j\epsilon_0\omega}{\sigma}} = Z_0 \sqrt{\frac{j\epsilon_0\omega}{\sigma}} \qquad (31)$$

This is a very small number and it means that while H in the metal may have a reasonable value, E is very small; thus Poynting's vector is small. The wave does not travel very far into the metal, since from Equation (17), Section 7.2, at low frequencies,

$$\gamma = j\frac{\omega}{c} \sqrt{-j\frac{\sigma}{\epsilon_0\omega}} = \sqrt{j\omega\mu\sigma} = (1+j) \sqrt{\frac{\omega\mu\sigma}{2}} = \frac{1+j}{\delta} \qquad (32)$$

δ here is the familiar skin depth already treated in Chapter 9. A wave incident normally on a good conductor travels only a few skin depths before becoming very small. We can easily show from (30) and (32) that

$$\frac{E}{H} = (1+j)\pi\frac{\delta}{\lambda}Z_0 = (1+j)R_s \qquad (33)$$

where λ is the free-space wavelength.

From the above we see that all good conductors are good reflectors. If the absorption coefficient k is a function of wavelength, as it may be in the visible, (28) shows that those colors that are strongly absorbed are strongly reflected, and a thin film of gold looks blue by transmitted light as the gold color is absorbed and reflected.

It is not difficult, but quite complicated, to calculate the reflection coefficient for a conductor at an arbitrary angle of incidence. The result is that a plane polarized wave in general becomes elliptically polarized. One industrial application of this is in the manufacture of tin-plated steel as used in tin cans. Formerly each sheet was inspected visually for holes in the tin plating. Automatic inspection was obtained by illuminating the sheet with polarized light, observing the reflected light through an arrangement of quarter-wave plates and polarizers so as to give no light when the reflection comes from tin. A hole showing reflection from steel then shows up as a bright spot. A phototube at the observation point causes the faulty region to be marked with paint and rejected.

13.4   Surface Guided Waves

We consider now a new type of wave, the surface wave, sometimes also called the ground wave or boundary layer wave. These are the waves used for radio propagation in the broadcast band (near 1 megacycle) in the daytime when ionospheric effects are absent. We seek a wave which is bound to the surface between a conductor (earth) and a dielectric (air). This wave will be present in both media and will propagate parallel to it. To be bound, the wave must decrease with amplitude as we leave the surface. Thus we shall seek a wave whose variation normal to the direction of propagation is a decreasing exponential rather than a trigonometric function.

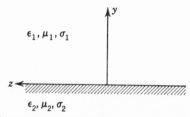

Fig. 13.4a. Propagation of guided waves over a lossy conductor.

We choose the plane of the conductor to be the xz plane, the conductor being in the region of negative y. Propagation will be in the $+z$ direction, as shown in Figure 13.4a, and we expect no variation of any of the components in the x direction. Near a good conductor we expect to find tangential H, normal E, and a small tangential E so as to permit a small portion of Poynting's vector to be normal to the conductor to make up for the ohmic losses in the latter. In the limit of infinite conductivity this conductor would terminate a plane wave: we wish to find a guided wave in the case of finite conductivity. In line with these considerations, we seek a wave with E_y, H_x, and E_z only, where we expect E_z to be small. No variation with x is expected.

Maxwell's equations are

$$\nabla \times \mathbf{E} = -j\omega\mu\mathbf{H}$$

and

$$\nabla \times \mathbf{H} = (\sigma + j\omega\epsilon)\mathbf{E} = j\omega\epsilon'\mathbf{E} \qquad (1)$$

where

$$\epsilon' = \epsilon + \frac{\sigma}{j\omega} = \epsilon - \frac{j\sigma}{\omega}$$

Here ϵ' will be real in region 1 and complex in region 2. With this restriction on ϵ' many of the considerations of Chapter 8 will still hold. In particular for any TM wave propagating in the z direction, we shall still have

$$H_x = \frac{-E_y}{Z_{\mathrm{TM}}} \qquad \text{where } Z_{\mathrm{TM}} = \frac{\gamma}{j\omega\epsilon'} \tag{2}$$

The wave equation for E_z is, in both media,

$$\nabla^2 E_z + \frac{\omega^2}{c^2} E_z = 0 \tag{3}$$

We choose $\qquad\qquad E_z = Y(y)Z(z) \tag{4}$

where we seek solutions of the form

$$Y = \{e^{\pm ky}\} \qquad Z = e^{-\gamma z} \tag{5}$$

To this end we divide (3) by E_z, obtaining

$$\frac{1}{Y}\frac{\partial^2 Y}{\partial y^2} + \underbrace{\frac{1}{Z}\frac{\partial^2 Z}{\partial z^2} + \frac{\omega^2}{c^2}}_{} = 0 \tag{6}$$

$$\longrightarrow\; = -k^2$$

We choose $-k^2$ for the separation constant because of the desired form of $Y(y)$ in (5). With this change in the sign of k^2 the arguments of Section 8.1 are still valid. For this case the transverse components of E can be determined by taking the gradient of a scalar potential where now

$$V = -\frac{1}{k^2}\frac{\partial E_z}{\partial z} \tag{7}$$

With the above as a basis, we choose now

$$\begin{aligned} E_{z1} &= A_1 e^{-k_1 y} e^{-\gamma z} \\ E_{z2} &= A_2 e^{k_2 y} e^{-\gamma z} \end{aligned} \tag{8}$$

where k_1 and k_2 are to be determined from the boundary conditions. Since tangential E is continuous, we have immediately

$$A_1 = A_2 = \text{say } A$$

Using the above equations we now have for the field components in both media:

$$\begin{aligned} E_{z1} &= A e^{-k_1 y} e^{-\gamma z} & E_{z2} &= A e^{k_2 y} e^{-\gamma z} \\ E_{y1} &= -\frac{\gamma A}{k_1} e^{-k_1 y} e^{-\gamma z} & E_{y2} &= \frac{\gamma A}{k_2} e^{k_2 y} e^{-\gamma z} \\ H_{x1} &= \frac{j\omega\epsilon_1' A}{k_1} e^{-k_1 y} e^{-\gamma z} & H_{x2} &= -\frac{j\omega\epsilon_2' A}{k_2} e^{k_2 y} e^{-\gamma z} \end{aligned} \tag{9}$$

Since tangential H is continuous we have

$$- \frac{j\omega\epsilon_2'}{k_2} = \frac{j\omega\epsilon_1'}{k_1} \qquad \text{or} \qquad k_1 = - \frac{\epsilon_1'}{\epsilon_2'} k_2 \qquad (10)$$

From (6), since γ must be the same in both media, we have

$$\gamma^2 = -k_1{}^2 - \frac{\omega^2}{c_1{}^2} = -k_2{}^2 - \frac{\omega^2}{c_2{}^2} \qquad (11)$$

where $c_1{}^2 = 1/\epsilon_1'\mu_0$ and $c_2{}^2 = 1/\epsilon_2'\mu_0$.

The two relations (10) and (11) are two relations between k_1 and k_2, enabling both quantities to be determined. Inserting (10) into (11) we have

$$k_1{}^2 = \omega^2 \left(\frac{1}{c_2{}^2} - \frac{1}{c_1{}^2} \right) + \left(\frac{\epsilon_2'}{\epsilon_1'} k_1 \right)^2 \qquad (12)$$

or, after some algebra,

$$k_1{}^2 = - \frac{\omega^2}{c_1{}^2} \frac{\epsilon_1'}{\epsilon_1' + \epsilon_2'}$$

and

$$k_2{}^2 = - \frac{\omega^2}{c_2{}^2} \frac{\epsilon_2'}{\epsilon_1' + \epsilon_2'} \qquad (13)$$

We see that if $\sigma = 0$ there is no bound wave, since both k_1 and k_2 will be imaginary. To demonstrate the nature of the solution with finite σ we let

$$\epsilon_1' = \epsilon_0 \qquad \text{and} \qquad \epsilon_2' = \epsilon_0 \left(K - j \frac{\sigma}{\omega\epsilon_0} \right) \qquad (14)$$

If now $\sigma/\omega\epsilon_0 \gg K$, then $\epsilon_2' = -j\sigma/\omega$. Under these conditions

$$\left| \frac{\epsilon_2'}{\epsilon_1'} \right| = \frac{\sigma}{\omega\epsilon_0} \gg 1$$

and (13) becomes

$$k_2{}^2 = - \frac{\omega^2}{c_2{}^2} = j\omega\mu\sigma \qquad \text{or} \qquad k_2 = \frac{1 + j}{\delta} \qquad (15)$$

where $\delta = \sqrt{2/\omega\mu\sigma}$, the usual expression for the skin depth in region 2. Also we have, since $c_1{}^2 = 1/\epsilon_0\mu_0 = c^2$,

$$k_1{}^2 = \frac{\omega^2}{c^2} \frac{\omega\epsilon_0}{j\sigma} \qquad \text{or} \qquad k_1 = \frac{\omega}{c} (1 - j) \sqrt{\frac{\omega\epsilon_0}{2\sigma}} \qquad (16)$$

Since $\omega/c = 2\pi/\lambda$ and the square root in (16) is a very small number, we find that the wave extends many wavelengths in the $+y$ direction in region 1, as expected. Inserting the value of k_1 into (11) we obtain

$$\gamma^2 = -k_1{}^2 - \frac{\omega^2}{c^2} = - \frac{\omega^2}{c^2} \left(1 - j \frac{\omega\epsilon_0}{\sigma} \right) \qquad (17)$$

Here $\omega\epsilon_0/\sigma \ll 1$ and we obtain on expansion

$$\gamma \approx j\frac{\omega}{c}\left(1 - j\,\frac{\omega\epsilon_0}{2\sigma}\right) = \alpha + j\beta \tag{18}$$

where $\alpha = \dfrac{\omega}{c}\dfrac{\omega\epsilon_0}{2\sigma}$ and $\beta = \omega/c$.

We note that the attenuation increases rapidly with frequency, showing that low frequencies are propagated quite efficiently. The above assumption $(\sigma/\omega\epsilon_0 \gg K)$ is good for sea water at frequencies below about 10 megacycles but is good for typical ground only below 20 kilocycles or so. For higher frequencies both the real and imaginary part of ϵ_2' must be obtained and the calculation is more difficult.

13.5   Ionospheric Propagation

The guided surface wave that we have been discussing is responsible for most of the low-frequency (below 1 megacycle, approximately) radio-propagation phenomena. The absorption of energy from the surface wave in ground losses increases with frequency and of course varies with the electric properties of the earth or sea water over which propagation takes place. Historically low frequencies were used almost exclusively for many years for radio communication (until about 1923). Experiments by radio amateurs, who were permitted to use only frequencies higher than 1.5 megacycles, and by the British Post Office showed that short waves provided a very powerful, though erratic, method of communicating over very large distances. Essentially this is due to the presence of ionized layers in the upper regions of the earth's atmosphere that can reflect radio waves of high frequency.

This mechanism is in general more efficient than ground-wave propagation because the wave travels in nonabsorbing "sky" for most of its path, being absorbed only when passing through or being reflected from an ionized layer, or at the surface of the earth if there are several reflections from the ionosphere. The ground wave, on the other hand, is continually absorbed along its path, and only if the absorption is small (at very low frequencies) can useful results be obtained at great distances.

The strongly absorbing resonant frequencies of air molecules and atoms lie in the ultraviolet region. The very short-wave ultraviolet part of the sun's spectrum can ionize atoms and molecules. There is then a layer of ionized gas at an altitude of about 300 kilometers. Above this height there is insufficient material to produce much ionization and below this height the short wavelength ultraviolet light that causes atomic ionization has been absorbed out. This layer is called the F_2 layer—sometimes there is a weak layer at 200 kilometers, called the F_1 layer. At these heights the absorption is mostly by atomic oxygen. Collisions between atoms of oxygen, formed at a lower level, are very infrequent at this pressure and recombination occurs at a very low rate. The ultraviolet wavelengths that cause ionization of oxygen molecules therefore pass easily through the F layers until they reach a low enough height (100 kilometers) so that molecular oxygen is encountered. At this height there is a sudden increase in electron concentration, called the E layer. These two layers, the F_2 layer at about 300 kilometers and the E layer at 100 kilometers, are the most important for radio communication. There are other layers—the D layer at 60 kilometers, caused by ozone, and sometimes, other weak layers. These are important mostly because of the absorption they cause, since they are too weak in general to cause reflection.

The action of an ionized layer on a radio wave is best understood by referring to Equations (25), (26), and (27), Section 13.3. Here by far the most important term is that due to the free electrons. The index of refraction n is

$$n = \sqrt{1 - \frac{N_e e^2}{m \epsilon_0 \omega^2}} = \sqrt{1 - \frac{\omega_p^2}{\omega^2}} \tag{1}$$

at radio frequencies. Here we define $\omega_p^2 = N_e e^2 / m \epsilon_0$, where ω_p is called the plasma frequency. At very low frequencies (about 100 kilocycles) the edge of the ionized layer is sufficiently sharp, measured in wavelengths, so that the ionized layer acts as a simple dielectric. There will of course be losses, and we can show that g in Equation (21), Section 13.3, is proportional to the collision frequency of the electrons with neutral atoms or molecules. The E layer is thus quite lossy, but the F_2 layer is not. At high frequencies a radio wave finds itself in a region of gradually decreasing dielectric constant. This causes a gradual turning of the wave, and if the ionization density is high enough and the angle of incidence not too small, the ray will be turned around in much the same way as total internal reflection.

There will in general be a critical angle of incidence such that smaller angles of incidence lead to penetration rather than reflection. The outgoing radio wave must point upward at least 3 degrees in order to escape being attenuated too much by ground-wave phenomena. Under these conditions the largest possible angle of incidence for the F layer is about 75 degrees. This is because of the geometry of the situation involved in the curvature of the earth and the height of the F layer. The detailed application of the above to the design of radio-propagation systems will not be treated in detail here.*   The full-scale solution of any propagation problem in which the curvature of the earth is taken into account is very complicated.

The above treatment has neglected the effect of the earth's magnetic field on the interaction between a plane wave and a group of electrons.   We shall neglect the effect of the H of the plane wave on the electron motion since it is much smaller than the force from E. The equation for the force on a charged particle is $\mathbf{F} = e(\mathbf{E} + \mathbf{v} \times \mathbf{B})$. If we consider only the component of the earth's magnetic field which is parallel to the direction of propagation (z), we have, calling this H_0,

$$\ddot{x} = \frac{e}{m} E_x + \frac{e}{m} \mu_0 H_0 \dot{y}$$
$$\ddot{y} = \frac{e}{m} E_y - \frac{e}{m} \mu_0 H_0 \dot{x} \tag{2}$$
$$\ddot{z} = 0$$

Since only x and y motion takes place, we can use complex notation.   Let

$$u = x + jy \qquad E = E_x + jE_y \qquad H = H_x + jH_y \tag{3}$$

Then (2) becomes

$$\ddot{u} - \frac{e}{m} E + j \frac{e}{m} \mu_0 H_0 \dot{u} = 0 \tag{4}$$

Maxwell's equations become

$$\frac{\partial E}{\partial z} = j\mu_0 \frac{\partial H}{\partial t} \qquad \text{and} \qquad \frac{\partial H}{\partial z} = -j\epsilon_0 \frac{\partial E}{\partial t} - jeN\dot{u} \tag{5}$$

We seek now solutions of (4) and (5).   Assume

$$E = Ae^{\pm j(\omega t - \beta z)} \qquad H = Be^{\pm j(\omega t - \beta z)}$$
$$u = Ce^{\pm j(\omega t - \beta z)} \tag{6}$$

Substituting (6) into (4) and (5) we obtain

$$-\frac{e}{m} A + \left(-\omega^2 \mp \frac{e}{m} \mu_0 H_0 \omega \right) C = 0$$
$$j\beta A - \mu_0 \omega B = 0 \tag{7}$$
$$\epsilon_0 \omega A + j\beta B + eN\omega C = 0$$

For a useful solution of (7) to exist, the determinant must vanish.

* See F. E. Terman, "Electronic and Radio Engineering," McGraw-Hill Book Company, Inc., New York, 1955.   This text gives a very full description of the actual phenomena, together with complete references.

This leads to

$$\beta^2 = \frac{\omega^2}{c^2} \left\{ 1 - \frac{N(e^2/m\epsilon_0)}{\omega^2 \pm e\mu_0 H_0 \omega/m} \right\} \tag{8}$$

Thus we have two indices of refraction; an ionized medium in the presence of a magnetic field has the properties of an anisotropic material, such as a double refracting crystal.

13.6   Waves Guided on a Dielectric Rod

At this time we return to the problem of guided waves and shall discuss a wave guided by a dielectric rod.   We wish to find TM waves traveling in the z direction which decrease in the radial direction outside the rod.   The discussion of Chapter 12 still holds, including the general solution for E_z

$$E_z = \left\{ \begin{matrix} J_n \\ N_n \end{matrix} (kr) \right\} \left\{ \begin{matrix} \sin \\ \cos \end{matrix} n\theta \right\} e^{\pm \gamma z} \tag{1}$$

Here we shall consider only $n = 0$ modes, and take the minus sign in $e^{\pm \gamma z}$. $e^{j\omega t - \gamma z}$ is assumed for all quantities.   Inside the rod only a J_0 term will be allowed for $N_0 \to \infty$ at the origin.   Outside we wish a combination of J_0 and N_0 that decreases with r so that the wave will remain close to the rod.   Such a combination can be had by referring to Appendix G, where it is shown that $H_0^{(1)}(x)$ is a solution of Bessel's equation which behaves as $\sqrt{1/x} \exp[+j(x - \pi/4)]$ at large arguments.   If the argument can be made imaginary, we then have the required combination of J_0 and N_0.   The solutions can be derived from

$$\begin{aligned} E_{z1} &= AJ_0(k_1 r) \\ E_{z2} &= BH_0^{(1)}(k_2 r) \end{aligned} \tag{2}$$

The solution of this problem can be found from (2) by using Section 8.1 and Faraday's law to compute H_θ and from the fact that for a wave to exist at all in both media at the same time we must have the propagation constants in each medium the same.   This means that the two γ's given by

$$\gamma^2 = k_1^2 - \omega^2 \epsilon_1 \mu_1 \qquad \text{and} \qquad \gamma^2 = k_2^2 - \omega^2 \epsilon_2 \mu_2 \tag{3}$$

must be the same leading to

$$k_1^2 - \omega^2 \epsilon_1 \mu_1 = k_2^2 - \omega^2 \epsilon_2 \mu_2 \tag{4}$$

At the surface of the rod we must have tangential E and H continuous. These two relations, together with (4) and the arbitrary choice of one of the amplitudes A or B in (2) to set the level, will give four relations among the four unknowns A, B, k_1, and k_2. There is the further restriction that k_2 must be imaginary.

PROBLEMS

1. Consider a layer of material having index of refraction n'' and of thickness d placed on the surface of semi-infinite material of index n'. Arrange n'' and d so that there is *no* reflected wave in the incident region (where $n = 1$). (This is the "coated-lens" technique mentioned in Section 13.1, the mathematics being quite similar to the quarter-wave transformer mentioned in Chapter 10.)

2. Consider a coaxial transmission line, inner conductor of radius a, outer conductor of radius c. From $r = a$ to $r = b$ the dielectric constant is ϵ_1 and from $r = b$ to $r = c$ it is ϵ_2. Assume a traveling wave with only E_z, H_θ, E_r, and no θ dependence. Exhibit a solution in the form of a number of simultaneous equations which must be satisfied. Do not attempt to solve these equations.

3. Develop the theory of guided TE and TM waves in an infinite dielectric slab of thickness a which is parallel to the xz plane. Let propagation be in the z direction and assume no variations in the x direction.

Useful References

1. Mason, Max, and Warren Weaver: "The Electromagnetic Field," Dover Publications, New York, 1929. This is an excellent book on the fundamental basic ideas behind this course. In particular a very careful discussion of dielectric phenomena is given.
2. Slater, John C., and Nathaniel H. Frank: "Electromagnetism," McGraw-Hill Book Company, Inc., New York, 1947. This book gives an excellent treatment of applications to optics, Huygens principle, Fresnel and Franhofer diffraction, as well as electricity and magnetism.
3. Slater, John C.: "Microwave Transmission," McGraw-Hill Book Company, Inc., New York, 1942. Quite good for transmission lines and antennas.
4. Smythe, William R.: "Static and Dynamic Electricity," McGraw-Hill Book Company, Inc., New York, 1950. This book treats advanced methods of solving boundary value problems and has excellent treatment of Bessel and Legendre functions.
5. Ramo, Simon, and John R. Whinnery: "Fields and Waves in Modern Radio," 2d ed., John Wiley & Sons, Inc., New York, 1953. Excellent on waveguides and antennas. Good use of Bessel functions in electrostatics.
6. Stratton, Julius Adams: "Electromagnetic Theory," McGraw-Hill Book Company, Inc., New York, 1941. Basic "bible" of the field. An advanced text, particularly complete in discussing radiation.
7. Sommerfeld, Arnold: "Electrodynamics" (in English), Academic Press, Inc., New York, 1952. Same remarks as Stratton. See also "Optics" by Sommerfeld.
8. Phillips, H. B.: "Vector Analysis," John Wiley & Sons, Inc., New York, 1933.
9. Panofsky, W., and M. Phillips: "Classical Electricity and Magnetism," Addison-Wesley Publishing Company, Reading, Mass., 1955. Excellent but quite advanced. Detailed treatment of relativity and radiation.
10. Slater, John C.: "Microwave Electronics," D. Van Nostrand Company,

Inc., Princeton, N.J., 1950. Good discussion of cavities and applications of theory to electronic devices.

11. Reich, Herbert J., Phillip F. Ordung, Herbert L. Krauss, and John G. Stalnik: "Microwave Theory and Techniques," D. Van Nostrand Company, Inc., Princeton, N.J., 1953. Good for applications, measuring techniques, etc. Also good discussion of klystrons, traveling wave tubes, etc.

12. Wayland, Harold: "Differential Equations Applied in Science and Engineering," D. Van Nostrand Company, Inc., Princeton, N.J., 1957. Good discussion of mathematical background.

13. Morse, Philip M., and Herman Feshbach: "Methods of Theoretical Physics," McGraw-Hill Book Co., Inc., New York, 1953. Advanced but very clear and complete on mathematical techniques. Very good for vector and tensor analysis.

14. Dwight, Herbert B.: "Tables of Integrals and Other Mathematical Data," 3d ed., The Macmillan Company, New York, 1957.

15. Peirce, B. O.: "A Short Table of Integrals," 3d ed., Ginn & Company, Boston, 1929.

Appendixes

A. Gradient and Line Integral

Differentiation in vector analysis uses the operator

$$\nabla = \left(\mathbf{i} \frac{\partial}{\partial x} + \mathbf{j} \frac{\partial}{\partial y} + \mathbf{k} \frac{\partial}{\partial z} \right) \tag{1}$$

$\nabla \phi$, called grad ϕ, is

$$\nabla \phi = \mathbf{i} \frac{\partial \phi}{\partial x} + \mathbf{j} \frac{\partial \phi}{\partial y} + \mathbf{k} \frac{\partial \phi}{\partial z} \tag{2}$$

Now the change in a scalar function ϕ resulting from a displacement $d\mathbf{r} = \mathbf{i}\, dx + \mathbf{j}\, dy + \mathbf{k}\, dz$ is

$$d\phi = \frac{\partial \phi}{\partial x}\, dx + \frac{\partial \phi}{\partial y}\, dy + \frac{\partial \phi}{\partial z}\, dz = d\mathbf{r} \cdot \nabla \phi \tag{3}$$

If we let the distance $ds = |d\mathbf{r}|$, then

$$\frac{d\phi}{ds} = \frac{\partial \phi}{\partial x} \frac{dx}{ds} + \frac{\partial \phi}{\partial y} \frac{dy}{ds} + \frac{\partial \phi}{\partial z} \frac{dz}{ds} = \frac{d\mathbf{r}}{ds} \cdot \nabla \phi \tag{4}$$

is called the derivative of ϕ in the direction of $d\mathbf{r}$. Since $d\mathbf{r}/ds$ is a vector of unit length, $d\phi/ds$ has its greatest value when $d\mathbf{r}$ is in the same direction as $\nabla \phi$. Since the gradient depends only on the values of ϕ in the neighborhood of a point, it is clearly independent of any coordinate system and the unit vectors above can be replaced by unit vectors along any three perpendicular axes and $\partial \phi / \partial x$, etc., replaced by derivatives along these new axes. If $\mathbf{u}$ is a unit vector tangent to a curve in space then $\mathbf{u} = d\mathbf{r}/ds$ where the direction in which s increases is defined. The line integral of a vector function along a path in space is the sum of the tangential components along this curve times the differential lengths along the curve, and is written as

$$\oint_A^B \mathbf{F} \cdot d\mathbf{r} \qquad (5)$$

We now consider a few properties of line integrals and their relation to $\nabla\phi$.

1. If a vector $\mathbf{F}$ is the gradient of a scalar function, the line integral between two end points a and b depends *only* on the end points and not on the path.

Assume $\mathbf{F} = \nabla\phi$. Then $\mathbf{F} \cdot d\mathbf{r} = d\mathbf{r} \cdot \nabla\phi = d\phi$ since the change in ϕ for a given displacement is the dot product of the gradient of ϕ taken with the displacement $d\mathbf{r}$. Thus

$$\int_a^b \mathbf{F} \cdot d\mathbf{r} = \int_a^b d\phi = \phi(b) - \phi(a) \qquad (6)$$

and depends only on the end points. It is obvious that the integral around a closed path $\oint \mathbf{F} \cdot d\mathbf{r}$ is zero for such a function. Conversely we now show that

2. If $\oint \mathbf{F} \cdot d\mathbf{r} = 0$ for every closed path in a region, there exists a ϕ such that $\mathbf{F} = \nabla\phi$. Let $\phi = \int_A^B \mathbf{F} \cdot d\mathbf{r}$ where A is a fixed point and B a variable point in space. $\phi = \int_A^B \mathbf{F} \cdot d\mathbf{r} = \int_A^B \mathbf{F} \cdot \dfrac{d\mathbf{r}}{ds} ds$ is a function of s which has a derivative

$$\frac{d\phi}{ds} = \mathbf{F} \cdot \frac{d\mathbf{r}}{ds} = \mathbf{F} \cdot \mathbf{u} \qquad (7)$$

where $\mathbf{u}$ is a unit tangent to the curve. This curve, however, can be chosen to have any direction we choose at B. Thus the derivative of ϕ at B is continuous in every direction at B and ϕ has a definite gradient at B. This means that

$$\frac{d\phi}{ds} = \frac{d\mathbf{r}}{ds} \cdot \nabla\phi = \mathbf{u} \cdot \nabla\phi \qquad (8)$$

Combining these last two equations we have

$$(\mathbf{F} - \nabla\phi) \cdot \mathbf{u} = 0 \qquad (9)$$

and for arbitrary $\mathbf{u}$ one has $\mathbf{F} = \nabla\phi$.

B. Simple Vector Analysis

Simple vector manipulation shows the following formulas to be true. The method used shows that it is true in rectangular coordinates, where it is known that

$$\text{grad } V = \mathbf{i}\frac{\partial V}{\partial x} + \mathbf{j}\frac{\partial V}{\partial x} + \mathbf{k}\frac{\partial V}{\partial z} \tag{1}$$

$$\text{div } \mathbf{A} = \frac{\partial A_x}{\partial x} + \frac{\partial A_y}{\partial y} + \frac{\partial A_z}{\partial z} \tag{2}$$

and

$$\text{curl } \mathbf{A} = \mathbf{i}\left(\frac{\partial A_z}{\partial y} - \frac{\partial A_y}{\partial z}\right)$$
$$+ \mathbf{j}\left(\frac{\partial A_x}{\partial z} - \frac{\partial A_z}{\partial x}\right) \tag{3}$$
$$+ \mathbf{k}\left(\frac{\partial A_y}{\partial x} - \frac{\partial A_x}{\partial y}\right)$$

The formulas below can easily be shown to be true for rectangular coordinates; hence they are true for any coordinate system, since vector relations are independent of the coordinate system.

1. $\mathbf{A} \cdot (\mathbf{B} \times \mathbf{C}) = \mathbf{B} \cdot (\mathbf{C} \times \mathbf{A}) = \mathbf{C} \cdot (\mathbf{A} \times \mathbf{B})$
2. $\mathbf{A} \times (\mathbf{B} \times \mathbf{C}) = \mathbf{B}(\mathbf{A} \cdot \mathbf{C}) - \mathbf{C}(\mathbf{A} \cdot \mathbf{B})$
3. $\text{div } (a\mathbf{F}) = a \text{ div } \mathbf{F} + (\mathbf{F} \cdot \text{grad } a)$
4. $\text{curl } a\mathbf{F} = a \text{ curl } \mathbf{F} + (\text{grad } a) \times \mathbf{F}$
5. $\text{div } (\mathbf{F} \times \mathbf{G}) = (\mathbf{G} \cdot \text{curl } \mathbf{F}) - (\mathbf{F} \cdot \text{curl } \mathbf{G})$
6. $\text{div curl } \mathbf{F} = 0 \quad$ for any vector $\mathbf{F}$
7. $\text{curl curl } \mathbf{F} = \text{grad div } \mathbf{F} - \nabla^2\mathbf{F}$

(This last equation is true in rectangular coordinates if we define $\nabla^2\mathbf{F} = \mathbf{i}\nabla^2 F_x + \mathbf{j}\nabla^2 F_y + \mathbf{k}\nabla^2 F$, the other operations being obvious in various coordinate systems.)

8. $\text{curl grad } a = 0 \quad$ for any scalar a

C. Stokes' Theorem

Stokes' theorem relates a surface integral to a line integral about the contour along the edge of this surface. It states that the line integral of a vector $\mathbf{F}$ around a closed line L in space is equal to the surface integral of the curl of $\mathbf{F}$ over the surfaces bounded by L.

$$\oint_L \mathbf{F} \cdot d\mathbf{s} = \int_S \nabla \times \mathbf{F} \cdot \mathbf{n} \, da \tag{1}$$

This presumes that a positive direction is defined for taking the line integral; i.e., $\mathbf{n}$ is up if we traverse the contour in a counterclockwise direction. We shall show that this theorem is true for an infinitesimal square; hence, by a simple extension, it is true for any surface. We choose the area to be $dx\, dy$, the normal $\mathbf{n}$ being in the z direction.

The surface integral is $\left(\dfrac{\partial F_y}{\partial x} - \dfrac{\partial F_x}{\partial y}\right) dx\, dy$ and the line integral is

$$F_x\, dx + \left(F_y + \frac{\partial F_y}{\partial x}\, dx\right) dy - \left(F_x + \frac{\partial F_x}{\partial y}\, dy\right) dx - F_y\, dy$$
$$= \left(\frac{\partial F_y}{\partial x} - \frac{\partial F_x}{\partial y}\right) dx\, dy \quad (2)$$

Thus the theorem is true for an infinitesimal area. In a large area the contributions to the line integral from each rectangle cancel except at the boundary. It is clear that the line integral along a smooth curve can be closely approximated by a jagged curve having elements parallel to the x and y axes, since $\mathbf{F} \cdot d\mathbf{s} = F_x\, dx + F_y\, dy$.

We have thus proved Stokes' theorem for surfaces lying in a plane. A more general surface can be handled by decomposing the vectors representing the tangent to the curve into three component vectors and the area into three projected areas, then proceeding as above. In general, we have for Stokes' theorem

$$\oint \mathbf{F} \cdot d\mathbf{s} = \int_S \operatorname{curl} \mathbf{F} \cdot \mathbf{n}\, da \quad (3)$$

D. Vector Operations in Orthogonal Curvilinear Coordinates

Let the three orthogonal coordinates be q_1, q_2, q_3. Here the three surfaces $q_1 = $ constant, $q_2 = $ constant, and $q_3 = $ constant all intersect at right angles, though the surfaces in general are curved. If we move a distance ds perpendicular to the surface $q_1 = $ constant, q_2 and q_3 do not change, but q_1 is increased by dq_1. Let the relation between ds_1 (a distance) and dq_1 (a change in the coordinate) be given by

$$ds_1 = h_1\, dq_1$$

and likewise

$$ds_2 = h_2\, dq_2 \qquad ds_3 = h_3\, dq_3 \quad (1)$$

It can be easily shown that the h's have the following values

Coordinate system	q_1	q_2	q_3	h_1	h_2	h_3
Rectangular	x	y	z	1	1	1
Cylindrical	r	θ	z	1	r	1
Spherical	r	θ	ϕ	1	r	$r \sin \theta$

Gradient. The component of the gradient of a scalar in any direction is its rate of change in that direction. Thus

$$\frac{dS}{ds_1} = \frac{1}{h_1}\frac{\partial S}{\partial q_1} \tag{2}$$

The components of the gradient in the various directions are

Coordinate system	Components of gradient		
Rectangular x,y,z	$\dfrac{\partial S}{\partial x}$	$\dfrac{\partial S}{\partial y}$	$\dfrac{\partial S}{\partial z}$
Cylindrical r,θ,z	$\dfrac{\partial S}{\partial r}$	$\dfrac{1}{r}\dfrac{\partial S}{\partial \theta}$	$\dfrac{\partial S}{\partial z}$
Spherical r,θ,ϕ	$\dfrac{\partial S}{\partial r}$	$\dfrac{1}{r}\dfrac{\partial S}{\partial \theta}$	$\dfrac{1}{r \sin \theta}\dfrac{\partial S}{\partial \phi}$

Divergence. Apply the divergence theorem

$$\int_V \nabla \cdot \mathbf{A}\, dv = \int_S \mathbf{A} \cdot \mathbf{n}\, da \tag{3}$$

to a small volume element $ds_1\, ds_2\, ds_3 = dv$, where the bounding coordinate surfaces are q_1, $q_1 + dq_1$, etc. Let $\mathbf{A}$ have the components A_1, A_2, A_3 along the three coordinate axes. The flux into the surface at q_1 is $(A_1\, ds_2\, ds_3)_{q_1}$ and the flux out of the opposite face is $(A_1\, ds_2\, ds_3)_{q_1+dq_1}$, where it should be noted that $ds_2\, ds_3$ may change with q_1 as well as A_1. The net flux leaving through these two surfaces is thus

$$-(A_1\, ds_2\, ds_3)_{q_1} + (A_1\, ds_2\, ds_3)_{q_1+dq_1}$$

$$= -(A_1\, ds_2\, ds_3) + (A_1\, ds_2\, ds_3) + \frac{\partial}{\partial q_1}(A_1\, ds_2\, ds_3)\, dq_1 \tag{4}$$

$$= \frac{1}{h_1 h_2 h_3}\frac{\partial}{\partial q_1}(A_1 h_2 h_3)\, dv$$

A similar argument holds for the other faces and we have

$$\text{div } \mathbf{A} = \frac{1}{h_1 h_2 h_3}\left[\frac{\partial}{\partial q_1}(A_1 h_2 h_3) + \frac{\partial}{\partial q_2}(A_2 h_1 h_3) + \frac{\partial}{\partial q_3}(A_3 h_1 h_2)\right] \tag{5}$$

Thus we have in the various coordinate systems

Rectangular: $\text{div } \mathbf{A} = \dfrac{\partial A_x}{\partial x} + \dfrac{\partial A_y}{\partial y} + \dfrac{\partial A_z}{\partial z}$ \hfill (6)

Cylindrical: $\text{div } \mathbf{A} = \dfrac{1}{r}\dfrac{\partial}{\partial r}(rA_r) + \dfrac{1}{r}\dfrac{\partial A_\theta}{\partial \theta} + \dfrac{\partial A_z}{\partial z}$ \hfill (7)

Spherical: $\text{div } \mathbf{A} = \dfrac{1}{r^2}\dfrac{\partial}{\partial r}(r^2 A_r) + \dfrac{1}{r \sin \theta}\dfrac{\partial}{\partial \theta}(\sin \theta A_\theta)$

$$+ \frac{1}{r \sin \theta}\frac{\partial A_\phi}{\partial \phi} \tag{8}$$

Laplacian.   The Laplacian of a scalar is $\nabla^2 S = \operatorname{div} \operatorname{grad} S$. This in general leads to

$$\nabla^2 S = \frac{1}{h_1 h_2 h_3} \left[\frac{\partial}{\partial q_1} \left(\frac{h_2 h_3}{h_1} \frac{\partial S}{\partial q_1} \right) + \frac{\partial}{\partial q_2} \left(\frac{h_1 h_3}{h_2} \frac{dS}{\partial q_2} \right) + \frac{\partial}{\partial q_3} \left(\frac{h_1 h_2}{h_3} \frac{\partial S}{\partial q_3} \right) \right] \quad (9)$$

In the various coordinate systems we have

Rectangular: $\nabla^2 S = \dfrac{\partial^2 S}{\partial x^2} + \dfrac{\partial^2 S}{\partial y^2} + \dfrac{\partial^2 S}{\partial z^2}$ $\quad (10)$

Cylindrical: $\nabla^2 S = \dfrac{1}{r} \dfrac{\partial}{\partial r} \left(r \dfrac{\partial S}{\partial r} \right) + \dfrac{1}{r^2} \dfrac{\partial^2 S}{\partial \theta^2} + \dfrac{\partial^2 S}{\partial z^2}$ $\quad (11)$

Spherical: $\nabla^2 S = \dfrac{1}{r^2} \dfrac{\partial}{\partial r} \left(r^2 \dfrac{\partial S}{\partial r} \right) + \dfrac{1}{r^2 \sin \theta} \dfrac{\partial}{\partial \theta} \left(\sin \theta \dfrac{\partial S}{\partial \theta} \right)$

$$+ \frac{1}{r^2 \sin^2 \theta} \frac{\partial^2 S}{\partial \phi^2} \quad (12)$$

Curl of a Vector.   Stokes' theorem states that for any vector **A**, $\oint \mathbf{A} \cdot d\mathbf{l} = \int_S (\nabla \times \mathbf{A} \cdot \mathbf{n})\, da$. Applying this to an approximately rectangular area bounded by q_1, $q_1 + dq_1$, q_2, and $q_2 + dq_2$, we have for the line integral about this circuit, approximately,

$$A_1 h_1\, dq_1 + A_2 h_2\, dq_2 + \frac{\partial}{\partial q_1} (h_2 A_2\, dq_2)\, dq_1 \quad (13)$$

$$- A_1 h_1\, dq_1 - \frac{\partial}{\partial q_2} (h_1 A_1\, dq_1)\, dq_2 - A_2 h_2\, dq_2$$

This is equal to

$$\left[\frac{\partial}{\partial q_1} (h_2 A_2) - \frac{\partial}{\partial q_2} (h_1 A_1) \right] dq_1\, dq_2 \quad (14)$$

Since this must be equal to $\operatorname{curl}_3 A\, ds_1\, ds_2$, we have

$$\operatorname{curl}_3 A = \frac{1}{h_1 h_2} \left[\frac{\partial}{\partial q_1} (h_2 A_2) - \frac{\partial}{\partial q_2} (h_1 A_1) \right] \quad (15)$$

with corresponding expressions for the other components. We thus have

Cylindrical coordinates: $(\operatorname{curl} A)_r = \dfrac{1}{r} \dfrac{\partial A_z}{\partial \theta} - \dfrac{\partial A_\theta}{\partial z}$

$(\operatorname{curl} A)_\theta = \dfrac{\partial A_r}{\partial z} - \dfrac{\partial A_z}{\partial r}$ $\quad (16)$

$(\operatorname{curl} A)_z = \dfrac{1}{r} \dfrac{\partial}{\partial r} (r A_\theta) - \dfrac{1}{r} \dfrac{\partial A_r}{\partial \theta}$

Spherical coordinates: $(\text{curl } A)_r = \dfrac{1}{r \sin \theta} \dfrac{\partial}{\partial \theta} (\sin \theta A_\phi)$

$$- \dfrac{1}{r \sin \theta} \dfrac{\partial A_\theta}{\partial \phi}$$

$$(\text{curl } A)_\theta = \dfrac{1}{r \sin \theta} \dfrac{\partial A_r}{\partial \phi} - \dfrac{1}{r} \dfrac{\partial}{\partial r} (rA_\phi) \quad (17)$$

$$(\text{curl } A)_\phi = \dfrac{1}{r} \dfrac{\partial}{\partial r} (rA_\theta) - \dfrac{1}{r} \dfrac{\partial A_r}{\partial \theta}$$

Rectangular coordinates: $(\text{curl } A)_x = \dfrac{\partial A_z}{\partial y} - \dfrac{\partial A_y}{\partial z}$

$$(\text{curl } A)_y = \dfrac{\partial A_x}{\partial z} - \dfrac{\partial A_z}{\partial x} \quad (18)$$

$$(\text{curl } A)_z = \dfrac{\partial A_y}{\partial x} - \dfrac{\partial A_x}{\partial y}$$

As an example of Equation (7), Appendix B, we compute $\nabla^2 F$ in rectangular coordinates:

$$\nabla^2 F = - \text{ curl curl } F + \text{grad div } F$$

$$(\nabla^2 F)_x = - \dfrac{\partial}{\partial y} \left(\dfrac{\partial F_y}{\partial x} - \dfrac{\partial F_x}{\partial y} \right) + \dfrac{\partial}{\partial z} \left(\dfrac{\partial F_x}{\partial z} - \dfrac{\partial F_z}{\partial x} \right)$$

$$+ \dfrac{\partial}{\partial x} \left(\dfrac{\partial F_x}{\partial x} + \dfrac{\partial F_y}{\partial y} + \dfrac{\partial F_z}{\partial z} \right)$$

$$= - \dfrac{\partial^2 F_y}{\partial x \partial y} + \dfrac{\partial^2 F_x}{\partial y^2} + \dfrac{\partial^2 F_x}{\partial z^2} - \dfrac{\partial^2 F_z}{\partial z \partial x} + \dfrac{\partial^2 F_x}{\partial x^2} + \dfrac{\partial^2 F_y}{\partial x \partial y} + \dfrac{\partial^2 F_z}{\partial x \partial z}$$

$$= \dfrac{\partial^2 F_x}{\partial x^2} + \dfrac{\partial^2 F_x}{\partial y^2} + \dfrac{\partial^2 F_x}{\partial z^2} = \nabla^2 F_x$$

$$(\nabla^2 F) = \mathbf{i}(\nabla^2 F_x) + \mathbf{j}(\nabla^2 F_y) + \mathbf{k}(\nabla^2 F_z) \quad (19)$$

Similar calculations can be made in cylindrical and spherical coordinates. These are long and tiresome. The results are

Cylindrical coordinates: $\nabla^2 A = \left(\nabla^2 A_r - \dfrac{2}{r^2} \dfrac{\partial A_\theta}{\partial \theta} - \dfrac{A_r}{r^2} \right) \mathbf{e}_r$

$$+ \left(\nabla^2 A_\theta + \dfrac{2}{r^2} \dfrac{\partial A_r}{\partial \theta} - \dfrac{A_\theta}{r^2} \right) \mathbf{e}_\theta + (\nabla^2 A_z) \mathbf{e}_z \quad (20)$$

Spherical coordinates:

$$\nabla^2 A = \left[\dfrac{1}{r} \nabla^2 (rA_r) - \dfrac{2}{r} \nabla \cdot A \right] \mathbf{e}_r$$

$$+ \left(\nabla^2 A_\theta + \dfrac{2}{r^2} \dfrac{\partial A_r}{\partial \theta} - \dfrac{A_\theta}{r^2 \sin^2 \theta} - \dfrac{2 \cos \theta}{r^2 \sin^2 \theta} \dfrac{\partial A_\phi}{\partial \phi} \right) \mathbf{e}_\theta \quad (21)$$

$$+ \left(\nabla^2 A_\phi - \dfrac{A_\phi}{r^2 \sin^2 \theta} + \dfrac{2 \cos \theta}{r^2 \sin^2 \theta} \dfrac{\partial A_\theta}{\partial \phi} + \dfrac{2}{r^2 \sin \theta} \dfrac{\partial A_r}{\partial \theta} \right) \mathbf{e}_\phi$$

In the above $\mathbf{e}_r$, $\mathbf{e}_\theta$, etc., are unit vectors in the r, θ, etc., directions, respectively. The calculation in spherical and cylindrical coordinates is essentially the same as for rectangular coordinates, i.e., no special value of $\nabla \cdot \mathbf{A}$ is assumed.

E. Uniqueness Theorem

Here we shall show that if a solution is obtained to a problem in electrostatics by any means it is a unique solution. Here we define a solution to be a potential function which satisfies Laplace's equation and matches the boundary conditions. The method of proof will be to suppose that two solutions V_1 and V_2 exist. We then prove that V_1 must equal V_2. Along the boundaries V_1 equals V_2, since both solutions must satisfy the boundary conditions. Since both are solutions of Laplace equations, $\nabla^2 V_1 = \nabla^2 V_2 = 0$ at all points, and hence $\nabla^2(V_1 - V_2) = 0$. We shall now use the divergence theorem which states that for any vector $\mathbf{F}$

$$\int_V \nabla \cdot \mathbf{F}\, dv = \int_S \mathbf{F} \cdot \mathbf{n}\, da \tag{1}$$

Here we choose

$$\mathbf{F} = (V_1 - V_2)\nabla(V_1 - V_2) \tag{2}$$

We then have

$$\int_V \nabla \cdot (V_1 - V_2)\nabla(V_1 - V_2)\, dv$$
$$= \int_S (V_1 - V_2)\nabla(V_1 - V_2) \cdot \mathbf{n}\, da \tag{3}$$

The integrand of the first integral can be expanded by Appendix A, Equation (3), to give

$$\int_V (V_1 - V_2)\nabla^2(V_1 - V_2)\, dv + \int_V [\nabla(V_1 - V_2)]^2\, dv$$
$$= \int_S (V_1 - V_2)\nabla(V_1 - V_2) \cdot \mathbf{n}\, da \tag{4}$$

The first and last integrals are zero if we take S to be the surface of the conductors where $V_1 = V_2$. Thus in the volume bounded by this surface

$$\int_V [\nabla(V_1 - V_2)]^2\, dv = 0 \tag{5}$$

However, $\nabla(V_1 - V_2)$ is a real number and its square must be positive or zero. Thus at all points we must have

$$\nabla(V_1 - V_2) = 0 \tag{6}$$

or
$$V_1 - V_2 = \text{constant} \tag{7}$$

The boundary conditions show that this constant must be zero; hence $V_1 = V_2$ at all points and the theorem is proved. The proof given here holds only for problems in which the boundary conditions involve conductors at fixed potentials. A more general proof is given by Stratton (see Reference 6).

F. Legendre Polynomials

The solution of Legendre's equation is discussed in detail in Smythe's "Static and Dynamic Electricity," page 133 (see Reference

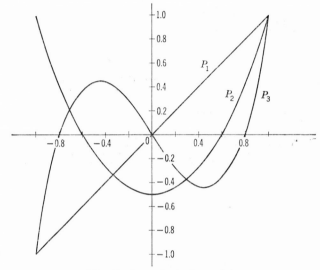

Fig. Fa. Legendre polynomials.

4). It is accomplished by the usual series expansion. The following formulas are also obtained from Smythe:

$$nP_{n-1} + (n+1)P_{n+1} = (2n+1)\mu P_n \tag{1}$$

$$P'_{n+1} - P'_{n-1} = (2n+1)P_n \tag{2}$$

$$\int_{-1}^{+1} [P_n]^2\, d\mu = \frac{2}{2n+1} \qquad \int_{-1}^{+1} P_n P_m\, d\mu = 0 \qquad \text{if } n \neq m \tag{3}$$

$$\int P_n\, d\mu = \frac{P_{n+1} - P_{n-1}}{2n+1} \tag{4}$$

$$P_0 = 1 \tag{5}$$

$$P_1 = \mu \tag{6}$$

$$P_2 = \tfrac{1}{2}(3\mu^2 - 1) \tag{7}$$

$$P_3 = \tfrac{1}{2}(5\mu^3 - 3\mu) \text{ etc.} \qquad \text{where } \mu = \cos\theta \tag{8}$$

$$n \text{ odd}: P_n(0) = 0 \tag{9}$$

$$n \text{ even}: P_n(0) = (-1)^{n/2} \frac{1 \cdot 3 \cdot 5 \cdots (n-1)}{2 \cdot 4 \cdot 6 \cdots (n)} \qquad (10)$$

Any $n: P_n(1) = 1$ (11)

Any $n: P_n(-\mu) = (-1)^n P_n(\mu)$ (12)

Any $n: P'_n(0) = -(n+1)P_{n+1}(0)$ (13)

Any $n: P'_n(1) = \frac{1}{2}n(n+1)$ (14)

Associated Legendre polynomials. These are also discussed in Smythe.

$$P_1{}^1 = (1 - \mu^2)^{\frac{1}{2}} = \sin\theta \qquad (15)$$

$$P_2{}^1 = 3(1 - \mu^2)^{\frac{1}{2}}\mu \qquad (16)$$

$$P_2{}^2 = 3(1 - \mu^2) \text{ etc.} \qquad (17)$$

$$\int_{-1}^{+1} P_n{}^m P_{n'}{}^{m'} \, d\mu = 0 \qquad \text{unless } n = n', \ m = m' \qquad (18)$$

when
$$\int_{-1}^{+1} [P_n{}^m]^2 \, d\mu = \frac{2}{2n+1} \frac{(n+m)!}{(n-m)!} \qquad (19)$$

G. Bessel and Hankel Functions

Bessel functions arise in the solution of Laplace's equation in cylindrical coordinates. They are one solution of Bessel's equation, i.e.,

$$\rho \frac{d}{d\rho}\left(\rho \frac{dR}{d\rho}\right) + (k^2\rho^2 - n^2)R = 0 \qquad (1)$$

If we let $r = k\rho$ this becomes

$$\frac{d^2R}{dr^2} + \frac{1}{r}\frac{dR}{dr} + \left(1 - \frac{n^2}{r^2}\right)R = 0 \qquad (2)$$

By the usual method of power series expansion one solution of (2) is

$$J_n(r) = \frac{1}{n!}\left(\frac{r}{2}\right)^n - \frac{1}{(n+1)!}\left(\frac{r}{2}\right)^{n+2} + \frac{1}{2!(n+2)!}\left(\frac{r}{2}\right)^{n+4} + \cdots \qquad (3)$$

These are called Bessel functions and are finite for $+r$, $J_n(0)$ being zero for integer $n \geq 1$, $J_0(0) = 1$. The $J_n(r)$ behave somewhat like a sine wave of slowly decreasing amplitude and slowly changing phase as r increases. If n is not an integer, the other solution of (2) is $J_{-n}(r)$. If n is an integer (the usual case), J_{-n} is related to J_n by a simple relation, so another solution must be sought. This is called a Neumann function, $N_n(r)$, which is similar to a Bessel function except that it goes to $-\infty$ at the origin. Asymptotic expansions for these functions are

$$\lim_{r\to 0} N_0(r) = \frac{2}{\pi} (\log r - 0.116) \tag{4}$$

$$\lim_{r\to 0} N_n(r) = -\frac{(n-1)!}{\pi} \left(\frac{2}{r}\right)^n \qquad n > 0 \tag{5}$$

$$\lim_{r\to\infty} J_n(r) = \sqrt{\frac{2}{\pi r}} \cos\left(r - \frac{2n+1}{4}\pi\right) \tag{6}$$

$$\lim_{r\to\infty} N_n(r) = \sqrt{\frac{2}{\pi r}} \sin\left(r - \frac{2n+1}{4}\pi\right) \tag{7}$$

It is sometimes convenient to choose those linear combinations of Bessel and Neumann functions that approach exponentials of imaginary argument at large values of the argument. Such combinations

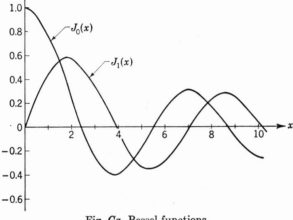

Fig. *Ga.* Bessel functions.

are called Hankel functions and are defined by

$$H_n^{(1)}(r) = J_n(r) + jN_n(r) \xrightarrow[r\to\infty]{} \sqrt{\frac{2}{\pi r}} e^{j(r-(2n+1/4)\pi)} \tag{8}$$

$$H_n^{(2)}(r) = J_n(r) - jN_n(r) \xrightarrow[r\to\infty]{} \sqrt{\frac{2}{\pi r}} e^{-j(r-(2n+1/4)\pi)} \tag{9}$$

When $n = l + \frac{1}{2}$, it is usual to define new functions as follows

$$
\begin{aligned}
j_l(r) &= \sqrt{\frac{\pi}{2r}} J_{l+\frac{1}{2}}(r) \\
n_l(r) &= \sqrt{\frac{\pi}{2r}} N_{l+\frac{1}{2}}(r)
\end{aligned}
\tag{10}
$$

These are called spherical Bessel functions. An obvious combination of these leads to spherical Bessel functions $h_l^{(1)}(r)$ and $h_l^{(2)}(r)$, as discussed in the chapter on spherical radiation.

The nomenclature for the Neumann functions $N_n(r)$ is not fixed. Many books call these Bessel functions of the second kind and write them as $Y_n(r)$ or $\bar{Y}_n(r)$.

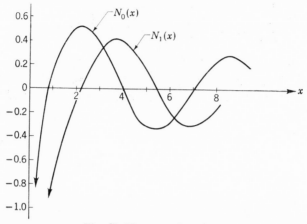

Fig. G*b*. Neumann functions.

Many formulas, integrals, and derivatives can be found for Bessel functions. Some of the more useful follow, where Z_n stands for either J_n or N_n,

$$\frac{d}{dr}[J_0(r)] = -J_1(r) \tag{11}$$

$$Z_{n-1}(r) + Z_{n+1}(r) = \frac{2n}{r} Z_n(r) \tag{12}$$

$$Z_{-n}(r) = (-1)^n Z_n(r) \qquad \text{if } n \text{ is integral} \tag{13}$$

$$\frac{d}{dr}[Z_n(r)] = \left[\frac{n}{r} Z_n(r) - Z_{n+1}(r)\right] \tag{14}$$

$$\frac{d}{dr}[r^n Z_n(r)] = r^n Z_{n-1}(r) \tag{15}$$

$$\int Z_1(r)\, dr = -Z_0(r) \tag{16}$$

$$\int r Z_0(r)\, dr = r Z_1(r) \tag{17}$$

$$\int r Z_0^2(r)\, dr = \frac{r^2}{2}[Z_0^2(r) + Z_1^2(r)] \tag{18}$$

$$\int r Z_n^2(r)\, dr = \frac{r^2}{2}[Z_n^2(r) - Z_{n-1}(r)Z_{n+1}(r)] \tag{19}$$

H. Fourier-series Expansions

1. Odd-step function

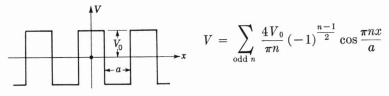

$$V = \sum_{\text{odd } n} \frac{4V_0}{\pi n} \sin \frac{\pi n x}{a}$$

2. Even-step function

$$V = \sum_{\text{odd } n} \frac{4V_0}{\pi n} (-1)^{\frac{n-1}{2}} \cos \frac{\pi n x}{a}$$

3. Parabola: $y = x^2$

$$y = \sum_{n=1}^{\infty} (-1)^n \left(\frac{2a}{\pi n}\right)^2 \cos \frac{\pi n x}{a} + \frac{a^2}{3}$$

4. Sawtooth: $V = \dfrac{V_0}{a} x$

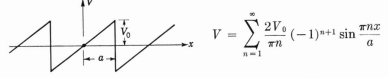

$$V = \sum_{n=1}^{\infty} \frac{2V_0}{\pi n} (-1)^{n+1} \sin \frac{\pi n x}{a}$$

5. Checkerboard: black rectangles $+V_0$, white rectangles $-V_0$

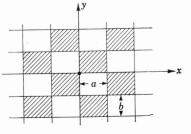

Origin at lower left corner of $+V_0$ square:

$$V = \sum_{l,m \text{ odd}} \frac{16V_0}{\pi^2 l m} \sin \frac{\pi l x}{a} \sin \frac{\pi m y}{b}$$

Origin at center of $+V_0$ rectangle:

$$V = -\sum_{l,m \text{ odd}} \frac{16V_0}{\pi^2 l m} (-1)^{l+m/2}$$

$$\cos \frac{\pi l x}{a} \cos \frac{\pi m y}{b}$$

6. Triangular wave

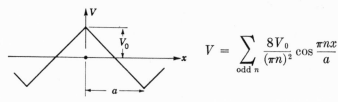

$$V = \sum_{\text{odd } n} \frac{8V_0}{(\pi n)^2} \cos \frac{\pi n x}{a}$$

7. Even δ function: one dimension

$$\delta(x) = 0, \; x \neq 0, \; \int_{-a}^{+a} \delta(x)dx = 1$$

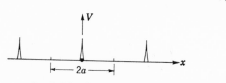

$$V = \frac{1}{2a} + \sum_{n=1}^{\infty} \frac{1}{a} \cos \frac{\pi n x}{a}$$

8. Odd δ function

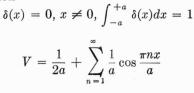

$$V = \sum_{n} \frac{2}{a} \sin \frac{\pi n c}{a} \sin \frac{\pi n x}{a}$$

9. Two-dimensional odd δ function at (c,d)

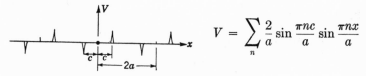

$$V = \sum_{l,m} \frac{4}{ab} \sin \frac{\pi l c}{a} \sin \frac{\pi m d}{b} \sin \frac{\pi l x}{a} \sin \frac{\pi m y}{b}$$

Index